STUDENT ACTIVITIES in Economics

TEACHER'S EDITION

Alan J. Carper

D1401354

BJU PRESS

Greenville, South Carolina

NOTE:
The fact that materials produced by other publishers may be referred to in this volume does not constitute an endorsement of the content or theological position of materials produced by such publishers. Any references and ancillary materials are listed as an aid to the student or the teacher and in an attempt to maintain the accepted academic standards of the publishing industry.

Activities Manual for ECONOMICS
Teacher's Edition

Alan J. Carper, M.B.A.

Produced in cooperation with the Bob Jones University School of Business Administration, the Department of Social Studies of the College of Arts and Science, and Bob Jones Academy.

ISBN 978-0-89084-810-4

15 14

Contents

How to Use the Activities Manual

These activities are designed to give you maximum flexibility. We have provided a ''menu'' of activities from which you can select the ones that will help you achieve your instructional goals. Before you begin each chapter, look over the activities and decide how you want to assign them. The *activity* codes and *skill* codes at the bottom of each page will help you decide.

Activity Codes

Each chapter has four to seven activities. The *activity* code tells you which sections of the chapter each activity covers. The code also tells you whether the activity is good for reinforcement, enrichment, or review.

- *Reinforcement* activities are based solely on the information in the textbook. They help students (1) to recognize and recall major terms and concepts in the chapter and (2) to ''put it all together.'' Some reinforcement activities cover the entire chapter. (Students can complete them as they read through the chapter or as they review for tests.) Other reinforcement activities apply to a specific section of the chapter. (Students can complete them as they read the section.)
- *Enrichment* activities go beyond the textbook. They help students (1) to apply information from the chapter, (2) to pursue subjects they find interesting, and (3) to develop special skills. Every student can benefit from these activities, but they are particularly useful for students who need a challenge. Most enrichment activities are related to a specific section in the chapter.
- *Chapter review* activities help students to prepare for the chapter test. They include crossword puzzles, games, and other interesting activities that review the chapter.

Alternative Uses of the Activities

Activities are useful for more than just homework. You can make them an integral part of your classroom discussion. Your students will especially appreciate your help in completing the more difficult activities.

- Homework—The students complete the activity at home.
- Class activity—The students complete the activity in class by themselves or in groups.
- Class discussion—You help the class complete the activity together in a classroom discussion.
- Lecture—You complete the activity on the chalkboard or overhead projector during your lecture, while the students take notes.
- Game—The students answer each question in a competition that pits team against team or ''every man for himself.''

Skill Codes

Every activity focuses on one of ten skills that economics students need to learn. Some activities teach specific skills such as graphing. Others teach basic thinking skills, such as recognizing terms.
Note: Each number in the chart below corresponds to the activity number for that chapter.

Chapter	1	2	3	4	5	6	7	8	9	10	11	12	13	14	15	16	17	18
1. Maps										1								
2. Charts					3						3	2	4-5			1		6
3. Graphs		3	2		3-4						2	3,5	3	1-2, 4				
4. Original Sources						1												
5. Research		1-2		3	2	2												
6. Recognition	3-5	4-5	3-4	1-2, 4	2, 5,7	3-4	5-7	4,6	5-6	4-5	4	1	6	6-7	6	4	4	7
7. Comprehension	3,6	4,6	3,5	5	6	5	7	5			4	6	6	3	6	4	4	7
8. Application	2						1-4	1-3	2-4	2-3	1,5	4	1-2	5	1-3, 5	2,3	1	1, 3, 4
9. Analysis	1		1	3	1				1	1				3	4		2-3	5
10. Synthesis																		2

Alternatives to Grading and Burdensome Records

You don't need to grade all the activities. You can complete some of them in class discussions, games, and lectures, as mentioned above, or you can use some of the ideas below.

- Check marks—Give simple pluses and minuses. You can use this information to decide borderline grades or—if you use them—"effort" grades.
- Extra credit—Let students do activities for extra credit, if they wish.
- Sporadic grades—Grade every third or fourth activity, but do not let students know which activities will be graded.
- Notebook—Make students keep their activities in a notebook. Collect the notebooks quarterly and grade them for neatness, completeness, and accuracy.

Economics

Economics in the News

Economic news and issues can be found throughout the pages of your newspaper. Everywhere one turns, economic choices are being made. For example, some recent newspapers had the following headlines:

> Japan and the U.S. Reach a New Five-Year Accord on Trade
> OPEC Ministers Agree Unanimously to Extend the Group's Daily Output Ceiling
> Stock Prices Slip but Bank Issues Surge
> Sales of Cars and Trucks Manufactured in North America Fall 12.9%

Find several issues of the same newspaper. Locate articles that address economic issues and complete the following.

1. Date and Page of Newspaper _____

   Headline and Brief Summary _____

   _____

   _____

2. Date and Page of Newspaper _____

   Headline and Brief Summary _____

   _____

   _____

3. Date and Page of Newspaper _____

   Headline and Brief Summary _____

   _____

   _____

4. Date and Page of Newspaper _____

   Headline and Brief Summary _____

   _____

   _____

5. Date and Page of Newspaper _____

   Headline and Brief Summary _____

   _____

   _____

6. Date and Page of Newspaper _____

   Headline and Brief Summary _____

   _____

   _____

Economics

Economic Choices

List five ''economic choices'' you have made already today.

1. *Answers will vary.* _____
2. _____
3. _____
4. _____
5. _____

Subjective Value

Give possible reasons that each of the following might have a high subjective value to one person and a low subjective value to someone else.

1. Lawn mower *Answers will vary, but one possible answer might be that a person with a lawn cutting business would highly value a lawn mower; thus, his subjective value would be relatively high. On the other hand, a person who has no yard to mow would place a relatively lower subjective value upon a lawn mower.*

2. Newspaper *Answers will vary, but one possible answer might be that a person with a need to read the classified advertising section would highly value a newspaper; thus, his subjective value would be relatively high. On the other hand, a person who cannot read would place a relatively lower subjective value upon having a newspaper.*

3. Candy bar *Answers will vary, but one possible answer might be that a person with a case of diabetes might highly value a candy bar as an emergency source of blood sugar; thus, his subjective value would be relatively high. On the other hand, a person who is allergic to one or more of a candy bar's ingredients would place a relatively lower subjective value upon having a candy bar.*

4. Jeep *Answers will vary, but one possible answer might be that a missionary in the outback of Australia would highly value a Jeep; thus, his subjective value would be relatively high. On the other hand, a five-year-old child would place a relatively lower subjective value upon having a Jeep.*

5. Cellular telephone *Answers will vary, but one possible answer might be that a doctor would highly value a cellular telephone if his job requires that he be notified in cases of emergency; thus, his subjective value would be relatively high. On the other hand, a person who values his privacy and wishes never to be disturbed would place a relatively lower subjective value upon having a cellular telephone.*

Economics

Word Scramble

Unscramble the following terms. After all words have been unscrambled, place the letters that are double underlined in the spaces provided at the bottom of this exercise and unscramble them to solve the riddle.

1. tastybiliaini   _i_ _n_ _s_ _a_ _t_ _i_ _a_ _b_ _i_ _l_ _i_ _t_ _y_

2. dogso   _g_ _o_ _o_ _d_ _s_

3. glycerinc   _r_ _e_ _c_ _y_ _c_ _l_ _i_ _n_ _g_

4. scot   _c_ _o_ _s_ _t_

5. sciencmoo   _e_ _c_ _o_ _n_ _o_ _m_ _i_ _c_ _s_

6. tuli   _u_ _t_ _i_ _l_

Riddle: What the economist found in the sand at the beach.

_r_ _d_ _a_ _l_ _o_ _s_ _l_ ⇒ _____ *dollars* _____ .

Matching

To the left of each number, place the letter of the definition or example that best corresponds to the item. Each answer is used only once.

A. intrinsic value
B. macroeconomics
C. microeconomics
D. normative economics

E. opportunity cost
F. services
G. utility

_E_ 1. regret

_F_ 2. intangible products

_B_ 3. study of large-scale economic events

_G_ 4. satisfaction

_C_ 5. study of the choices of individual people, households, and businesses

_D_ 6. ''Feeding the poor should be our greatest economic priority.''

_A_ 7. ''As a ditch digger I *should* be paid $100 per hour. After all, it took years of study to perfect my digging technique!''

Chapter Review   **Skills: Recognition/Comprehension**   **3**

Economics

Multiple Choice

Choose the response that best answers the question or completes the sentence.

D 1. Which of the following would you consider to be an "economic good"?
  A. an old, worn-out tire found in the city landfill
  B. the assistance of a paid tour guide
  C. money in one's bank account
  D. a computer

B 2. Which of the following is *not* one of the three types of goods described in your text?
  A. free goods
  B. opportunity goods
  C. economic goods
  D. nuisance goods

D 3. You have decided to quit your job in the country in order to go to college in the city. Which of the following would *not* be an opportunity cost of going to college?
  A. the loss of the $15 per hour you were earning in the country
  B. the money you have to spend on your books
  C. the loss of the pleasant environment of the country as opposed to the city
  D. the additional earning power you will have as a result of being a college graduate

C 4. You have only one evening to prepare for two tests the next day. If you concentrate on studying economics and ignore English, you will receive a 93 on your economics test and a 72 on your English test. If, on the other hand, you study English and ignore economics, you will receive a 91 on your English test and an 83 on your economics test. The opportunity cost of receiving a 91 on your English test rather than a 72 is a
  A. 19 point gain on your English test.
  B. 10 point loss on your English test.
  C. 10 point loss on your economics test.
  D. 21 point gain on your economics test.

C 5. Which of the following would be considered a question of *microeconomics*?
  A. "What is the inflation in the United States?"
  B. "What percentage of income does the average Japanese person save?"
  C. "How much should General Motors charge for its new car model?"
  D. "When will the stock market reach its peak?"

Economics

Crossword Puzzle

Fill in the blanks on the crossword puzzle with the words that best correspond to the definitions or statements provided.

ACROSS

4. satisfaction that a person loses by foregoing the next best choice
7. Menger said that it could be worth more than diamonds.
9. a tangible thing that has a measurable life span
10. a common-sense science
12. one of the things that the "man of God" should "follow after" (I Timothy 6:11)
13. worth determined by the nature of the product itself
14. types of goods and services that have a price tag of zero
15. the father of the Austrian school of economic thought
16. The unregenerate world views economics as the "_____."
18. economic statement of opinion
19. Its value was debated in contrast to that of water.
20. the "economist" in Luke 12:42
21. an imaginary unit of satisfaction
22. a biblical king in the book of Ecclesiastes who contemplated the idea of insatiability

23. usefulness
24. the idea that everything is limited in quantity
25. the study of large-scale choices
26. There are no infinite resources; rather, everything is _____.

DOWN

1. worth determined by usefulness to the buyer
2. kinds of goods and services that bear a negative economic cost
3. An intangible product is known as a _____.
4. the satisfaction a person receives from a choice
5. a statement of economic fact
6. Economics is the science of _____.
8. the idea that everyone has unlimited wants
11. the study of choices made by small, individual units
12. what the world cannot give but Christ can (John 14:27)
17. the school of economic thought that emphasizes the free market, private property, and the limited role of government

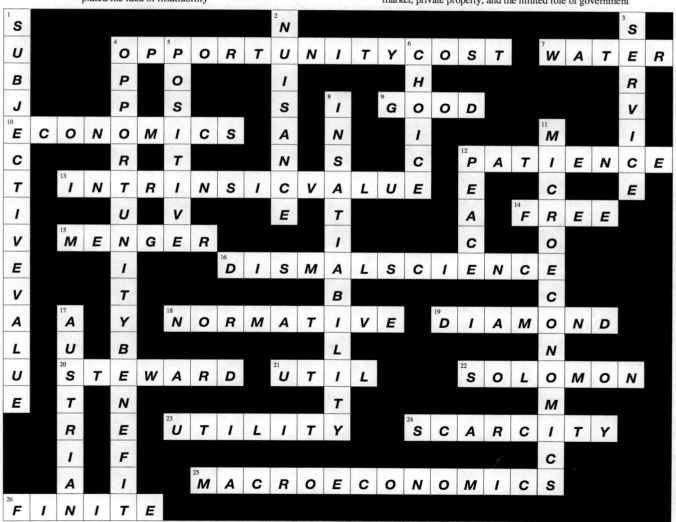

Name _____

Short Answer

Fill in the blanks with the word, phrase, or list that best answers the question or completes the sentence.

1. Economics is the common-sense science of how and why people make the choices they do. As a science, economics always begins with the _____*observation*_____ of choices.

2. People, businesses, and governments must make choices because of the conflict caused by the two contrary principles of _____*insatiability*_____ and _____*scarcity*_____.

3. Most goods carry a price tag that is greater than zero. Such goods are called _____ _____*economic goods*_____.

4. In 1871 Karl Menger solved an economic riddle called the Diamond-Water Paradox. Some argued that diamonds were more valuable than water, while others argued the opposite case. Which group was correct? *Actually, both groups were correct because Menger reasoned that value is determined by the subject (the receiver of the good) rather than the object itself; hence his new theory was called the principle of subjective value.*

5. "The whole of economics can be reduced to a single lesson," said economist Henry Hazlitt, "and that lesson can be reduced to a single sentence." In your own words, what was that sentence? *Your students, of course, will use their own words, but Hazlitt's words were, "The art of economics consists in looking not merely at the immediate but at the longer effects of any act or policy; it consists in tracing the consequences of that policy not merely for one group but for all groups."*

6. Explain the difference between positive and normative economic statements. *A positive economic statement is an assertion of observable economic fact. A normative economic statement is one of personal opinion.*

Diminishing Marginal Utility

Bring into the class a student who is not a member of the class and who has just finished some vigorous exercising. (Perhaps you can get a student straight from a physical education class.) Have him sit down before the class and tell him that you are conducting an experiment in economics and that you wish for him to drink several premeasured 2-ounce glasses of some athletic thirst-quenching drink and for him to tell you how satisfying each of them was on a utility scale of 1 to 20, with 20 utils being the most satisfying and 1 being the least satisfying. Have him drink one glassful and report his satisfaction. Have him continue drinking and reporting until he cannot drink anymore. Each student in the class should record each of his reports on the following marginal utility schedule. After all responses are entered, enter a marginal utility curve on the graph provided. How well did your results conform to William Jevons's principle of diminishing marginal utility?

This would be a good place to discuss the futility of seeking satisfaction with material possessions.

Marginal Utility Schedule					
Glass #	Marginal Satisfaction Provided by This Glass	+	Previous Level of Total Satisfaction	=	New Total Overall Satisfaction
1					
2					
3					
4					
5					
6					
7					
8					
9					
10					
11					
12					

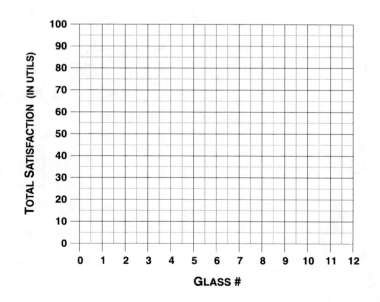

Economics

Law of Demand

Ask one of your parents how many cans of soup (or some other nonperishable grocery item) he or she would be willing to purchase at five progressively higher prices. Begin with an extremely low price, such as five cents per can, and raise the price to an extremely high price, such as $4.50 per can. Graph your results on the following graph. Be sure to label the horizontal axis of your graph.

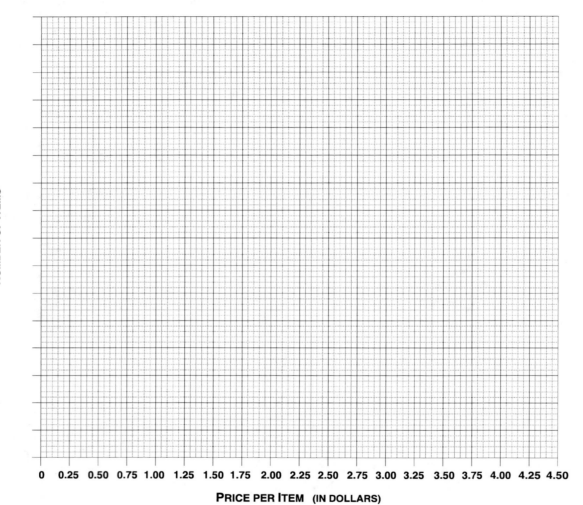

NUMBER OF ITEMS

0   0.25   0.50   0.75   1.00   1.25   1.50   1.75   2.00   2.25   2.50   2.75   3.00   3.25   3.50   3.75   4.00   4.25   4.50

PRICE PER ITEM   (IN DOLLARS)

Economics

Graphing

1. Market research has determined that a certain retail business will be able to sell its new *Volcano!* model electric hair dryer in the following quantities at each of the prices given in the demand schedule below. Use this information to construct a demand curve for the hair dryers on the graph provided. Label the demand curve "demand$_1$."

Demand Schedule	
Price	Quantity Demanded (Units)
$ 6.00	1,000
8.00	700
10.00	450
12.00	300
14.00	175
16.00	125
18.00	95
20.00	70
22.00	50
24.00	35
26.00	20
28.00	10
30.00	5

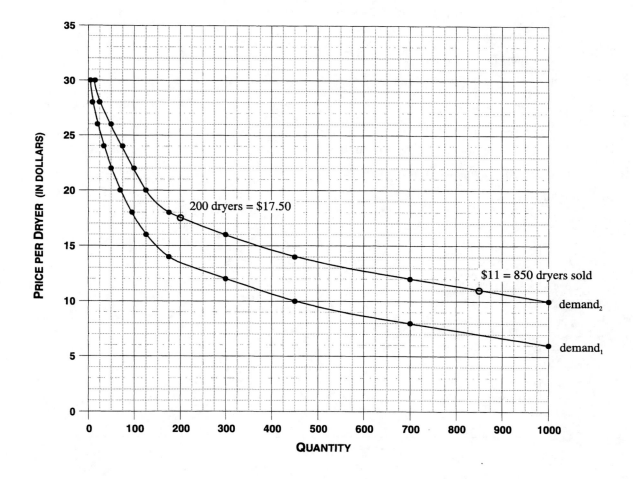

200 dryers = $17.50

$11 = 850 dryers sold

demand$_2$

demand$_1$

2. Suppose that the popularity of a new hairstyle suddenly increases the demand for the *Volcano!* hair dryer. Because of this change in consumer preference, the demand schedule has changed as seen in the following demand schedule. Add the new demand curve to the graph you just completed and label it "demand₂."

Demand Schedule	
Price	Quantity Demanded (Units)
$10.00	1,000
12.00	700
14.00	450
16.00	300
18.00	175
20.00	125
22.00	100
24.00	75
26.00	50
28.00	25
30.00	15

a. On demand₂ approximately how many *Volcano!* hair dryers will be demanded at a price of $11.00? ____850____

b. On demand₂ about what price would the store have to charge if it wishes to sell 200 *Volcano!* hair dryers? ____approximately $17.50____

3. Answer these questions based on the graph below.

a. Beginning at point #3, if the price of the good were to rise (everything else remaining constant), to which new point would you move? ___4___

b. Beginning at point #1, if the price of the good were to rise and you were to receive an increase in income (assume the good is a normal good), to what new point would you move? ___4___

c. Beginning at point #4, if you were planning to purchase the good next week but outside of the store you heard a manager say that the price was going to triple, to what new point would you immediately move? ___6___

d. Beginning at point #6, if the price of the good were to fall *and* you were to receive an increase in income (assume that the good is an inferior good), to what new point would you move? ___3___

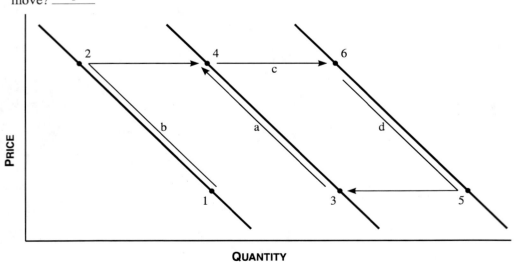

Economics

Word Scramble

Unscramble the following words. After all words have been unscrambled, place the letters that are double underlined in the spaces provided at the bottom of this exercise and unscramble them to solve the riddle.

1. recip __p__ __r__ __i__ __c__ __e__

2. grailman __m__ __a__ __r__ __g__ __i__ __n__ __a__ __l__

3. tisbestutu __s__ __u__ __b__ __s__ __t__ __i__ __t__ __u__ __t__ __e__

4. meddan __d__ __e__ __m__ __a__ __n__ __d__

5. vreuc __c__ __u__ __r__ __v__ __e__

6. morlan __n__ __o__ __r__ __m__ __a__ __l__

Riddle: By paying her a compliment, the economist hoped to make her his

__p__ __e__ __m__ __n__ __t__ __e__ __m__ __c__ __o__ __l__ ⇒ __complement__ .

Matching

To the left of each number, place the letter of the definition or example that best corresponds to the item. Each answer is used only once.

A. change in demand
B. demand
C. demand curve
D. inferior good

E. marginal utility
F. normal good
G. substitute good

__G__ 1. chicken or beef

__E__ 2. satisfaction gained by one more unit of input

__C__ 3. a graphic representation of the law of demand

__B__ 4. the act of buying

__A__ 5. a shift of a demand curve

__D__ 6. travel on a city bus

__F__ 7. something that one purchases more of as his income rises

Economics

Multiple Choice

Choose the response that best answers the question or completes the sentence.

_A_ 1. Which economist developed the principle of diminishing marginal utility?
A. William Jevons
B. Adam Smith
C. Karl Menger
D. Friedrich von Hayek

_C_ 2. Which of the following is *not* one of the three functions of price?
A. Prices provide incentives.
B. Prices transmit information.
C. Prices increase utility.
D. Prices redistribute income.

_C_ 3. The law of demand states that as the _____ of a good rises, other things being held constant, the _____ will fall.
A. price, quality
B. supply, quantity supplied
C. price, quantity demanded
D. quantity demanded, price

_A_ 4. Which of the following will *not* lead to a change in demand?
A. a change in the price of the good
B. a change in the income of buyers
C. a change in price expectations
D. a change in preferences

_B_ 5. Assume that going out to dinner at a nice restaurant is a normal good. What will happen to your demand curve for this good if your income rises?
A. It will rise.
B. It will shift to the right.
C. It will shift to the left.
D. You will move up along the demand curve to the left.

_D_ 6. Assume that fountain pens and fountain pen ink are complementary goods. A severe shortage in one of the main ingredients has caused the price of fountain pen ink to rise from $2 per bottle to $2,000 per bottle. What will happen to the demand for fountain pens?
A. It will increase.
B. It will remain unchanged.
C. It will increase for a short time then decrease.
D. It will decrease.

Economics

Short Answer

Fill in the blanks with the word or phrase that best answers the question or completes the sentence.

1. The pastor of your church asked you to clean the inside of the church building. You asked a friend to come and help you do the job. Without telling you, your friend put out the word that help was needed. The day of the cleanup arrived and so did 500 fellow church members. In the end you found that because everyone was bumping into each other, it took *longer* to clean the church with all the ''help'' than if you and your friend had done it alone. You could say that the job suffered from a case of ___diminishing marginal utility___.

2. Freidrich von Hayek wrote an article describing how prices automatically transmit information to producers and consumers. The article was called ___The Use of Knowledge in Society___.

3. Assume that manufacturer A develops a new kind of razor which ''revolutionizes the shaving experience.'' It seems that the company has designed the razor to conform perfectly to the face of the user by means of a gel-filled cushion. Further assume that while costing consumers twice as much as its next best competing model made by manufacturer B, this new razor has immediately won 75% of the shaving market. Describe how the three functions of the price mechanism would work in a free market. *Wording will vary. As manufacturer B notices its sales dipping, it becomes concerned and begins an investigation. It soon discovers that its former customers are willing to pay twice as much for manufacturer A's new razor. Thus (1) the price has transmitted information about consumer preferences. Wishing to stay in business, manufacturer B (2) has incentive to produce a similar razor. Once its new razor goes on the market, it regains much of its old market share, and (3) wealth is redistributed away from manufacturer A to itself.*

4. Why does the law of demand work the way it does? *Wording will vary. Each person has a subjective value for a particular good; thus, some are willing to pay more for it than others. As the price of the good falls, some consumers who before found that the price was above their subjective values now find the price below their subjective values, leading them to make a purchase. Hence, as the price of a good falls, the quantity demanded of that good rises and vice versa.*

5. What is the difference between a *change in quantity demanded* and a *change in demand?* *Wording will vary. A change in quantity demanded is the change in the number of items purchased as a result of a change in the price. A change in demand is a situation where more or less of a good is purchased without a change in the good's price. A change in demand is represented by a shift of the demand curve either to the right or left.*

6. List the four conditions that could lead to a change in demand.
   - *a change in consumer income*
   - *a change in the price of related goods*
   - *a change in tastes and preferences*
   - *a change in expectations about the future price of the good*

Economics

Combination of Supply and Demand

One of the most interesting things about the laws of supply and demand is that the laws do not apply only to goods for sale in stores. On the contrary, the laws of supply and demand apply to a great many other facets of economic life. For example, in the labor market you are the supplier and your employer is the demander. If the cost of labor to the firm (wages and other benefits) is greater than the equilibrium price of labor, a surplus of labor (unemployment) will be the result. If, on the other hand, the cost of labor to the business is below the equilibrium price, a shortage of labor will result. Below is a supply and demand schedule for labor for the Quantum Corporation. Note that the quantities are in terms of hours of labor per week; therefore, each forty hours equals one employee. Plot the supply and demand schedules on the graph provided and answer the questions that follow.

Quantum Corporation Labor Demand and Supply Schedule		
Cost Per Hour of Labor	Quantity of Labor Demanded (in hours)	Quantity of Labor Supplied (in hours)
$60.00	12,000	72,000
50.00	14,000	70,000
40.00	20,000	64,000
30.00	28,000	54,000
20.00	42,000	42,000
14.00	54,000	32,000
10.00	66,000	22,000
4.00	86,000	4,000

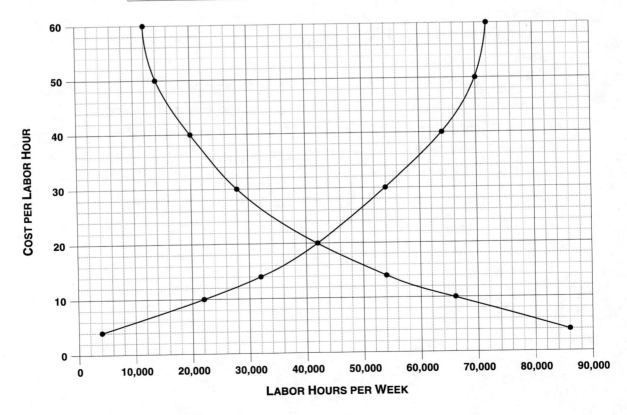

1. Why does the Quantum Corporation's labor demand curve slope downward and to the right?
   Answers will vary, but your students should mention the fact that as the cost per hour of labor declines, profits for the firm increase; therefore, the firm is willing to employ more labor.

2. What costs go into making up the "cost of labor"? *Answers will vary, but your students should include items such as wages, medical benefits, dental benefits, life insurance, disability insurance, unemployment compensation contributions that the employer must make to the state unemployment compensation fund per employee, the employer's portion of Social Security contributions, vacation pay, sick pay, costs in maintaining employee lounges and cafeterias, and programs for employees who abuse alcohol and drugs.*

3. What is the equilibrium cost per hour of labor, and how many employees will be employed at that cost? *$20 per hour and 1,050 workers (42,000 hours of labor per week)*

4. Let us suppose that the Quantum Corporation is a union shop; that is, each worker must be a member of the International Brotherhood of Computer Part Workers (IBCPW). And the current labor contract calls for wages of $12 per hour and benefits of $8 per hour, which create for the firm a total cost of labor of $20 per hour. Suppose that the current labor contract is due to expire at the end of the month and the union is calling for a 30% increase in wages and benefits. Under the threat of a strike, the management of Quantum concede to the demands.
   a. What will be Quantum's new cost of labor per hour? *$26 ($20 x 1.30)*
   b. What will be the total quantity of labor hours that workers will be willing to provide at the new cost per hour of labor? *approximately 49,000 hours*
   c. What is the total quantity of labor hours and workers per week that the Quantum Corporation will be willing to employ at the now higher cost per labor hour? *about 33,000 hrs. and 825 workers*
   d. Given your answers to questions 3 and 4c, how much unemployment will result from the 30% increase in labor cost? *Two hundred twenty-five employees will lose their jobs (1,050 - 825).*

5. What has this exercise shown you? *Answers will vary, but your students should have gained the knowledge that unemployment is a cost phenomenon. That is, if the demanded price of labor is greater than the cost of labor, a surplus of labor (unemployed labor) will result. Anything that drives up the cost of labor (such as increased wages, expanded benefits, increases in federally mandated minimum wages, and lowered productivity on the part of workers) will eventually lead to higher unemployment. On the other hand, anything that drives down the cost of labor (such as lower wages, reduced benefits, and increased productivity on the part of workers) will increase employment of labor.*

Economics

Graphing

1. Market research has determined that a certain retail business will be willing to sell its new *Volcano!* model electric hair dryer in the following quantities at each of the prices given in the supply schedule below. Use this information to construct a supply curve for the hair dryers on the graph provided. Label the supply curve "supply₁."

Supply Schedule	
Price	Quantity Supplied (Units)
$ 6.00	100
8.00	500
10.00	725
13.00	850
17.00	900
30.00	1,000

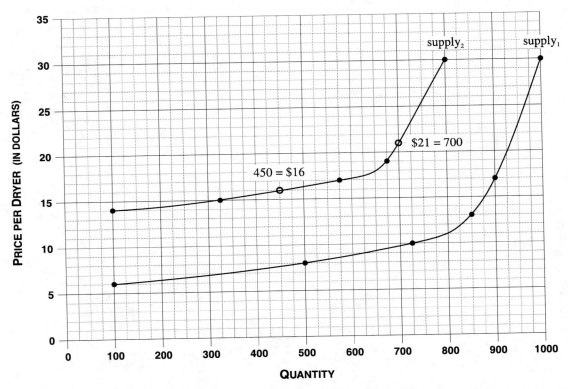

2. Suppose that the cost of the heating elements used in the hair dryers doubled in price, causing the firm to reevaluate the quantities they would be willing to sell at any given price. Because of this change, the supply schedule has been modified as seen below. Add a new supply curve to the graph you just completed and label it "supply₂."

Supply Schedule	
Price	Quantity Supplied (Units)
$ 14.00	100
15.00	325
17.00	575
19.00	675
30.00	800

a. On supply$_2$ approximately how many *Volcano!* hair dryers will be supplied at a price of $21.00? _____700_____

b. On supply$_2$ approximately what price would customers have to pay if they wished to buy 450 *Volcano!* hair dryers? _____$16_____

3. Answer these questions based on the graph below.

   a. Beginning at point #1, if the price of the good were to rise (everything else remaining constant), to which new point would you move? _____4_____

   b. Beginning at point #5, if the price of the good were to fall *and* the firm was able to receive a discount on the price it paid for the raw materials used in production, to which new point would you move? _____3_____

   c. Beginning at point #2, to which point would you eventually move if you were able to receive a discount on the price the firm paid for the raw materials used in production, but at the same time the employees demanded and received an increase in wages that was the same amount as the discount? _____2_____

   d. Beginning at point #5, if the price of the good were to fall and a substitute good were to fall in price, to what new point would you move? _____1_____

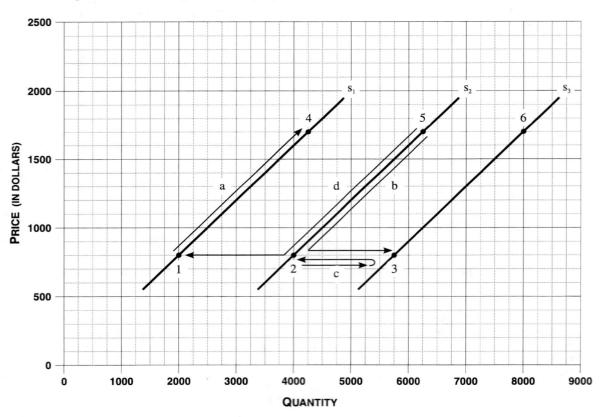

4. Provided below are supply and demand schedules for the Lexington Slugger baseball bat. Plot both supply and demand curves on the graph provided; complete and label the graphs and answer the questions that follow. *Be sure to mark the graph to prove your answers.*

Lexington Slugger Baseball Bats Supply and Demand Schedule

Price Per Bat	Quantity Supplied	Quantity Demanded
$4.00	1,000	8,000
6.00	2,500	5,500
10.00	4,000	4,000
16.00	4,750	2,250
32.00	6,000	1,500
52.00	7,000	1,000

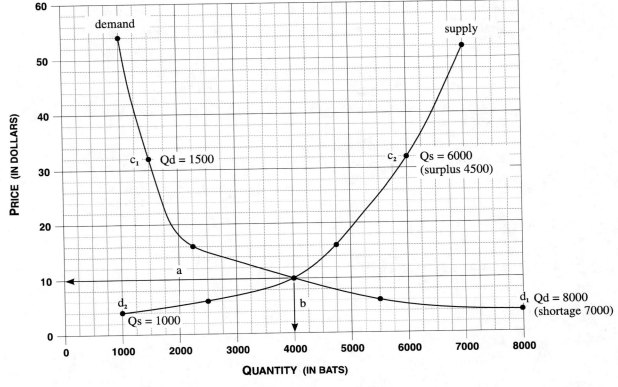

a. What is the market equilibrium price for the Lexington Slugger? _____ *$10.00*

b. What quantity of baseball bats will be sold at the equilibrium price? _____ *4,000*

c. What would be the surplus or shortage of Lexington Sluggers if the price was set at $32.00 per bat? *surplus of 4,500 (QS 6,000 – QD 1,500)*

d. What would be the surplus or shortage of Lexington Sluggers if the price was set at $4.00 per bat? *shortage of 7,000 (QD 8,000 – QS 1,000)*

Economics

True/False

Write *T* for True or *F* for False.

___T___ 1. The law of supply shows how the quantity supplied changes as the price that buyers are willing to pay changes.

___F___ 2. A typical supply curve slopes downward from left to right.

___T___ 3. If the price of a good rises, quantity supplied increases.

___T___ 4. A leftward shift of the supply curve indicates that a seller is willing to sell less of a good at every possible price.

___F___ 5. Technological improvements cause a good's supply curve to shift to the left.

___F___ 6. Thomas Malthus was a ''Utopian Economist'' who believed that the world was getting better and better.

___T___ 7. A greeting card manufacturer gets a special reduced price on envelopes. This lower cost of production will cause the supply curve to shift to the right.

___T___ 8. On a supply and demand graph, a price floor keeps the price above the equilibrium market price.

___T___ 9. On a supply and demand graph, there is only one price at which sellers will sell all they wish to sell at the same time that buyers will purchase all they wish to buy.

___F___ 10. The market solution to a surplus is to stimulate enough demand in order to absorb the excess.

Matching

To the left of each number, place the letter of the definition or example that best corresponds to the item. Each answer is used only once.

A. leftward shift of the supply curve   E. equilibrium price
B. price floor   F. change in quantity supplied
C. surplus   G. shortage
D. price ceiling   H. change in supply

___F___ 1. caused by a change in the price buyers are willing to pay

___A___ 2. a result of cutting production

___B___ 3. a barrier preventing a price from falling

___H___ 4. caused by a change in production costs

___E___ 5. no surpluses or shortages

___C___ 6. caused by the price's being higher than the market price

___G___ 7. solved by allowing the price to rise

___D___ 8. rent control

Economics

Word Search

Search the puzzle for the words listed below. Then connect the letters vertically, horizontally, diagonally, backwards, or forwards. *(Multiword combinations have no spaces separating the words.)*

surplus
price ceiling
supply
price floor
shortage
equilibrium

products
Malthus
technology
market price
rent control

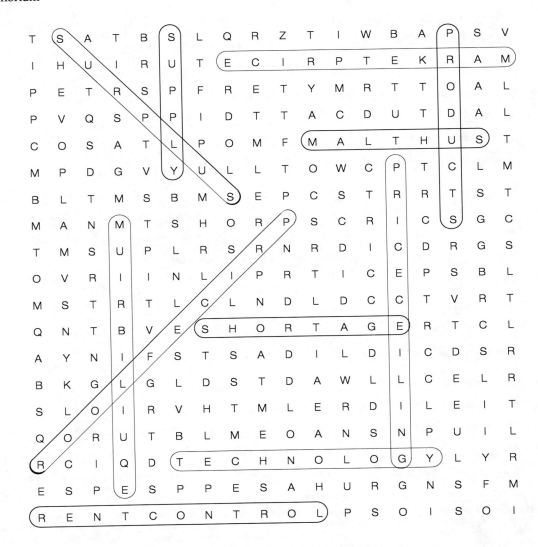

Economics

Short Answer

Fill in the blanks with the word, phrase, or list that best answers the question or completes the sentence.

1. _____*Supply*_____ is defined as the amount of goods and services business firms are willing and able to provide at different prices.

2. The law of supply says that as the price consumers are willing to pay for a good ____*rises*____, suppliers will be willing to supply a greater quantity.

3. Why does the law of supply work the way it does? *Wording will vary, but the students should recognize that the profit motive "drives" the law of supply. That is, when buyers are wiling to pay a higher price, suppliers become more willing to sell greater quantities in order to receive greater profits.*

4. What three conditions will cause a shift of the supply curve for a good or service?
   - *a change in technology*
   - *a change in production costs*
   - *a change in the prices of other goods*

5. Why will a shortage always occur when the price of a good is held below its equilibrium price?
   Wording will vary, but the students should mention that when the price of a good is below its equilibrium price, the law of demand leads consumers to demand a greater quantity while the law of supply leads suppliers to provide a smaller quantity—a situation that eventually leads to a shortage.

6. What are the three possible solutions to a surplus?
   - *increase demand*
   - *decrease supply*
   - *allow the price to fall to the equilibrium market price*

7. What do you think would happen if the government passed a law that made $1.00 the maximum price a merchant could charge for a good which has an equilibrium market price of 89 cents? Why?
   If the government set the maximum allowable price above the equilibrium market price, no shortage would occur. However, if the government passed a law setting the maximum price below the equilibrium price, a shortage would occur. For example, if the government passed a law forbidding merchants to charge more than $3 for a can of soup, the economy would be unaffected.

   The value of this question arises from the fact that conditions often change. For instance, many state legislatures have set maximum interest rates that banks can charge on loans. When these laws were passed, the rates were higher than the market interest rate; therefore, the economy suffered no ill effects. As inflation grew in the late 1970s, banks were forced to pay higher rates of interest on deposits but were unable to recoup their costs since the market interest rate on loans "bumped" up against the interest rate ceilings. Banks were losing money on loans, so they stopped lending until the laws were changed.

Economics

Name _____

Chapter 4   **Activity 1**

©1995 BJU Press. Reproduction prohibited.

Word Scramble

Unscramble the following words. After all words have been unscrambled, place the letters that are double underlined in the spaces provided at the bottom of this exercise and unscramble them to solve the riddle.

1. prentensehirepru

   e n t r e p r e n e u r s h i p

2. dehlooshus   h o u s e h o l d s

3. suchdeel   s c h e d u l e

4. placait   c a p i t a l

5. oldem   m o d e l

6. reverse   r e s e r v e

Riddle: The "disease" from which many consumers suffer.

n n i p o u c t m o s ⟹ __consumption__.

Matching

To the left of each number, place the letter of the definition or example that best corresponds to the item. Each answer is used only once.

A. budget surplus   E. financial capital
B. crowding out   F. profit
C. dissaving   G. real capital
D. interest   H. transfer payment

__D__ 1. factor payment for financial capital

__C__ 2. borrowing by individuals

__A__ 3. tax revenues = $1 million; government spending = $900,000

__F__ 4. factor payment for entrepreneurship

__H__ 5. welfare

__B__ 6. government borrowing prevents business borrowing

__G__ 7. tools used by business firms

__E__ 8. loans to business firms

Chapter Review   **Skill: Recognition**   23

Economics

Economic Models

On the blank schedule provided below, make an observation of the relationship between two variables and record your results. Examples might include the number of students that come in the school's front door during five 10-minute intervals prior to 8 A.M., the number of students that finish a foot race at various stopwatch times, the number of people who bring 2, 3, 4, 5, or 6 books to class, and so on. Be creative! After you have posted your results on the schedule, plot your observations on the blank line graph provided.

VARIABLE #1 _____

VARIABLE #2 _____

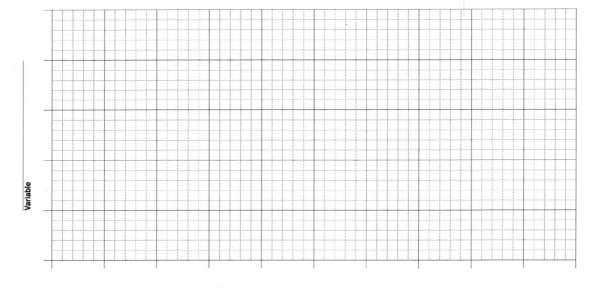

Observation Schedule	
Variable #1	Variable #2

Comment on the advantages and disadvantages of the schedule and the line graph methods of modeling. *Answers will vary, but the students will probably note that the observation schedule provides limited information, while the line graph provides a greater amount of information since points may be plotted on the line graph between observed plotted points.*

_____

Economics

Factors of Production

Think of three specific goods and then describe some specific types and uses of natural resources, labor, and financial capital that went into their production.

Example:

Product: _____ *computer* _____

- Land: *the plastic, glass, metal, wire, and other natural resources that go into the computer's production*

- Labor: *the work of production personnel on the computer assembly line, the services of the computer firm's accountants, the labor of the firm's research and development department, the efforts of the salespeople, and the services of the janitorial staff*

- Financial Capital: *the funds that are used to purchase the equipment needed to manufacture the computers; the equipment needed to prepare, package, and ship the finished product*

Product #1 _____

- Land: _____
  _____
  _____

- Labor: _____
  _____
  _____

- Financial Capital: _____
  _____
  _____

Product #2 _____

- Land: _____
  _____
  _____

- Labor: _____
  _____
  _____

- Financial Capital: _____
  _____
  _____

Product #3 _____

- Land: _____
  _____
  _____

- Labor: _____
  _____
  _____

- Financial Capital: _____
  _____
  _____

Extra! Extra!

Select one of the three products you surveyed in the previous question. Discuss some specific areas in which a firm would use entrepreneurship to direct, organize, and plan the production of the product.

Answers will vary. _____

_____
_____
_____
_____
_____
_____
_____
_____
_____
_____
_____
_____
_____
_____
_____
_____
_____
_____
_____
_____
_____

Economics

Multiple Choice

Choose the response that best answers the question.

__B__ 1. What is the chief advantage of the line graph over the schedule?
   A. The line graph is more scientific than the schedule.
   B. The line graph displays more information than the schedule.
   C. The line graph is more accurate than the schedule.
   D. The line graph is easier to read than a schedule.

__B, D__ 2. Which of the following are the two basic participants in the circular flow model?
   (Choose two answers.)
   A. government
   B. households
   C. financial markets
   D. business firms
   E. Federal Reserve Bank

__D__ 3. Which of the following would not be considered ''land''?
   A. hogs
   B. diamonds
   C. water
   D. money

__A__ 4. What is the most important factor of production?
   A. entrepreneurship
   B. financial capital
   C. labor
   D. land

__A__ 5. Which of the following is not a factor payment?
   A. transfer payments
   B. wages
   C. profits
   D. interest

__D__ 6. Which of the following is a type of dissaving?
   A. depositing money into a checking account
   B. spending all of one's income
   C. a loan from a financial institution to a business firm
   D. a household's withdrawal from a bank account

Economics

Short Answer

Fill in the blanks with the word, phrase, or list that best answers the question or completes the sentence.

1. Economists use _____*models*_____ to explain to students how economics works and to predict future economic events.

2. A _____*schedule*_____ is a type of economic model which provides a limited number of observations. A _____*line graph*_____, on the other hand, is used to link the limited number of observations in order to provide a much greater amount of information.

3. The two major participants in the circular flow are _____*households*_____ and _____*business firms*_____.

4. Another name for the sum of all goods and services produced by business firms and sold to final consumers is _____*gross national product*_____.

5. List the four factors of production and the factor payments associated with them.

Factor of Production	Factor Cost
Land (or natural resources)	Rent
Labor	Wages
Financial capital	Interest
Entrepreneurship	Profits

6. In your own words, what is entrepreneurship? *Answers will vary, but your students should identify the fact that entrepreneurship is the activity of creatively planning, organizing, and directing the first three factors of production in unique ways in order to develop new and useful goods and services. It would also be beneficial if they recognized that without entrepreneurship, economic progress would be seriously hampered.*

7. What is a "transfer payment"? *A transfer payment is a payment of money or goods made by government to persons for which no specific economic repayment is expected.*

8. To an economist, what is "savings"? *Savings is money that is placed with a financial institution either on deposit or in payment of a loan.*

9. The government is said to have a _____*deficit or budget deficit*_____ whenever its spending exceeds its tax receipts.

10. James Buchanan won the Nobel Prize for economics in 1986 for his development of public choice theory. What is public choice theory? *Answers will vary. Public choice theory is the analysis of the economic choices made by government.*

Economics

National Economic Goals and the News

The four national economic goals are constantly in the media. Below are listed a few examples of headlines found in some newspapers on the same day. Try to locate some for yourself and record your results in the spaces provided below. *You may wish to point out that although the national economic goals are sometimes contradictory and mutually exclusive, the media often chastise public officials if all the goals are not met!*

Average Weekly Pay of Factory Workers in May Rose to $449.35

A Bipartisan Panel Urged a $1,000 Federal Income-Tax Credit for Each Child

U.S. Budget Deficit Widened to Record

Swords-into-Plowshares Programs Stumble, Stranding Defense Workers

1. Date and Page of Newspaper _____
   Headline and Brief Summary _____
   _____
   _____

2. Date and Page of Newspaper _____
   Headline and Brief Summary _____
   _____
   _____

3. Date and Page of Newspaper _____
   Headline and Brief Summary _____
   _____
   _____

4. Date and Page of Newspaper _____
   Headline and Brief Summary _____
   _____
   _____

5. Date and Page of Newspaper _____
   Headline and Brief Summary _____
   _____
   _____

6. Date and Page of Newspaper _____
   Headline and Brief Summary _____
   _____
   _____

Economics

Name _____

Chapter 5   **Activity 2**

National Economic Goals

Explain each of the four national economic goals found on pages 67-68 of your text to three people: a junior high student, a middle-aged person, and an older person. Ask your subjects to rank the four goals in order of importance (with 1 being the most important and 4 being the least important). Also ask them to explain their reasons for ranking their choices as they did. *As students discuss their results in class, note possible correlations between the subjects' responses and their age, gender, economic station, etc.*

National Economic Goals & Personal Preferences

Subject	Low Unemployment Rate	Stable Prices	Economic Growth	Fair Distribution of Income	Reasons
Junior High School Student					
Middle-Aged Adult (35-50)					
Older Adult (Over 55)					

Matching

Match the terms with the definitions and examples.

A. capital goods
B. capital intensive
C. *Communist Manifesto*
D. egalitarian fairness
E. labor intensive
F. libertarian fairness
G. savings

__F__ 1. distribution of the nation's income based upon each individual's productivity

__D__ 2. distribution of the nation's income based upon the equality of each individual

__C__ 3. "from each according to his ability, to each according to his need"

__E__ 4. using relatively more human workers than equipment

__A__ 5. productive equipment

__B__ 6. using relatively more equipment than human workers

__G__ 7. the source of funds for businesses to purchase more productive equipment

Skills: Research/Recognition

Economics

The Distribution Question: Who Will Receive What Is Produced?

The distribution question is actually best asked as follows: "Who will receive the nation's income?" As the United States has grown older, its people have experienced a change in the sources of their income. The table below lists the personal income data for several years and the sources from which income was derived. Beside each source is that source's percentage of total income. Use the information to answer the questions that follow.

			Sources of Personal Income 1929-1990 (billions of dollars)*					
Year	**Total Personal Income**	**Wage and Salary Income**		**Dividend and Interest Income**		**Government Transfer Payments**		**All Other Sources**	
1929	$ 84.3	$ 50.5	59.9%	$ 12.7	15.1%	$ 1.5	1.8%	$ 19.6	23.2%
1940	77.6	49.9	64.3	9.3	12.1	3.1	4.0	15.3	19.7
1950	228.1	147.2	64.5	18.4	8.1	15.2	6.7	47.3	20.7
1960	409.2	272.8	66.6	38.4	9.4	28.8	7.0	69.2	16.9
1970	831.0	551.5	66.4	92.7	11.2	84.6	10.2	102.2	12.3
1980	2,265.4	1,376.6	60.8	331.1	14.6	321.5	14.2	236.2	10.4
1990	4,673.8	2,745.0	58.7	842.6	18.0	687.6	14.7	398.6	8.5
1993	5,387.6	3,080.4	57.2	854.1	15.9	911.6	16.9	541.5	10.1

* Source: Economic Report of the President, February 1994, Table B-26

1. In which year was total personal income down from the previously listed period? _____**1940**_____

2. In which listed year were government transfer payments at their lowest percentage of total personal income? _____**1929**_____ What was the percentage? _____**1.8%**_____

3. In which listed year were government transfer payments at their greatest percentage of total personal income? _____**1993**_____ What was the percentage? _____**16.9%**_____

4. In which listed year was wage and salary income at its greatest percentage of total personal income? _____**1960**_____ What was the percentage? _____**66.6%**_____

5. In which listed year was wage and salary income at its lowest percentage of total personal income? _____**1993**_____ What was the percentage? _____**57.2%**_____

6. On the graph provided on the next page, plot the percentage contribution toward total personal income for each of the categories of income. To make the graph more understandable, you might want to use four different colored pencils. Discuss your results in class, especially as your graph relates to the distribution question.

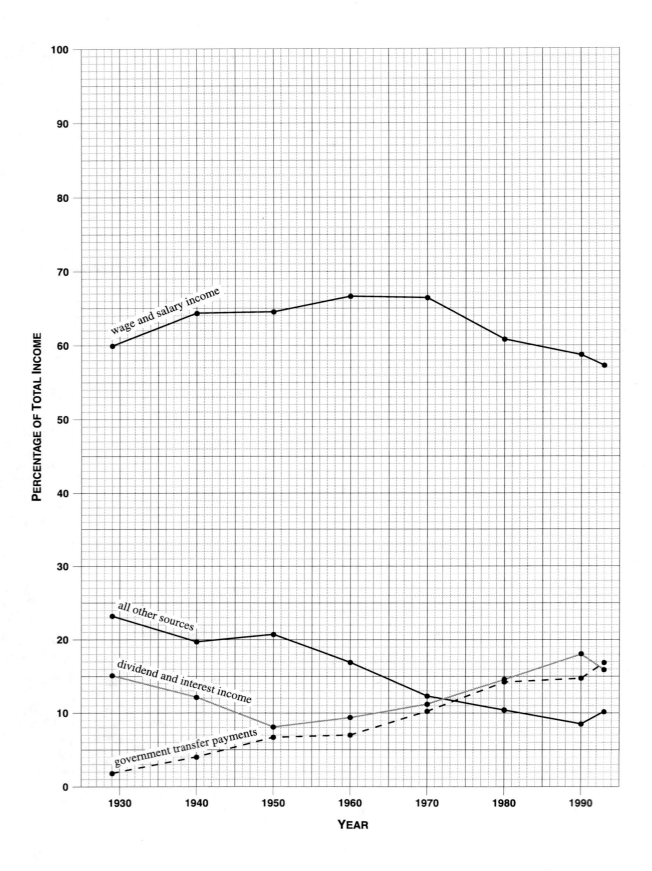

The Output Question and Interest Rates

The output question is really a question of the mixture of capital goods and consumer goods a nation believes is best. In a command economy, a central authority sets this mixture, but in a market economy, the mixture is determined by the market interest rate. As businesses experience an increased demand for their goods, they borrow money to purchase the capital goods needed to produce the goods that will earn them future profits. As interest rates rise (because of increased demand for business loans), consumers reduce their consumption spending in order to deposit their money in bank accounts. Thus, as interest rates rise, consumption expenditures fall, savings rise, and business investment increases.

The interest rate is the going price on borrowed money. Interest rates vary depending on who is doing the borrowing and for how long. Three important interest rates are the discount rate, the federal funds rate, and the prime rate. The discount rate is the rate the Federal Reserve Bank charges commercial banks. The federal funds rate is the rate banks charge one another for overnight loans when one is temporarily short of funds. The prime rate is the rate commercial banks charge their most creditworthy business borrowers.

These rates are important to economists, but more important than the rates themselves is the *change* in the rates. A change in interest rates signals a change in the economy. The *Economic Report of the President,* found in most public libraries, contains a wealth of economic information. On the graph below, plot the federal funds rate, the discount rate, and the prime rate as given in the *Economic Report of the President* table called "Bond Yields and Interest Rates." For easier reading, use three different colored pencils.

Money Market Interest Rates and Mortgage Rates: 1970 to 1993														
Type	1970	1975	1980	1981	1983	1984	1985	1987	1988	1989	1990	1991	1992	1993
Federal Reserve discount rate	5.95	6.25	11.77	13.42	8.50	8.80	7.69	5.66	6.20	9.21	8.10	5.69	3.52	3.02
Federal funds, effective rate	7.18	5.82	13.36	16.38	9.09	10.23	8.10	6.66	7.57	10.87	10.01	8.46	6.25	6.00
Prime rate charged by banks	7.91	7.86	15.27	18.87	10.79	12.04	9.93	8.21	9.32	6.93	6.98	5.45	3.25	3.00

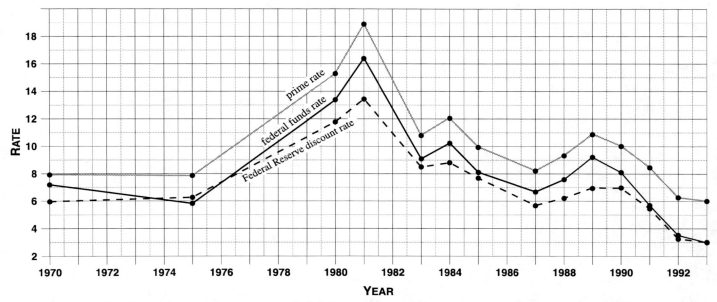

If the students do not have access to a copy of the Economic Report of the President, *you may wish to refer them to the* Statistical Abstracts of the United States. *If you do not wish this to be an overnight assignment, you may give your students the rates. Discuss the effects that these shifts had on the economy.*

Name _____

Economics

Chapter 5   **Activity 5**

Multiple Choice

Choose the response that best answers the question or completes the sentence.

___C___ 1. Which of the following is *not* one of the national economic goals mentioned in your text?
A. a low rate of unemployment
B. a healthy rate of economic growth
C. a positive balance of trade with other nations
D. a stable price level

___A___ 2. The consumer good/capital good tradeoff is really a tradeoff between
A. spending and saving.
B. saving and transfer payments.
C. labor intensive and capital intensive business practices.
D. libertarian and egalitarian fairness.

___B___ 3. What is the market solution to the output question?
A. Let a committee decide the correct mixture between capital goods and consumer goods.
B. Allow the interest rate to find its own free market level.
C. Allow each business the freedom to decide its own capital/labor mix.
D. Give the legislature the power to control income redistribution.

___A___ 4. What input question must every society answer?
A. How will the nation's goods be produced?
B. Who will receive the goods that a nation produces?
C. How many goods will the nation produce?
D. What types of goods shall the nation produce?

___D___ 5. What view of economics leads nations to introduce economic assistance programs such as food stamps, Social Security, and housing assistance?
A. libertarianism
B. economic Darwinism
C. economic leveling
D. safety-net egalitarianism

Economics

Short Answer

Fill in the blanks with the word, phrase, or list that best answers the question or completes the sentence.

1. _____ **Unemployment** _____ exists when someone who wishes to work cannot find a job.

2. The term _____ **economic growth** _____ refers to an increase in the quantity of goods and services a nation can produce.

3. In your own words, what is the difference between extensive and intensive economic growth?
   Answers will vary, but it is important that your students distinguish between the two by noting that extensive growth is economic growth based upon finding and using more resources. Intensive growth, however, is economic growth based upon using existing resources more efficiently.

4. List five consumer goods and five capital goods. After the list briefly describe the consumer good/capital good tradeoff. *The students should distinguish between goods that are used by final consumers and those used in the production of other goods or services. Answers will vary.*

Consumer Goods	Capital Goods
Shampoo	A school's chalkboard
Running shoes	Hair clippers
Ball-point pen	Corporate jet
Potato chips	Welding machine
Doll	Road grader

   The consumer good/capital good tradeoff states that a nation cannot produce everything it wishes. If it wishes to produce consumer goods, it gives up the ability to produce some capital goods and vice versa.

5. In the free market, what do rising and falling interest rates indicate? *Answers will vary. A rising interest rate is evidence that demand for consumer goods has increased to the point that business firms are demanding more loans in order to purchase more capital goods. A falling interest rate indicates the opposite situation.*

6. Why would a nation's government favor a labor intensive economy? *A nation's government might favor a labor intensive economy because such an economy uses more human labor than does a capital intensive economy. A capital intensive economy might lead to a temporarily higher unemployment rate.*

7. The distribution question asks, "Who will receive what is produced?" but the real question is *"Who will receive the nation's money, which provides the ability to purchase the nation's production?"*

Economics

Crossword Puzzle

Fill in the blanks on the crossword puzzle with the word or phrase that best corresponds to the definitions or statements provided. Multiword answers will have no spaces separating the words.

ACROSS

3. The libertarian concept of fairness has been dubbed "economic _____."
4. economic growth that comes from employing more resources
7. "If any would not _____, neither should he eat."
8. Egalitarian _____ holds that every person deserves a portion of the nation's wealth.
9. He brought communism to China.
10. This kind of good is used to create other goods.
13. welfare for which one must work
14. An economic goal of most nations is to have a stable _____ _____.
15. What the nation produces is dependent upon how much people consume versus how much people _____.

18. This question asks, "How will the nation's goods be produced?"

DOWN

1. the father of communism
2. the term denoting a firm that uses relatively more equipment than human labor
4. equal distribution of the nation's income
5. _____ fairness argues that a person's income is dependent upon how well he satisfies others' wants.
6. An economic goal for which most nations strive is a low _____ level.
11. Karl Marx's book was called *The Communist* _____.
12. Karl Marx's middle name
16. Karl Marx's friend and coauthor
17. This question asks, "What will be produced?"

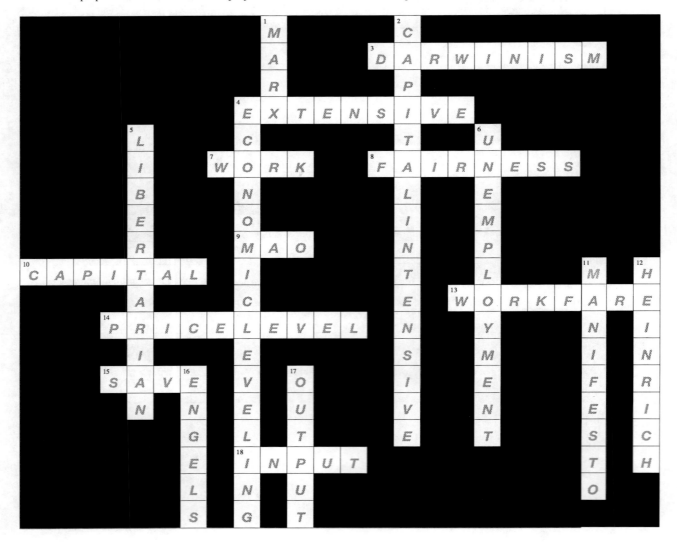

Economics

The Former Soviet Union: An Example of the Tenets of Centralized Socialism

Virtually every nation on earth has established a constitution which serves as the basis for all of their laws. In addition to serving as a basis of law, a nation's constitution serves as a manifesto, or declaration, of the ideological principles under which the nation seeks to guide itself. Where better to look, therefore, to find the principles of centralized socialism, than the constitution of the former Soviet Union? After reading the excerpts from the *Constitution (Fundamental Law) of the Union of Soviet Socialistic Republics,* answer the questions that follow.

КОНСТИТУЦИЯ

(ОСНОВНОЙ ЗАКОН)

СОЮЗА СОВЕТСКИХ СОЦИАЛИСТИЧЕСКИХ РЕСПУБЛИК

Принята на внеочередной седьмой сессии Верховного Совета СССР девятого созыва 7 октября 1977 года

☆

ИЗДАНИЕ ВЕРХОВНОГО СОВЕТА СССР
МОСКВА ○ 1977

Chapter 1

THE POLITICAL SYSTEM

Article 1. The Union of Soviet Socialist Republics is a socialist state of the whole people, expressing the will and interests of the workers, peasants, and intelligentsia, the working people of all the nations and nationalities of the country.

Article 2. All power in the USSR belongs to the people.

The people exercise state power through Soviets of People's Deputies, which constitute the political foundation of the USSR.

All other state bodies are under the control of, and accountable to, the Soviets of People's Deputies.

Article 3. The Soviet state is organized and functions on the principle of democratic centralism, namely the electiveness of all bodies of state authority, from the lowest to the highest, their accountability to the people, and the obligation of lower bodies to observe the decision of higher ones. Democratic centralism combines central leadership with local initiative and creative activity and with the responsibility of each state body and official for the work entrusted to them.

Article 8. Work collectives take part in discussing and deciding state and public affairs, in planning production and social development, in training and placing personnel, and in discussing and deciding matters pertaining to the management of enterprises and institutions, the improvement of working and living conditions, and the use of funds allocated both for developing production and for social and cultural purposes and financial incentives.

Chapter 2

THE ECONOMIC SYSTEM

Article 10. The foundation of the economic system of the USSR is socialist ownership of the means of production in the form of state property (belonging to all the people) and collective farm-and-cooperative property.

Socialist ownership also embraces the property of trade unions and other public organizations which they require to carry out their purposes under their rules.

The state protects socialist property and provides conditions for its growth.

No one has the right to use socialist property for personal gain or other selfish ends.

Article 11. State property, i.e., the common property of the Soviet people, is the principal form of socialist property.

The land, its minerals, waters, and forests are the exclusive property of the state. The state owns the basic means of production in industry, construction, and agriculture; means of transport and communication; the banks; the property of state-run trade organizations and public utilities, and other state-run undertakings; most urban housing; and other property necessary for state purposes.

Article 12. The property of collective farms and other cooperative organizations, and of their joint undertakings, comprises the means of production and other assets which they require for the purposes laid down in their rules. The land held by collective farms is secured to them for their free use in perpetuity.

The state promotes development of collective farm-and-cooperative property and its approximation to state property.

Collective farms, like other land users, are obliged to make effective and thrifty use of the land and to increase its fertility.

Article 13. Earned income forms the basis of the personal property of Soviet citizens. The personal property of citizens of the USSR may include articles of everyday use, personal consumption and convenience, the implements and other objects of a small-holding, a house, and earned savings. The personal property of citizens and the right to inherit it are protected by the state.

Citizens may be granted the use of plots of land, in the manner prescribed by law, for a subsidiary small-holding (including the keeping of livestock and poultry), for fruit and vegetable growing, or for building an individual dwelling. Citizens are required to make rational use of the land allotted to them. The state and collective farms provide assistance to citizens in working their small-holdings.

Property owned or used by citizens shall not serve as a means of deriving unearned income or be employed to the detriment of the interests of society.

Article 14. The source of the growth of social wealth and of the well-being of the people, and of each individual, is the labor, free from exploitation, of Soviet people.

The state exercises control over the measure of labor and of consumption in accordance with the principle of socialism: "From each according to his ability, to each according to his work." It fixes the rate of taxation on taxable income.

Socially useful work and its results determine a person's status in society. By combining material and moral incentives and encouraging innovation and a creative attitude to work, the state helps transform labor into the prime vital need of every Soviet citizen.

Article 15. The supreme goal of social production under socialism is the fullest possible satisfaction of the people's growing material and cultural and intellectual requirements.

Relying on the creative initiative of the working people, the socialist emulation and scientific and technological progress, and by improving the forms and methods of economic management, the state ensures growth of the productivity of labor, raising of the efficiency of production and of the quality of

work, and dynamic, planned, proportionate development of the economy.

Article 16. The economy of the USSR is an integral economic complex comprising all the elements of social production, distribution, and exchange on its territory.

The economy is managed on the basis of state plans for economic and social development, with due account of the sectoral and territorial principles, and by combining centralized direction with the managerial independence and initiative of individual and amalgamated enterprises and other organizations, for which active use is made of management accounting, profit, cost, and other economic levers and incentives.

Article 18. In the interests of the present and future generations, the necessary steps are taken in the USSR to protect and make scientific, rational use of the land and its mineral and water resources, and the plant and animal kingdoms, to preserve the purity of air and water, ensure reproduction of natural wealth, and improve the human environment.

Chapter 3

SOCIAL DEVELOPMENT AND CULTURE

Article 20. In accordance with the communist ideal ''The free development of each is the condition of the free development of all,'' the state pursues the aim of giving citizens more and more real opportunities to apply their creative energies, abilities, and talents, and to develop their personalities in every way.

Article 23. The state pursues a steady policy of raising people's pay levels and real incomes through increase in productivity.

In order to satisfy the needs of Soviet people more fully, social consumption funds are created. The state, with the broad participation of public organizations and work collectives, ensures the growth and just distribution of these funds.

Chapter 4

FOREIGN POLICY

Article 28. The USSR steadfastly pursues a Leninist policy of peace and stands for strengthening of the security of nations and broad international cooperation.

The foreign policy of the USSR is aimed at ensuring international conditions favorable for building communism in the USSR, safeguarding the state interests of the Soviet Union, consolidating the positions of world socialism, supporting the struggle of peoples for national liberation and social progress, preventing wars of aggression, achieving universal and complete disarmament, and consistently implementing the principle of the peaceful coexistence of states with different social systems.

In the USSR war propaganda is banned.

Chapter 7

THE BASIC RIGHTS, FREEDOMS, AND DUTIES OF CITIZENS OF THE USSR

Article 40. Citizens of the USSR have the right to work (that is, to guaranteed employment and pay in accordance with the quantity and quality of their work, and not below the state-established minimum), including the right to choose their trade or profession, type of job and work in accordance with their inclination, abilities, training and education, with due account of the needs of society.

This right is ensured by the socialist economic system, steady growth of the productive forces, free vocational and professional training, improvement of skills, training in new trades or professions, and development of the systems of vocational guidance and job placement.

Article 42. Citizens of the USSR have the right to health protection.

This right is ensured by free, qualified medical care provided by state health institutions; by extension of the network of therapeutic and health-building institutions; by the development and improvement of safety and hygiene in industry; by carrying out broad prophylactic measures; by measures to improve the environment; by special care for the health of the rising generation, including prohibition of child labor, excluding the work done by children as part of the school curriculum; and by developing research to prevent and reduce the incidence of disease and ensure citizens a long and active life.

Article 43. Citizens of the USSR have the right to maintenance in old age, in sickness, and in the event of complete or partial disability or loss of the breadwinner.

This right is guaranteed by social insurance of workers and other employees and collective farmers; by allowance for temporary disability; by the provision by the state or by collective farms of retirement pensions, disability pensions, and pensions for loss of the breadwinner; by providing employment for the partially disabled; by care for the elderly and the disabled; and by other forms of Social Security.

Article 44. Citizens of the USSR have the right to housing.

This right is ensured by the development and upkeep of state and socially owned housing; by assistance for cooperative and individual house building; by fair distribution, under public control, of the housing that becomes available through fulfillment of the program of building well-appointed dwellings, and by low rents and low charges for utility services. Citizens of the USSR shall take good care of the housing allocated to them.

Article 45. Citizens of the USSR have the right to education.

This right is ensured by free provision of all forms of education, by the institution of universal,

compulsory secondary education, and broad development of vocational, specialized secondary, and higher education, in which instruction is oriented toward practical activity and production; by the development of extramural, correspondence, and evening courses; by the provision of state scholarships and grants and privileges for students; by the free issue of school textbooks; by the opportunity to attend a school where teaching is in the native language; and by the provision of facilities for self-education.

Article 49. Every citizen of the USSR has the right to submit proposals to state bodies and public organizations for improving their activity, and to criticize shortcomings in their work.

Officials are obliged, within established time-limits, to examine citizens' proposals and requests, to reply to them, and to take appropriate action.

Persecution for criticism is prohibited. Persons guilty of such persecution shall be called to account.

Article 50. In accordance with the interest of the people and in order to strengthen and develop the socialist system, citizens of the USSR are guaranteed freedom of speech, of the press, and of assembly, meetings, street processions, and demonstrations.

Exercise of these political freedoms is ensured by putting public buildings, streets, and squares at the disposal of the working people and their organizations, by broad dissemination of information, and by the opportunity to use the press, television, and radio.

Article 52. Citizens of the USSR are guaranteed freedom of conscience, that is, the right to profess or not to profess any religion, and to conduct religious worship or atheistic propaganda. Incitement of hostility or hatred on religious grounds is prohibited.

In the USSR, the church is separated from the state, and the school from the church.

Articles 54. Citizens of the USSR are guaranteed inviolability of the person. No one may be arrested except by a court decision or on the warrant of a procurator.

Article 56. The privacy of citizens, and of their correspondence, telephone conversations, and telegraphic communications is protected by law.

1. According to the constitution of the former USSR, what was the "foundation of the economic system" of the USSR? _Article 10: the socialist ownership of the means of production_

2. To whom did the land, its minerals, waters, and forests belong? _Article 11: They were the exclusive property of the state._

3. According to Article 13, what were citizens allowed to own? _Citizens were allowed to keep their earned income, articles for everyday use and for personal consumption and convenience, personal tools, a house, and their personal savings._

4. According to Article 14, what determined a person's status in society? _the social usefulness of a person's work and its results_

5. According to Article 15, who managed the economy, and what was the goal of management of the economy? _The economy was managed on the basis of state plans with the goal of satisfaction of people's material, cultural, and intellectual requirements._

6. Article 23 gives us an insight into the attitude of the government of the former Soviet Union toward the distribution question. What do you believe was that attitude? _Answers will vary, but students should note that the Soviets tended toward a command system with a high emphasis on egalitarian fairness. However, according to Article 23, pay was determined by a worker's productivity._

7. What did Article 40 guarantee to every citizen? _a job_

8. Articles 42 through 45 indicate that certain free services were guaranteed to each citizen. List those services. _free health care, disability income, financial maintenance in old age, low-rent housing, education_

9. Article 52 ensured that the church was separate from the state and that the school was separate from the _church._

Economics

Economic Systems and Public Opinion

Different people have vastly different opinions about the government's role in the economy. Some hold that the government should be severely limited to what Adam Smith believed should be the three functions of government; others believe the government should provide goods, services, and transfer payments to citizens while at the same time heavily regulating businesses or owning businesses outright. You saw in Figure 6-1 of your text (page 85) that economic systems can be loosely termed capitalistic or socialistic based on the degree of personal ownership of property and the degree to which people are allowed to answer the three economic questions discussed in Chapter 5. In the United States, as majority opinion goes, so goes the economic system.

Therefore, it is important to be able to correctly gauge the economic philosophies of others.

Find four people with considerable differences in their opinions of the government's role and ask them to rank their agreement with the statements below. Following the opinion questionnaire is a series of four continuums of the same type found in Chapter 6. After recording your subjects' responses to the questions, use your personal judgment and place an X on each person's line indicating the mix of personal responsibility and governmental responsibility which they appear to favor. Compare the placement of the X's with the various economic systems listed in your text and indicate the probable type of economic system that each person favors.

Statement	Subject #1	Subject #2	Subject #3	Subject #4
Which Statement About Ownership of Property Is Closest to What You Believe?				
I believe that in order to prevent exploitation of the workers, the government should own all factories and businesses.				
I believe that to combat greed and exploitation of workers, the government should own the companies in the United States' key industries (only), including health care, banking, transportation, and energy production companies.				
I believe that private individuals, not government, should own the factories and businesses of the United States.				
Which Statement About Business Decision Making Is Closest to What You Believe?				
I believe that to promote fairness and safety and to prevent exploitation of the workers at the hands of greedy business people, the government should heavily regulate all American business.				
I believe that some government regulation of businesses is necessary (but only the minimal amount necessary to protect the health and safety of workers and consumers.)				
I believe that no government regulation is necessary.				
Which Statement About Income Redistribution Is Closest to What You Believe?				
I believe that all income should be distributed evenly to all citizens, regardless of their ability to work.				
I believe that to prevent poverty, a financial "safety net" should exist beneath which citizens should not be allowed to fall.				
I believe that government should not engage in income redistribution. A person's income should be based solely on his or her work. Any needed charity should be provided through nongovernmental channels.				

Socialistic systems   Capitalistic Systems

Subject #1 favors a _____ economic system.

Socialistic systems   Capitalistic Systems

Subject #3 favors a _____ economic system.

Socialistic systems   Capitalistic Systems

Subject #2 favors a _____ economic system.

Socialistic systems   Capitalistic Systems

Subject #4 favors a _____ economic system.

Economics

Word Scramble

Unscramble the following words. After all words have been unscrambled, place the letters that are double underlined in the spaces provided at the bottom of this exercise and unscramble them to solve the riddle.

1. varzittiponia   p   r   i   v   a   t   i   z   a   t   i   o   n

2. mimmcsonu   c   o   m   m   u   n   i   s   m

3. denews   s   w   e   d   e   n

4. amda   a   d   a   m

5. cradlia   r   a   d   i   c   a   l

6. apureone   e   u   r   o   p   e   a   n

Riddle: Because of the reforms sweeping through the formerly Communist nations of Eastern Europe, perhaps the answer to the question "What is socialism?" is "Socialism is the long hard struggle from capitalism to   p   t   c   i   s   a   m   i   l   a   ⇒

    capitalism   ."

Matching

To the left of each number, place the letter of the definition or example which best corresponds to the item. Each answer is used only once.

A. classic liberal capitalism
B. communism
C. European social democracy
D. mercantilism

E. radical capitalism
F. welfare state
G. worker management socialism

   F   1. Sweden

   A   2. Adam Smith's idea of the ideal economic system

   B   3. Government is no longer necessary, since everyone is acting in the best interest of others.

   D   4. Gold and silver in the government's treasury are what is important.

   E   5. No government exists, since everyone is acting in his own best interest.

   G   6. Yugoslavia

   C   7. Government takes possession of key industries.

Economics

©1995 BJU Press. Reproduction prohibited.

Name _____

Chapter 6   **Activity 4**

Multiple Choice

Choose the response which best answers the question or completes the sentence.

__C__1. In what year did mercantilism end?
A. 1500
B. 476
C. 1776
D. 1871

__B__2. Which of the following was not one of the strategies of mercantilism?
A. sponsor exploration expeditions in order to locate gold and silver
B. refuse to sell goods and services to foreign nations
C. encourage colonization
D. arrange all foreign relationships so that competition is limited

__D__3. What does "laissez faire" mean?
A. peaceful work
B. invisible hand
C. beautiful idleness
D. let alone

__A__4. Which of the following is *not* one of the distinguishing characteristics of a capitalistic economy?
A. Workers decide all questions of policy for their particular business.
B. Individuals own a majority of the factors of production.
C. The government does not own the businesses that are cornerstones of the economy.
D. Most economic decisions are made by individuals.

__A__5. According to Adam Smith, why do the butcher and baker provide our dinner?
A. because it is in their own best interest to do so
B. because of benevolence
C. because the law forces them to provide quality goods and services
D. because it ultimately enriches the state

__C__6. In which of the following economic systems does the government not exist?
A. European social democracy
B. classic liberal capitalism
C. communism
D. radical socialism

__D__7. Which of the following would a European social democracy be least likely to confiscate?
A. a hospital
B. a nuclear power plant
C. a telephone company
D. a shoe factory

Chapter Review   **Skill: Recognition   43**

Economics

Short Answer

Fill in the blanks with the word, phrase, or list which best answers the question or completes the sentence.

1. A ___*favorable balance of trade*___ is said to exist when a nation sells more goods and services than it purchases.

2. Why did mercantilism promote colonization? *Colonies were used to produce goods which could not be produced by the mother country.*

3. According to Adam Smith, what was the root problem with mercantilism? *the mistaken assumption that money (gold and silver) was wealth*

4. Why is radical capitalism unscriptural? *because it holds that government is not a legitimate authority, whereas Scripture decrees that government is ordained by God*

5. In the eighteenth century, what did the word *liberal* mean? *A liberal was a person who believed in liberty.*

6. According to Karl Marx, "The history of all hitherto existing society is the history of ___*class struggle*___."

7. According to your text, why does it appear that Scripture supports capitalism as opposed to socialism? *Answers will vary, but the idea should be that capitalism supports the scriptural concepts of accountability, rewarding diligence, penalizing indolence, and personal ownership of property.*

Corporate Ownership: The Stock Certificate

If you wish to become a part owner of a corporation, you must purchase shares of stock in that corporation. Two types of stock are available for purchase in American corporations: common stock and preferred stock. Common stock represents true ownership of the firm. That is, if you own 10,000 shares of common stock in a corporation which has 100,000 common shares outstanding, you own 10% of the corporation. As owners of the corporation, common shareholders also own all of the corporation's profits. After all expenses have been paid, the remaining profits may either be distributed to the common shareholders in the form of "dividends" or be retained by the firm to assist in the purchase of needed assets. The decision concerning the combination of dividends and retained profits is made by the corporation's board of directors, a group elected by the common shareholders. As the firm's profits increase, dividends paid to the common shareholders may likewise increase. Because they are the owners of the corporation, however, common shareholders are the last to be paid if the firm fails. If a corporation files bankruptcy, all of the firm's assets (land, buildings, equipment, raw materials, inventory, etc.) are sold. The first to be paid are employees who have wages due them; next is the government, which is paid any outstanding tax bills. The third group to be paid is creditors such as banks and other lenders. After the creditors have been paid, any leftover money is paid to the common shareholders in proportion to their ownership in the firm.

The second type of stock is preferred stock. Do not let the word *preferred* fool you into thinking that preferred stock is significantly better than common stock. Comparing preferred stock to common stock is like comparing apples to oranges. Both have their advantages and disadvantages. Since preferred stock is not representative of true ownership of the firm, preferred shareholders usually do not have the right to vote on matters of importance to the corporation. To the corporation, preferred stock is much like debt. The dividend which is paid to preferred shareholders is fixed, like interest on a loan. The word *preferred* merely refers to the fact that preferred shareholders receive their dividends before common shareholders receive theirs. Like common stockholders, however, preferred shareholders are not guaranteed any dividends. If the firm pays out all of its money in meeting its expenses, it is not obligated to pay any dividends to either common or preferred stockholders. Finally, in case the firm files for bankruptcy, the preferred shareholders receive their share of the firm's money (if there is any left!) immediately before the common shareholders.

When a person buys common or preferred stock, he is said to be a shareholder. Each person's claims on the firm may be recorded on a share certificate. Many shareholders elect not to receive printed share certificates, but rather to have their ownership recorded electronically so that they can sell their shares at a moment's notice without having to locate their shares and sign them over to a new owner. On the next page is a share certificate on a corporation with all of the important features explained. Study it carefully and then answer the questions about the stock certificate.

- A human figure with plainly discernible features must appear with at least a 3/4 frontal view on all New York Stock Exchange certificates. Delicate flesh tones are engraved next to heavy shadows to make the artwork hard to reproduce.

- SEC Registration Number assigned by the Securities and Exchange Commission

- Name of issuer

- Number of shares

- The CUSIP number is a security identification number assigned to every stock certificate and every corporate and municipal bond. The Committee on Uniform Securities Identification Procedures is set up by the American Banker's Association.

- Stocks are printed on specially made paper incorporating little colored discs, called planchettes, which are treated with chemicals. Security devices can automatically sense the planchettes.

1. What is the name of the firm which issued this stock? *Banc One Corporation*

2. What kind of stock is represented by this share certificate? *common stock*

3. How many shares of ownership does this stock certificate represent? *280 shares*

4. What is the SEC Registration Number of the share certificate? *P029090*

5. What is the CUSIP number of the stock? *559438 10 1*

6. What does CUSIP stand for? *Committee on Uniform Securities Identification Procedures*

7. What are the offices of the two persons whose signatures are found at the bottom of the certificate on behalf of the issuing corporation? *secretary and chairman*

8. What is the name given to the special colored spots found on the face of the certificate?

   planchettes

Economics

Corporate Ownership: How to Become Incorporated

Many people mistakenly believe that the only ones who need to incorporate are pin-striped executives in multimillion-dollar businesses. One of the primary advantages of incorporating is the limitation of personal financial liability. Follow carefully this scenario. You started a little business in which you sell home care products such as soaps and cleaners. Late one evening on his way home from an appointment in which he was demonstrating your products, one of your employees fell asleep at the steering wheel, and his car slammed into a chemical manufacturing facility, causing over $10 million in damages. As a sole proprietor you are liable to pay for all of the damages not covered by insurance, perhaps necessitating the sale of your home and most of your possessions. Because a corporation is a legal entity separate from its managers, it may be sued and its assets sold to satisfy legal claims, but in most cases claimants cannot take away the personal wealth of the owners or managers.

In order to enjoy this protection from personal financial liability, more and more people in sole proprietorships are electing to incorporate and are finding it to be a relatively easy process. The first step in incorporating is to contact an attorney, since he will be familiar with the incorporation laws in your particular state. The total cost to incorporate may range from $300 to $800 or more, depending upon the fees charged by the incorporating attorney, fees charged by the state, and the cost of printing the stock certificates, seals, and other administrative ''hardware'' needed by the corporation.

The second step is for one to file a ''Articles of Incorporation'' form with his state's secretary of state. The purpose of the Articles of Incorporation is to inform the state as to the existence of the corporation and to register the names and addresses of each main officer of the firm. The filing of the Articles of Incorporation will be done by the attorney.

To show how easy it is to complete, a blank Articles of Incorporation form has been provided with the information needed to fill in the blanks. While the example is for the state of South Carolina, most states' Articles of Incorporation forms are very similar. Given the following information, complete the blank form.

Line 1   The name of the proposed corporation is Universal Widgets.

Line 2   Given

Line 3   The firm's address is 3131 Mockingbird Lane in the city of Greenville (Greenville County), South Carolina 29600. Since you will conduct the business of the firm, enter your name as the registered agent.

Line 4   In some cases, corporations issue two or more kinds (classes) of common shares. One class receives dividends but does not have the power to vote while the other receives little or no dividends but has the power to vote. For this example, assume that there is only one class of stock and the firm will be issuing 100,000 shares.

Line 5   Leave blank, since you want the existence of the corporation to begin the day the Articles are filed with the secretary of state.

Line 6   Leave blank.

Line 7   Many smaller corporations choose not to have a board of directors because all of the stock is owned by a handful of people who do not need to have others acting on their behalf. The shareholders will, in such cases, manage all of the affairs of the corporation. Such is the case with Universal Widgets; therefore, place an X in the box signifying that the corporation will not have a board of directors.

Line 8   Many smaller corporations composed of a small number of major shareholders realize that if one of the main shareholders/managers should die, the surviving spouse may be unable to step in to help run the firm. Thus, in order to help surviving spouses, the shareholders/managers may decide to purchase the shares of deceased shareholders. Universal Widgets so elects this provision.

Line 9   Leave blank. Universal Widgets has no optional provisions to include.

Line 10 Place your name, the firm's address, your signature as an incorporator, and today's date.

STATE OF SOUTH CAROLINA
SECRETARY OF STATE

ARTICLES OF INCORPORATION FOR A STATUTORY CLOSE CORPORATION

1. The name of the proposed corporation is ___*Universal Widgets*___.

2. This corporation is a statutory close corporation, pursuant to Chapter 18, Title 33 of the 1976 South Carolina Code, as amended.

3. The initial registered office of the corporation is ___*3131 Mockingbird Lane*___
   Street & Number

   ___*Greenville, SC*___ ___*Greenville*___ ___*29600*___,
   City   County   Zip Code

   and the initial registered agent is ___*student's name*___.

4. The corporation is authorized to issue shares of stock as follows. Complete *a* or *b*, whichever is applicable:

   a. ☒ If the corporation is authorized to issue a single class of shares, the total number of shares authorized is ___*100,000*___.

   b. ☐ The corporation is authorized to issue more than one class of shares:

Class of Shares	Authorized No. of Each Class

   The relative rights, preferences, and limitations of the shares of each class, and of each series within a class, are as follows:

5. The existence of the corporation shall begin when these articles are filed with the secretary of state unless a delayed date is indicated (See §33-1-230(b)): _____.

6. Unless otherwise specified below, the transfer of shares of stock shall be subject to the restrictions set out in §§33-18-110 through 33-18-110 of the 1976 South Carolina Code, as amended. Specify any variations in the statutory format in §§33-18-110 through 33-18-110:

7. Unless otherwise specified below, the corporation shall have a board of directors. (See §33-18-210.)
   ☒ This corporation elects not to have a board of directors.

8. Check if applicable: ☒ This corporation elects to apply the provisions of §§33-18-140 through 33-18-170 of the 1976 code, which give the estate of a deceased shareholder the right to compel the corporation to purchase the deceased shareholder's shares. Specify any variations in the statutory format.

9. The optional provisions which the corporation elects to include in the articles of incorporation are as follows (See §33-2-102 and the applicable comments thereto; and 35-2-105 and 35-2-221 of the 1976 South Carolina Code):

10. The name and address of each incorporator is as follows (only one is required):

Name	Address	Signature
student's name	*3131 Mockingbird Lane Greenville, SC 29600*	*student's signature*

11. I, _____, an attorney licensed to practice in the State of South Carolina, certify that the corporation to whose articles of incorporation this certificate is attached has complied with the requirements of Chapter 2, Title 33 of the 1976 South Carolina Code relating to the articles of incorporation.

Date ___*today's date*___

___*student's signature*___
(Signature)

___*student's name*___
(Type or Print Name)

___*student's address*___
(Address)

The third step in incorporating is to file a request with the government to receive an employer identification number (also known as a taxpayer ID number). Just as individual workers must have Social Security numbers for tax purposes, a corporation must have a taxpayer ID number to assist the Internal Revenue Service in its job of collecting taxes on profits and on the corporation's employees. Given the following information, complete the blank Application for Employer Identification Number on the next page.

Line 1	Enter the name of the corporation "Universal Widgets."
Line 2	Leave blank since the trade name is the same as the corporation.
Line 3	Enter your name here.
Lines 4a & 4b	Enter the firm's street address.
Lines 5a & 5b	Enter "Same as box 4a & 4b."
Line 6	Enter the county name and state for Universal Widgets.
Line 7	Enter your name as the president of the corporation.
Line 8a	Place an X in the "other corporation (specify)" box and write "statutory close corporation."
Line 8b	Enter "South Carolina" beside "State."
Line 9	Indicate that you are starting a new business.
Line 10	Enter today's date.
Line 11	In business it is useful to know two terms. *Calendar year* runs from January 1 to December 31 of the same year. *Fiscal year,* or *accounting year,* refers to a twelve-month period that the business uses for bookkeeping purposes. At the end of the fiscal year, the business counts its inventory, balances and "closes out" its books, and begins the next day as the first day of the new fiscal year. Often a firm chooses to have the fiscal year to be the calendar year. In the case of Universal Widgets, however, the fiscal year will end on June 30 of each year.
Line 12	Universal Widgets will begin paying wages on the first day of next month.
Line 13	Universal Widgets will have only five nonagricultural employees during the next twelve months.
Line 14	Universal Widgets will be manufacturing widgets.
Line 15	Universal Widgets is a manufacturing enterprise. The principal raw material is titanium.
Line 16	Universal Widgets will be selling its product to the government for use in SSBN's (nuclear ballistic submarines); therefore, check the "other" and explain.
Line 17a	Universal Widgets has never before applied for an Identification Number.
	Print your name as president of Universal Widgets, add (803) 421-5253 as the firm's hypothetical telephone number, and sign as the firm's president.
Lines 17b & 17c	Leave blank.

Form **SS-4** | **Application for Employer Identification Number** | EIN

1 Name of applicant (True legal name) (See instructions.)

Universal Widgets

2 Trade name of business, if different from name in line 1 | **3** Executor, trustee, "care of" name

student's name

4a Mailing address (street address) (room, apt., or suite no.) | **5a** Address of business (See instructions.)

3131 Mockingbird Lane | **same as 4a**

4b City, state, and Zip Code | **5b** City, state, and Zip Code

Greenville, SC 29600 | **same as 4b**

6 County and state where principal business is located

Greenville County, South Carolina

7 Name of principal officer, grantor, or general partner (See instructions.) ▶ **student's name**

8a Type of entity (Check only one box.) (See instructions.)

- ☐ Individual SSN _____
- ☐ Farmer's coop. ☐ Estate ☐ Trust
- ☐ Plan administrator SSN _____ ☐ Partnership
- ☐ REMIC ☐ Personal service corp. ☒ Other corp. (specify) **statutory close corporation**
- ☐ State/local government ☐ National guard ☐ Church or church-controlled organization
- ☐ Other nonprofit organization (specify) _____ If nonprofit organization enter GEN (if applicable) _____
- ☐ Federal government/military ☐ Other (specify) ▶ _____

8b If a corporation, give name of foreign country (if applicable) or state in the U.S. where incorporated. ▶ | Foreign country | State

South Carolina

9 Reason for applying (Check only one box.)

- ☒ Started new business
- ☐ Hired employees
- ☐ Created a pension plan (specify type) ▶ _____
- ☐ Banking purpose (specify) ▶ _____
- ☐ Changed type of organization (specify) ▶ _____
- ☐ Purchase going business
- ☐ Created a trust (specify) ▶ _____
- ☐ Other (specify) ▶ _____

10 Date business started or acquired (mo., day, yr.) (See instructions.)

today's date

11 Enter closing month of accounting year. (See instructions.)

June

12 First date wages or annuities were paid or will be paid (mo., day, yr.). **Note:** If applicant is a withholding agent, enter date income will first be paid to nonresident alien (mo., day, yr.). . . . . ▶ **first day of next month**

13 Enter highest number of employees expected in the next 12 months. **Note:** If the applicant does not expect to have any employees during the period, enter "0." ▶ | Nonagricultural **5** | Agricultural | Household

14 Principal activity (See instructions.) ▶ **manufacturing widgets**

15 Is the principal business activity manufacturing? . . . . ☒ Yes ☐ No

If "Yes," principal product and raw material used ▶ **product—widgets; raw material—titanium**

16 To whom are most of the products sold? Please check the appropriate box. | ☐ Business (wholesale)

☐ Public (retail) ☒ Other (specify) ▶ **government (for use in SSBNs)** | ☐ N/A

17a Has the applicant ever applied for an identification number for this or any other business? . . . . ☐ Yes ☒ No

Note: If "Yes," please complete lines 17b and 17c.

17b If you checked the "Yes" box in line 17a, give applicant's true name and trade name, if different from name shown on prior application.

True name ▶ | Trade name ▶

17c Enter approximate date, city, and state where the application was filed and the previous employer identification number if known.

Approximate date when filed (mo., day, yr.) | City and state where filed | Previous EIN

Under penalties of perjury, I declare that I have examined this application, and to the best of my knowledge and belief, it is true, correct, and complete. | Telephone number (include area code)

Name and title (Please type or print clearly.) ▶ **student's name, President** | **(803) 421-5253**

Signature ▶ **student's signature** | Date ▶ **today's date**

Once the Articles of Incorporation and the Application for an Employer Identification Number have been completed and mailed, the majority of the work required to become incorporated has been done. Your attorney will provide a kit containing stock certificates and a corporate seal, which may be necessary when documenting incorporation by conducting official business such as opening bank accounts and filing accounting documents.

While most sole proprietors can see the obvious benefits of incorporating, they are reluctant to do so since corporations may pay taxes at a higher rate than sole proprietorships. To encourage incorporation, the United States government has created a corporate status for small businesses which allows them to continue being taxed at the lower personal income tax rates. Small businesses that fit in this category are referred to as "Subchapter S corporations," or more commonly "S corporations." A business may incorporate as an S corporation if it has fewer than 35 shareholders and only one type of stock (common or preferred), and within the type of stock it has outstanding, it may not have both voting and nonvoting common stock. If one meets these requirements and desires to become an S corporation, an IRS Form 2553 (shown below and on the next page) will need to be filed with the federal government.

Form **2553** (Rev. September 1993) Department of the Treasury	**Election by a Small Business Corporation** (Under section 1362 of the Internal Revenue Code) ▶ For Paperwork Reduction Act Notice, see p. 1 of instructions.	OMB No. 1545-0146 Expires 8-31-96

Notes: 1. This election, to be an "S corporation," can be accepted only if all the tests are met under Who May Elect on page 1 of the instructions; all signatures in Parts I and III are originals (no photocopies); and the exact name and address of the corporation and other required form information are provided.

2. Do not file Form 1120S, U.S. Income Tax Return for an S Corporation, until you are notified that your election is accepted.

Part I **Please Type or Print**	**Election Information**	
	Name of corporation (see instructions)	**A** Employer ID number (EIN)
	Number, street, room or suite no. (If P.O. box, see instructions.)	**B** Date incorporated
	City or town, state, and Zip Code	**C** State of incorporation

D Election is to be effective for tax year beginning (month, day, year) . . . . ▶ / /

E Name and title of officer or legal representative whom the IRS may call for more information | **F** Telephone number of officer or legal representative ( )

G If the corporation changed its name or address after applying for the EIN shown in A, check this box. . . . . ▶ ☐

H If this election takes effect for the first tax year the corporation exists, enter month, day, and year of the earliest of the following: (1) date the corporation first had shareholders, (2) date the corporation first had assets, or (3) date the corporation began doing business . . . . ▶ / /

I Selected tax year: Annual return will be filed for tax year ending (month and day) ▶ _____

If the tax year ends on any date other than December 31, except for an automatic 52-53-week tax year ending with reference to the month of December, you must complete Part II on the back. If the date you enter is the ending date of an automatic 52-53-week tax year, write "52-53-week year" to the right of the date. See Temporary Regulations section 1.441-2T(e)(3).

J Name and address of each shareholder's spouse having a community property interest in the corporation's stock, and each tenant in common, joint tenant, and tenant by the entirety. (A husband and wife and their estates are counted as one shareholder in determining the number of shareholders without regard to the manner in which the stock is owned.)	**K** Shareholder's Consent Statement— Under penalties of perjury, we declare that we consent to the election of the above-named corporation to be an "S corporation" under section 1362(a) and that we have examined this consent statement, including accompanying schedules and statements, and to the best of our knowledge, it is true.		**L** Stock owned		**M** Social security number or employer identification number (see instructions)	**N** Shareholder's tax year ends (month and day)
	Signature	Date	Number of shares	Dates acquired		

For this election to be valid, the consent of each shareholder, shareholder's spouse having a community property interest in the corporations stock, and each tenant in common, joint tenant, and tenant by the entirety must either appear above or be attached to this form. (See instructions for Column K if a continuation sheet or a separate consent statement is needed.)

Under penalties of perjury, I declare that I have examined this election, including accompanying schedules and statements, and to the best of my knowledge and belief, it is true, correct, and complete.

Signature of officer ▶ _____ Title ▶ _____ Date ▶ _____

Part II Selection of Fiscal Tax Year (All corporations using this part must complete item O and one of items P, Q, or R.)

O Check the applicable box below to indicate whether the corporation is:

    1. ☐ A new corporation adopting the tax year entered in item I, Part I.

    2. ☐ An existing corporation retaining the tax year entered in item I, Part I.

    3. ☐ An existing corporation changing to the tax year entered in item I, Part I.

P Complete item P if the corporation is using the expeditious approval provisions of Revenue Procedure 87-32, 1987-2 C.B. 396, to request: (1) a natural business year (as defined in section 4.01(1) of Rev. Proc. 87-32, or (2) a year that satisfies the ownership tax year test in section 4.01(2) of Rev. Proc. 87-32. Check the applicable box below to indicate the representation statement the corporation is making as required under section 4 of Rev. Proc. 87-32.

1. Natural Business Year ▶ ☐ I represent that the corporation is retaining or changing to a tax year that coincides with its natural business year as defined in section 4.01(1) of Rev. Proc. 87-32 and as verified by its satisfaction of the requirements of section 4.02(1) of Rev. Proc. 87-32. In addition, if the corporation is changing to a natural business year as defined in section 4.01(1), I further represent that such tax year results in less deferral of income to the owners than the corporation's present tax year. I also represent that the corporation is not described in section 3.01(2) of Rev. Proc. 87-32. (See instructions for additional information that must be attached.)

2. Ownership Tax Year ▶ ☐ I represent that shareholders holding more than half of the shares of the stock (as of the first day of the tax year to which the request relates) of the corporation have the same tax year or are concurrently changing to the tax year that the corporation adopts, retains, or changes to per item I, Part I. I also represent that the corporation is not described in section 3.01(2) of Rev. Proc. 87-32.

Note: If you do not use item P and the corporation wants a fiscal tax year, complete either item Q or R below. Item Q is used to request a fiscal tax year based on a business purpose and to make a back-up section 444 election. Item R is used to make a regular section 444 election.

Q Business Purpose—To request a fiscal tax year based on a business purpose, you must check box Q1 and pay a user fee. See instructions for details. You may also check box Q2 and/or box Q3.

1. Check here ▶ ☐ if the fiscal year entered in item I, Part I, is requested under the provisions of section 6.03 of Rev. Proc. 87-32. Attach to Form 2553 a statement showing the business purpose for the requested fiscal year. See instructions for additional information that must be attached.

2. Check here ▶ ☐ to show that the corporation intends to make a back-up section 444 election in the event the corporation's business purpose request is not approved by the IRS. (See instructions for more information.)

3. Check here ▶ ☐ to show that the corporation agrees to adopt or change to a tax year ending December 31 if necessary for the IRS to accept this election for S corporation status in the event: (1) the corporation's business purpose request is not approved and the corporation makes a back-up section 444 election, but is ultimately not qualified to make a section 444 election, or (2) the corporation's business purpose request is not approved and the corporation did not make a back-up section 444 election.

R Section 444 Election—To make a section 444 election, you must check box R1 and you may also check box R2.

1. Check here ▶ ☐ to show the corporation will make, if qualified, a section 444 election to have the fiscal tax year shown in item I, Part I. To make the election, you must complete Form 8716, Election to Have a Tax Year Other Than a Required Tax Year, and either attach it to Form 2553 or file it separately.

2. Check here ▶ ☐ to show that the corporation agrees to adopt or change to a tax year ending December 31 if necessary for the IRS to accept this election for S corporation status in the event the corporation is ultimately not qualified to make a section 444 election.

Part III Qualified Subchapter S Trust (QSST) Election Under Section 1361(d)(2)

Income beneficiary's name and address	Social security number
Trust's name and address	Employer identification number

Date on which stock of the corporation was transferred to the trust (month, day, year) . . . . ▶   / /

In order for the trust named above to be a QSST and thus a qualifying shareholder of the S corporation for which this Form 2553 is filed, I hereby make the election under section 1361(d)(2). Under penalties of perjury, I certify that the trust meets the definitional requirements of section 1361(d)(3) and that all other information provided in Part III is true, correct, and complete.

Signature of income beneficiary or signature and title of legal representative or other qualified person making the election   Date

Economics

Chapter 7   **Activity 3**

Corporate Income Taxes

One of the greatest objections to incorporating is the threat of higher income tax rates. By looking at the current corporate tax rate schedule below, you can see how high these rates actually are.

Corporate Tax Rates			
Taxable Income		Tax Liability	
Over	But Not Over	Calculation	Of the Amount of Taxable Income Over
$0	$ 50,000	$ 0 + 15%	$0
50,000	75,000	7,500 + 25%	50,000
75,000	100,000	13,750 + 34%	75,000
100,000	335,000	22,250 + 39%	100,000
335,000	——	113,900 + 34%	335,000

At first glance the above corporate tax table may appear confusing, but it is relatively easy to use. For example, if Universal Widgets had a taxable income for the year of $60,000, then its tax liability would be $10,000. This amount was found by following these simple steps.

Step 1   Find which of the five corporate tax "brackets" the corporation's income falls within. In the case of Universal Widgets, the taxable income of $60,000 falls within the "Over $50,000 but Not Over $75,000."

Step 2   Find the minimum tax for the bracket. In the case of Universal Widgets, this amount equals $7,500.

Step 3   Determine the amount of taxable income the corporation has in excess of the lowest income required for the bracket in which it finds itself. For Universal Widgets this amount is $10,000 ($60,000 taxable income - $50,000 lowest income to be in the bracket).

Step 4   Multiply the bracket's tax rate by the amount found in step 3 to determine the additional tax for the bracket. For Universal Widgets this equals $2,500 (.25 x $10,000).

Step 5   Add the minimum tax for the bracket (found in step 2) to the additional tax (found in step 4) to determine the total tax liability. For Universal Widgets the total tax liability is $10,000 ($7,500 + $2,500).

Now it is your turn to try a few!

Show your calculations and final answers for the following taxable incomes. (Round answers to the nearest whole dollar.) Note: The answers you calculate will be used in the next activity.

1. $1,000

   a. Tax Bracket "Over _____ $ 0 _____ but Not Over _____ $50,000 _____"

   b. Minimum tax for this bracket = _____ $ 0 _____

   c. Amount of taxable income over the lowest income required to be in the bracket =
   _____ $1,000 ($1,000 – 0) _____

   d. Additional tax for the bracket = _____ $150 ($1,000 X .15) _____

   e. Total tax due = _____ $150 ($ 0 + 150) _____

2. $50,000

    a. Tax Bracket "Over _____ $0 _____ but Not Over _____ $50,000 _____ "

    b. Minimum tax for this bracket = _____ $0 _____

    c. Amount of taxable income over the lowest income required to be in the bracket =

        _____ $50,000 ($50,000 – 0) _____

    d. Additional tax for the bracket = _____ $7,500 ($50,000 X .15) _____

    e. Total tax due = _____ $7,500 ($0 + 7,500) _____

3. $75,000

    a. Tax Bracket "Over _____ $50,000 _____ but Not Over _____ $75,000 _____ "

    b. Minimum tax for this bracket = _____ $7,500 _____

    c. Amount of taxable income over the lowest income required to be in the bracket =

        _____ $25,000 ($75,000 – 50,000) _____

    d. Additional tax for the bracket = _____ $6,250 ($25,000 X .25) _____

    e. Total tax due = _____ $13,750 ($ 7,500 + 6,250) _____

4. $100,000

    a. Tax Bracket "Over _____ $75,000 _____ but Not Over _____ $100,000 _____ "

    b. Minimum tax for this bracket = _____ $13,750 _____

    c. Amount of taxable income over the lowest income required to be in the bracket =

        _____ $25,000 ($100,000 – 75,000) _____

    d. Additional tax for the bracket = _____ $8,500 ($25,000 X .34) _____

    e. Total tax due = _____ $22,250 ($13,750 + 8,500) _____

5. $335,000

    a. Tax Bracket "Over _____ $100,000 _____ but Not Over _____ $335,000 _____ "

    b. Minimum tax for this bracket = _____ $22,250 _____

    c. Amount of taxable income over the lowest income required to be in the bracket =

        _____ $235,000 ($335,000 – 100,000) _____

    d. Additional tax for the bracket = _____ $91,650 ($235,000 X .39) _____

    e. Total tax due = _____ $113,900 ($22,250 + 91,650) _____

6. $450,000

    a. Tax Bracket "Over _____ $335,000 _____ but Not Over _____ – – – _____ "

    b. Minimum tax for this bracket = _____ $113,900 _____

    c. Amount of taxable income over the lowest income required to be in the bracket =

        _____ $115,000 ($450,000 – 335,000) _____

    d. Additional tax for the bracket = _____ $39,100 ($115,000 X .34) _____

    e. Total tax due = _____ $153,000 ($113,900 + 39,100) _____

Economics

Marginal Corporate Income Tax Rates

One word which is heard quite often in economics is the term *marginal*. Very simply defined, the word *marginal* means "where you are right now." For example, in Chapter 2 you learned about the principle of diminishing *marginal* utility, a principle which states that the amount of satisfaction you receive from something *right now* is less than the satisfaction you received from the previous input.

In economics and business, the tax rate which should be of concern is not the rate found in the corporate tax table, but rather the marginal tax rate, the tax rate which you are paying *right now*. For example, we saw in the previous exercise that if a corporation had a taxable income of $60,000, it would fall in the 25% corporate tax bracket, but when the final tax liability was calculated, it was

found that the firm paid $10,000 in taxes. Therefore, the corporation's marginal tax rate was 17% ($10,000 / $60,000 = .17). Thus, the way to calculate a firm's marginal tax rate is to divide its total tax liability by its total taxable income.

To illustrate the burden corporations bear in higher marginal tax rates as their incomes increase, calculate the marginal tax rates (in percentages rounded to tenths) for each of the problems found in the previous activity. After you have calculated the marginal tax rates, plot your findings on the graph. As a basis for comparison, the marginal tax rates for sole proprietorships at each of the given levels of taxable income have been provided. Place the sole proprietorship rates on the same graph using a different colored pencil. Comment on your findings.

You do not need to recompute the total tax liability for each income category. Merely divide the tax liability which you already calculated by the total taxable income to determine the marginal corporate tax rate.

A. Taxable income: $1,000

    Marginal Tax Rate: <u>15% ($150 / $1,000)</u>

    Marginal Sole Proprietorship Tax Rate: 15%

B. Taxable income: $50,000

    Marginal Tax Rate: <u>15% ($7,500 / $50,000)</u>

    Marginal Sole Proprietorship Tax Rate: 23.4%

C. Taxable income: $75,000

    Marginal Tax Rate: <u>18.3% ($13,750 / $75,000)</u>

    Marginal Sole Proprietorship Tax Rate: 24.9%

D. Taxable income: $100,000

    Marginal Tax Rate: <u>22.3% ($22,250 / $100,000)</u>

    Marginal Sole Proprietorship Tax Rate: 25.7%

E. Taxable income: $335,000

    Marginal Tax Rate: <u>34% ($113,900 / $335,000)</u>

    Marginal Sole Proprietorship Tax Rate: 27.3%

F. Taxable income: $450,000

    Marginal Tax Rate: <u>34% ($153,000 / $450,000)</u>

    Marginal Sole Proprietorship Tax Rate: 27.5%

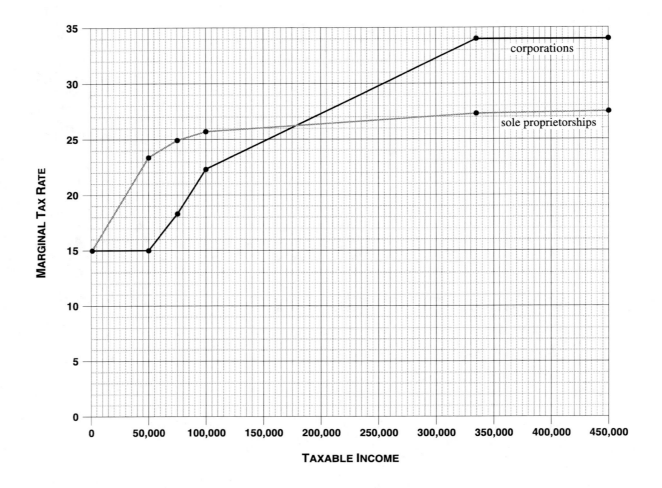

Comments on your findings: *Answers will vary, but your students should note that the marginal corporate tax rate is stable at 15% for taxable income levels of $0 to $50,000. It rises sharply to over 22% for a taxable income level of $100,000, then rises gradually to 34% for incomes at the $335,000 level, and then stabilizes. Compared to the rates paid by sole proprietorships, corporations pay a lower tax rate up to a taxable income level of approximately $180,000, above which sole proprietorships experience lower marginal tax rates. S corporations pay the same tax rates as the sole proprietorship; thus, if a sole proprietor wishes to limit his liability and expects to have a taxable income level over $180,000, he should elect to incorporate as an S corporation.*

Economics

©1995 BJU Press. Reproduction prohibited.

Name _____

Word Search

proprietorship
creditor
liability
partnership
surety
cosigner
limited

corporation
stockholder
shares
directors
CEO
regulation
secrecy

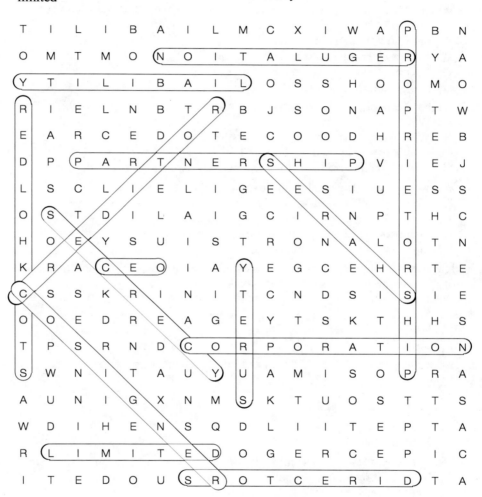

Economics

Multiple Choice

Choose the response which best answers the question or completes the sentence.

___D___ 1. What is the most common form of business ownership in America today?
   A. limited partnership
   B. general partnership
   C. private corporation
   D. sole proprietorship

___A___ 2. Which of the following is *not* an advantage of the sole proprietorship form of business ownership?
   A. unlimited financial liability
   B. ease in entering and exiting the market
   C. freedom to be one's own boss
   D. ability to keep information secret

___D___ 3. Which of the following questions is *not* answered by a general partnership agreement?
   A. Who are the partners?
   B. What is each partner responsible to do?
   C. How are the profits to be divided?
   D. What is the degree of financial responsibility each partner will bear?

___C___ 4. What is probably the greatest disadvantage of a partnership?
   A. a limited ability to raise money
   B. a difficulty in exiting the market
   C. total personal financial liability for each partner
   D. too much control by outsiders

___C___ 5. If a corporation has one million shares outstanding and you wish to own one-tenth of the firm, how many shares must you purchase?
   A. 1,000
   B. 10,000
   C. 100,000
   D. 100,001

___A___ 6. A corporation which is owned by the public and managed by the government is called a _____ corporation.
   A. public
   B. government
   C. private
   D. limited

___B___ 7. Which of the following most correctly follows the corporate organizational structure?
   A. board of directors→stockholders→president→senior vice presidents
   B. stockholders→board of directors→president→senior vice presidents
   C. stockholders→president→board of directors→senior vice presidents
   D. board of directors→president→senior vice presidents→stockholders

Economics

Short Answer

Fill in the blanks with the response that best answers the question or completes the sentence.

1. The sole proprietorship is a very popular form of business ownership. Currently, about _____ *74 %* _____ of all of America's businesses are sole proprietorships.

2. A sole proprietor is responsible to pay all obligations of the firm, even if it requires him to use his own funds. Your text refers to this responsibility as *unlimited personal financial liability.*

3. When speaking of a partnership, one is usually referring to a _____ *general* _____ partnership.

4. List four advantages of the partnership form of business ownership. *greater management skills, greater chance of keeping competent employees, greater sources of financing, ease of formation and freedom to manage*

5. In what way is being a general partner in a business the same as being a surety? *A general partner is liable to pay all debts of the business, whether or not he incurred them or was even aware of their existence. As a general partner, he is cosigning every obligation to which his partner is binding the business.*

6. What were J. C. Penney's "Penney Principles"? *to serve the public, as nearly as we can, to its complete satisfaction; to offer the best possible dollar's worth of quality and value; to strive constantly for a high level of intelligent and helpful service; to charge a fair profit for what we offer and not all the traffic will bear; to apply this test to everything we do: "Does it square with what is right and just?"*

7. What is the primary advantage of the corporate form of business ownership? *Limited personal financial liability of the shareholders; this feature allows people to purchase a portion of the company knowing they can lose only the amount of their investment.*

Matching

To the left of each number, place the letter(s) of the type(s) of business ownership that best corresponds to the word or phrase. *NOTE: Some descriptions apply to more than one form of business ownership. Indicate all that apply.*

A. sole proprietorship
B. partnership
C. limited partnership
D. corporation

B,C,D 1. more than one owner

C 2. One of the owners invests money but has nothing to do with managing the firm.

A 3. one owner

D 4. Every owner's financial liability is limited to his investment.

D 5. Owners have "shares."

A,B 6. Owner is totally liable for the debts of the firm.

A,B,C 7. If the owner dies, the firm dies.

A 8. Most American business firms are of this type.

B 9. Few American business firms are this type.

Economics

Measuring Competitive Performance: The Role of the Income Statement

No matter what form of competition under which a business operates, there must be some measure available to tell the managers if they are being successful. In a basketball game, a scoreboard is visible so that the teams and spectators know the standings. In a pie-eating contest, one can judge each contestant's progress by the number of empty pie plates before him. Business and economics are no different. The goal of practically every corporation is to earn profits. Managers use the "income statement" to gauge a corporation's progress toward this goal.

An income statement is a financial statement which measures the profitability of a business over time. The following is an example of an income statement for Universal Widgets Corporation (UWC).

Universal Widgets, Incorporated Income Statement for the Year Ended December 31, 1995	
Sales	$ 4,000,000.00
Less: Cost of Goods Sold	3,000,000.00
Equals: Gross Profit	$ 1,000,000.00
Less: Selling and Administrative Expenses	440,000.00
Less: Depreciation Expense	100,000.00
Equals: Operating Profit (Earnings Before Interest and Taxes [EBIT])	$460,000.00
Less: Interest Expense	40,000.00
Equals: Earnings Before Taxes (EBT)	$ 420,000.00
Less: Corporate Profit Taxes	142,800.00
Equals: Net Income (Earnings After Taxes [EAT])	$ 277,200.00
Net Income (Earnings After Taxes [EAT])	$ 277,200.00
Less: Preferred Stock Dividends	20,000.00
Equals: Earnings Available to Common Shareholders (EATCS)	$ 257,200.00
Divided By: Number of Common Shares Outstanding	205,760
Equals: Earnings Per Share (EPS)	$ 1.25
Divided By: Most Recent Share Price	5.00
Equals: Shareholders' Return	25.00%

The first thing to notice about the statement is that it covers a period of time. Some income statements report a firm's revenues and expenditures for a month, some cover one quarter (three months), and some a year. In our example, the income statement covers the "Year Ended December 31, 1995." Notice how each item is presented in a successive fashion so that profits (or losses) can be seen after each expense category is subtracted.

Universal Widgets sold $4 million worth of products during 1995 from which we subtract its cost of goods sold of $3 million. Cost of goods sold is the sum of all the costs UWC incurred in the production of their products. The resulting gross profit of $1 million is the difference between the firm's sales revenues and the cost to produce its goods. From gross profit we subtract operating expenses. UWC had a selling and administrative expense of $440,000, which represents the costs of advertising, paying salespeople, and running its office.

The next item on the statement is depreciation expense. When a business purchases small items in the course of doing business, it counts those costs as part of sales and administrative expenses so that its taxes will be reduced. However, when a business buys a factory or a large piece of equipment, the government will not permit all of the expense to be subtracted in the same year because to do so would reduce tax revenues too much. Instead, the government allows a business to deduct part of the cost each year over a period of several years until the full amount is deducted. This annual deduction is called depreciation. In the UWC example, depreciation expense equaled $100,000 leaving $460,000 in earnings before interest and taxes were paid.

Businesses borrow money from banks and other sources. The interest that the firm pays each year is deducted from its earnings before interest and taxes. During 1995 UWC paid $40,000 in interest, leaving $420,000 as earnings before taxes were paid. As you

saw in the previous chapter of this activity book, corporate taxes are computed by subjecting a firm's earnings before taxes (EBT) to the government's corporate tax rates. According to the tax table in the previous chapter, UWC's tax burden is $142,800, leaving $277,200 in earnings after taxes (EAT). Earnings after taxes represents the firm's profits.

Technically, earnings after taxes is the end of the income statement, but many income statements show the supplemental information shown here. After paying all of its expenses, a firm must pay its preferred shareholders (if it has any) before paying common shareholders their portion of the profits. After paying $20,000 in preferred dividends to its preferred shareholders, Universal Widgets had $257,200 left in earnings available to the common shareholders. EATCS may be paid out as dividends to the common shareholders or may be kept by the company for later use.

One final number that is very important is earnings per share (EPS). Earnings per share represents the amount of money each share earned after taxes during the year. EPS is roughly comparable to the interest one earns on deposit at a bank and is critical in determining the market price of the stock. For example, if you found that your savings account earned $1.25 in interest last year would you be pleased or disappointed? The answer, of course, depends upon how much you had on deposit. If you had only $1 on deposit, you should be very pleased because you earned a 125% return ($1.25/$1). You would probably deposit more money in your bank and its popularity would rise. If, however, you had $1,000 on deposit, you would be disappointed since you earned only a .125% return ($1.25/$1,000). Rather than depositing more money in the bank, you and all other depositors would hurry to withdraw your funds. Likewise, if EPS is low as a percentage of the share's price, investors will sell their stock, causing its price to fall. On the other hand, if EPS is high as a percentage of the share's price, the price of the stock will tend to rise. In our example, earnings per share is $1.25, and the share price is $5 per share, which is equivalent to a 25% return ($1.25/$5).

With the figures below, construct an income statement for the Hypotheticon Corporation for the fiscal year ended December 31, 1996. A corporate tax table has been included.

Selling and Administrative Expenses . . . $150,000.00
Cost of Goods Sold $500,000.00
Price of the Common Stock $5.00
Interest Expense $300,000.00
Number of
  Common Shares Outstanding 625,000
Sales $2,500,000.00
Depreciation Expense $300,000.00

Corporate Tax Rates			
Taxable Income		Tax Liability	
Over	But Not Over	Calculation	Of the Amount of Taxable Income Over
——	$ 50,000	$ 0 + 15%	——
$ 50,000	75,000	7,500 + 25%	$ 50,000
75,000	100,000	13,750 + 34%	75,000
100,000	335,000	22,250 + 39%	100,000
335,000	——	113,900 + 34%	335,000

Hypotheticon Corporation Income Statement for the Year Ended December 31, 1996	
Sales	**$ 2,500,000.00**
Less: Cost of Goods Sold	**500,000.00**
Equals: Gross Profit	**$ 2,000,000.00**
Less: Selling and Administrative Expenses	**150,000.00**
Less: Depreciation Expense	**300,000.00**
Equals: Operating Profit (Earnings Before Interest and Taxes [EBIT])	**$ 1,550,000.00**
Less: Interest Expense	**300,000.00**
Equals: Earnings Before Taxes (EBT)	**$ 1,250,000.00**
Less: Corporate Profit Taxes ($113,900 +[($1,250,000 - $335,000) × .34])	**425,000.00**
Equals: Net Income (Earnings After Taxes [EAT])	**$ 825,000.00**
Net Income (Earnings After Taxes [EAT])	**$ 825,000.00**
Less: Preferred Stock Dividends	**200,000.00**
Equals: Earnings Available to Common Shareholders (EATCS)	**$ 625,000.00**
Divided By: Number of Common Shares Outstanding	**625,000**
Equals: Earnings Per Share (EPS)	**$ 1.00**
Divided By: Most Recent Share Price	**5.00**
Equals: Shareholders' Return	**20.00%**

Economics

A Moment in the Life of a Stock: Reading the Stock Ticker

In July 1991 a special event took place in New York City. Victorious American troops, fresh from vanquishing Saddam Hussein's army in the Persian Gulf War, marched through the city in a shower of scraps of paper. Such is the traditional "ticker tape" parade which is given in honor of those who have performed heroic exploits. What, though, is "ticker tape"? In today's electronic age, the question should be "What *was* ticker tape?" Ticker tape was a long role of one-inch wide paper which, after being run through a printing device, recorded the name, quantity, and price of every share traded on one of the stock markets at the moment of its trade. The stock ticker enabled shareholders to see immediately if their shares were going up or down in price, helping them in their buying or selling decisions. No longer do Wall Street stock analysts stand by their tickers reading their tapes. The old paper and ink ticker has given way to electronic display boards in brokers' offices, television displays for the home viewer, and wristwatch style displays for the investor on the go.

While today's investor can know the most recent price paid for any given stock within moments of its trade, he still relies on the codes developed over one hundred years ago. At first glance the information displayed on a modern ticker can be quite intimidating to those who do not understand its special language. Consider the following:

$$ICE_{1\ 1/4}\ SODA_{36\ 3/4}\ OJ_{2s\ 5\ 5/8}\ GRIT_{9s\ 4\ 7/8}\ EGG_{1000s\ 40\ 5/8}$$

At first glance, the above ticker symbols look like a restaurant server's shorthand for a breakfast order, but in reality it is the written record of almost $50,000 worth of stock traded in a few seconds. The *symbol* is the alphabetic code which represents the name of the corporation. While many symbols are alphabetically similar to a corporation's name, it seems that others simply reflect someone's sense of humor. For example, the five firms represented in the above ticker are *(ICE)* Arctic Alaska Fisheries, Inc., a fishing fleet and at-sea fish processing firm; *(SODA)* A&W Brands, Inc., a producer of soft drink concentrates; *(OJ)* Orange Juice Company, Inc., a grower of citrus groves and producer of juice products; *(GRIT)* Grub/Ellis Realty, Inc., a real estate investment company; and *(EGG)* EG&G, Inc., an electronics company. If you know a company's symbol and you wish to discover its name, you may consult the stock listing in the *Wall Street Journal* or in the *Standard & Poor's Security Owner's Stock Guide,* or better yet, call a stockbroker who merely has to type the symbol into his quotron computer in order to receive a host of data about the company.

The second item to note is the current price of the shares. Notice that *ICE* has a 1 1/4 beside its symbol. This means that the trade which just took place saw the stock sold for $1.25 per share. Likewise, A&W Brands sold for $36.75, Orange Juice Company for $5.625, Grub/Ellis Realty $4.875, and EG&G stock sold for $40.625 per share.

The third and final item of interest found in the ticker is the volume, or the number of shares involved in the trade being displayed on the ticker. If a stock's symbol is immediately followed by the price then only one "round lot," or 100 shares, was traded. If an *S* precedes the price, then more than one round lot was traded. For example, the 2S that precedes the price for OJ's trade indicates that two round lots, or 200 shares, were involved in the trade. Likewise, the 9S used for GRIT indicates that 900 shares were traded. What about EGG which has a 1000S preceding the price? Were 100,000 shares traded? No. Trades involving more than 900 shares (9S) are displayed in absolute numbers; thus *EGG*$_{1000S\ 40\ 5/8}$ means that 1,000 shares were traded at $40.625.

On the next page is provided a page from the *Standard & Poor's Security Owner's Stock Guide,* which is available at most public libraries. Given this information and the following hypothetical stock ticker, complete the table found on the next page.

58 COR-CRO — Standard & Poor's

¶ S&P 500 # MidCap 400 • Options

Index	Ticker Symbol	Name of Issue (Call Price of Pfd. Stocks) Market	Com. Rank. & Pfd. Rating	Par Val.	Inst. Hold Cos	Inst. Hold Shs. (000)	Principal Business	Price Range 1971-92 High	1971-92 Low	1993 High	1993 Low	1994 High	1994 Low	Aug. Sales in 100s	August, 1994 Last Sale Or Bid High	Low	Last	%Div Yield	P-E Ratio
1	CGA	✓Cornerstone Natural Gas ....AS	NR	10¢	8	584	Nat'l gas process'g,transp	10¾	¼	1 13/16	⅜	3¼	1 7/16	1759	2¾	2 9/16	2 9/16	...	d
¶2•1	GLW	✓Corning Inc ....NY,B,Ch,P,Ph	A–	50¢	530	120158	Sp'lty mat,commun,csmr prd/sv	43⅛	3⅛	39	24	34⅜	27⅝	92610	31¾	29	30⅞	2.2	15
3	GLWPrM	Corning Del L.P. 6%61"MIPS'(62 51.80) 2	†A	50	..	...	Subsid of Corning Inc	....	....	....	....	50¾	48	4572	50	48	49	6.1	..
4	AGR	Corporacion Banc Espana ADS63... NY	NR	0	52	7447	General banking, Spain	....	....	23⅛	17	23⅞	18⅛	12231	22⅜	19¾	21	3.3	12
5	COY	Corporate High Yield Fund ....NY	NR	10¢	5	4	Closed-end investment co	....	....	15⅝	14⅝	15¾	12	5924	13¼	12½	13¼	11.6	..
6	KYT	Corporate High Yield Fd II ....NY	NR	10¢	..	...	Closed-end investment co	....	....	15	14¾	14¾	11½	2938	12¾	11⅝	12⅛	11.6	..
7	CTZ	✓Corpus Christi Bancshares........AS,Ph	B–	5	2	142	General banking, Texas	....	....	15¼	6	11¾	8¾	53	10⅛	9¾	10a	2.5	9
8	CCAX	✓Corrections Corp Amer ....NNM	B–	1	28	2877	Supplies prison mgmt svcs	16½	3	10¼	6¼	17⅞	8⅞	9391	17⅝	15¼	17½	...	45
9	CO	✓Corrpro Co........NY,Ch	NR	No	35	2306	Corrosion ctrl engineer'g svc	....	....	21	11	24¼	11⅝	2509	16⅞	14⅛	14¼	...	17
10	CORX	✓Cortex Pharmaceuticals ....NSC	NR	0.001	17	8618	Dvlp stge:therapeutic drug R&D	4¾	5/16	2¾	1 5/16	2 1/16	¾	23892	1⅛	¾	1 1/16	...	d
11	COSCB	✓Cosmetic Center Cl'B'(vtg) ....NNM	B+	1¢	17	431	Retails cosmetic/beauty aids	16¼	3⅛	18¾	10	20½	14½	417	18¼	16	18¼	...	19
12	COSCA	✓ Cl'A' ....NNM	B+	1¢	33	1151		16	3⅛	18¾	10¾	21	15½	1784	18¾	16¼	18⅜	...	19
13•3	COTTF	✓Cott Corp........NNM	NR	No	156	33388	Mfr non-alchoholic beverages	14	4⅜	37¾	11⅜	31⅜	9⅞	225102	12⅜	9⅞	10⅞	♦0.7	16
14	CSLI	✓Cotton States Life Ins64 ....NNM	B+	1	7	296	Insurance: life,health	9¾	1¾	8	6½	8⅛	6½	2411	8⅛	6⅞	8	2.0	7
15	CTF	Counsellors Tandem........NY,Ch	NR	1¢	10	750	Closed-end investment co	14¾	3⅜	16⅞	14	16¼	11½	560	13½	12¾	13⅜	...	..
16•4	CCR	✓Countrywide Credit Indus ...NY,B,Ch,P	B+	5¢	230	80897	Services mtge loans	19⅞	1/32	23⅜	15¼	19⅛	12⅞	128011	15⅝	13⅞	14⅞	s2.2	7
17	COU	✓Courtaulds, plc ADR56........AS,B,Ch	NR	58p25	1	383	Rayon yarn, British Isles	10½	⅞	10¼	6⅝	8⅝	7¼	73	8¼	7⅞	7⅞a	2.8	26
18	CUZ	✓Cousins Properties ....NY	NR	1	77	10063	Real estate develop: jt vent	21¼	3/16	18⅜	14¼	18	15⅛	3486	17¾	16⅜	16¾	5.3	22
19•4	CVTY	✓Coventry Corp ....NNM	NR	1¢	145	12035	Hlth benefit svcs/oper HMO's	12⅜	3½	22⅛	8¾	26⅞	15¾	150682	22½	15¾	21½	...	24
20	CPAK	✓CPAC Inc ....NNM	B	1¢	17	585	Chem/equip for imaging indus	10¼	7/16	9¼	6¾	14¼	7¾	1889	14¼	10	13½	1.9	15
21	CPBI	✓CPB Inc ....NNM	A–	No	21	833	Commercial banking, Hawaii	33	8¼	29¾	24½	29½	24½	121	28¼	26½	26½	3.3	10
¶22•5	CPC	✓CPC Intl ....NY,B,C,Ch,P,Ph	A+	25¢	675	96995	International food processor	51⅝	2⅞	51⅛	39⅞	54½	44¼	94509	54½	48⅞	53⅜	2.5	17
#23	CPY	✓CPI Corp........NY,Ch,Ph	B+	40¢	112	12730	Photo studio/lab,elec publ'g	34¾	3⅜	20⅞	13¾	18⅛	14	3179	18⅛	17⅛	18	3.1	24
#24•6	CBRL	✓Cracker Brl Old Ctry ....NNM	A	50¢	207	23981	Restaurant & gift stores	30⅝	7/16	34¼	22½	29⅛	21¼	92107	27¼	22	25½	0.1	21
25	CRFT	✓Craftmade Intl ....NNM	NR	1¢	20	856	Mkt ceiling fans,light kits	7½	2	13¼	6⅞	12⅜	8⅞	2742	10½	9⅝	10⅛	0.4	15
26	CRG	✓Craig Corp59........NY,B,Ch,P,Ph	C	25¢	24	1076	Supermkt chain,real estate	26⅝	¾	13⅛	7⅛	12⅞	10⅝	1019	12⅝	10⅝	10⅞	...	d
27	Pr	Cl'A' com60Pref (1 Vote)........NY	B–	1¢	5	572	banking investment in Calif	18	6⅝	12½	6¾	12⅝	10	773	11⅝	10	10⅜	...	..
¶28•4	CR	✓Crane Co ....NY,B,Ch,P,Ph	B+	1	240	19091	Mfr industrial,consumer prd	30	1 11/16	30⅞	22⅝	29½	24⅛	6377	26⅝	25⅛	26⅛	2.9	12
29	CRD.B	✓Crawford & Co Cl'B' ....NY,Ch,Ph	A	1	59	12757	Insurance claim adj service	30	¼	24¼	15	17	14¾	1523	16¼	15½	16	3.1	15
30	CRD.A	✓ Class'A' (non-vtg)........NY	A	1	54	12592		29¼	10	23	15½	17¾	15½	2074	16	15½	15⅞	3.5	14
¶31•6	CYR	✓Cray Research ....NY,B,Ch	B	1	243	19979	Scientific computer/software	135¾	15/16	30⅞	20⅝	33¾	19⅛	23812	21¾	20¼	21⅝	...	10
32	CAP.EC	Creative Computer Appl........ECM	B–	No	3	12	Hlthcare ind info systems	11	¼	1½	1	1 11/16	7/16	3439	1 11/16	1⅛	1 7/16	...	d
33•7	CREAF	Creative Technology63 ....NNM	NR	63..	..	...	IBM compatible audio/video pd	11⅜	5⅜	19¼	8¾	24	9¾	202263	21½	16	18	...	16
34	CMOS	✓Credence Systems........NNM	NR	.001	57	5201	Mfr semiconductor test eqp	....	....	15	10	28	14½	50313	23¾	17¼	22¼	...	18
35	CACC	✓Credit Acceptance........NNM	NR	No	47	5011	Auto dealers financial svcs	11¼	4⅜	26	9⅞	33¼	20	12892	33¼	28¾	30½	...	41
36	CRLP	Credit Lyonnais64 ....Pa	NR	180	..	...	Intl banking:France	901	385	795	456	856	415	....	493	415	475	2.1	d
37	CEI	✓Crescent Real Estate Eq ....NY,Ph	NR	1¢	55	6737	Real estate investment trust	....	....	....	....	29¾	25	11046	29¾	25⅜	29⅝	6.2	d
#38•4	CF	✓Crestar Financial........NY	B+	5	245	18972	Commercial bkg,Virginia	39¾	2¾	46½	35⅛	49¾	39⅜	14204	49¾	47¼	48¼	3.3	12
39	CFR	✓CRI Liquidating REIT65........NY,Ph	NR	1¢	26	515	Real estate investment trust	13⅜	9¼	10½	7¾	8¾	5¼	3006	5⅝	5¼	5½	⊙15.8	5
40	CMM	✓CRIIMI MAE ....NY,Ph	NR	1¢	38	1554	Real estate investment trust	10	6¼	12¾	9¾	12	9⅜	10612	11¼	10½	10⅝	10.9	12
41	CGW	Cristalerias de Chile ADS66 ...NY,Ch,Ph	NR	66..	33	2186	Mfr glass containers,Chile	....	....	....	....	31	16⅝	9044	19⅝	17¼	18	2.6	18
42	CXIM	✓Criticare Systems........NNM	B–	4¢	10	712	Mfr patient monitor'g instr	12½	1¾	3⅜	1 11/16	2⅝	1¾	3210	2 9/16	1⅞	2 3/16	...	..
#43•8	CNK	✓Crompton & Knowles ....NY,Ch,Ph	A+	10¢	201	31373	Spec chemicals,ind'l mchy	23⅞	5/16	27¼	17⅝	24⅛	15⅞	43706	17¼	15⅞	15⅞	3.0	14
#44	ATX.A	✓Cross (A.T.) Cl'A' ....AS,B,Ch,P,Ph	B	1	111	10258	Fine writing instruments	41	1 15/16	20¼	12⅜	17⅝	12⅝	4590	16⅞	15½	16⅜	3.9	36
45	XTO	✓Cross Timbers Oil........NY,Ph	NR	1¢	68	9096	Oil & gas dvlpmt, prod'n	....	....	18⅞	12⅞	15⅜	12½	2223	15⅛	14⅜	14⅝	2.1	..

Reproduced by permission of *Standard & Poor's*, a division of McGraw-Hill, Inc.

CF$_{3s\ 48 1/4}$ CPBI$_{2000s\ 27}$ CXIM$_{2\ 3/16}$ ATX.A$_{4s\ 15\ 3/4}$ CBRL$_{8s\ 24}$ CYR$_{40000s\ 21\ 1/8}$

Stock Ticker Interpretation				
Symbol	**Company Name**	**Principal Business**	**Price Per Share (on ticker)**	**Volume (shares traded in transaction on ticker)**
CF	Crestar Financial	Commercial banking, Virginia	$48.25	300
CPBI	***CPB, Inc.***	***Commercial banking, Hawaii***	***27.00***	***2,000***
CXIM	***Criticare Systems***	***Manufacturing of patient monitoring instruments***	***2.1875***	***100***
ATX.A	***A. T. Cross***	***Fine writing instruments***	***15.75***	***400***
CBRL	***Cracker Barrel Old Country***	***Restaurants and gift stores***	***24.00***	***800***
CYR	***Cray Research***	***Scientific computer/software***	***21.125***	***40,000***

Economics

A Day in the Life of a Stock: How to Read the Stock Pages

Whenever a corporation is formed, stock is created to evidence its ownership for those who created the firm. Over time, however, the original owners of a firm sell their stock to others; thus, the firm's shares become an investment to be traded among many investors. Implicit in being an investor is an understanding of how to read the stock pages of the newspaper. The stock pages of a newspaper provide a snapshot of an entire day in the life of a stock. It is imperative for those involved in economics and business to be able to read the stock pages, for they provide the day-to-day vital signs of companies. Below is a portion of a stock report as it might appear in a local newspaper.

52 Wks. Hi	Lo	Stock	Sym	Div	Yld %	PE	Vol 100s	Hi	Lo	Close	Net Chg
$18\frac{1}{8}$	$14\frac{1}{2}$	BostCelts	BOS	1.40	8.4	9	32	17	$16\frac{5}{8}$	$16\frac{5}{8}$	$-\frac{1}{4}$
$20\frac{5}{8}$	$16\frac{1}{2}$	BostEdsn	BSE	1.58	7.8	13	252	$20\frac{3}{8}$	20	$20\frac{1}{4}$	$+\frac{1}{8}$
$16\frac{3}{4}$	$14\frac{1}{8}$	BostEdsn pf		1.46	8.8	$\cdots$	3	$16\frac{5}{8}$	$16\frac{5}{8}$	$16\frac{5}{8}$	$+\frac{1}{8}$
$30\frac{3}{8}$	$16\frac{1}{8}$	Bowater	BOW	1.20	4.8	12	393	$25\frac{1}{2}$	$25\frac{1}{4}$	$25\frac{1}{4}$	$-\frac{1}{2}$
$36\frac{3}{4}$	$20\frac{1}{2}$	BriggsStrat	BGG	1.60	4.4	13	372	$36\frac{5}{8}$	36	$36\frac{3}{8}$	$\cdots$
▲ $84\frac{7}{8}$	$55\frac{3}{8}$	BrisMyrsSqb	BMY	2.40	2.8	23	9577	$85\frac{1}{4}$	$83\frac{3}{4}$	$84\frac{5}{8}$	$+\frac{1}{2}$
$37\frac{3}{4}$	$24\frac{1}{2}$	BritAir	BAB	2.10	7.1	$\cdots$	401	$29\frac{5}{8}$	$29\frac{3}{8}$	$29\frac{3}{8}$	$\cdots$
$49\frac{7}{8}$	38	BritGas	BRG	2.79	6.0	12	567	47	$46\frac{1}{2}$	$46\frac{5}{8}$	-1
$86\frac{1}{4}$	$63\frac{7}{8}$	BritPetrol	BP	4.75	6.7	10	1023	$70\frac{3}{4}$	$70\frac{1}{8}$	$70\frac{3}{8}$	$-\frac{1}{4}$

Your first task is to determine the market in which your stock is traded. Newspapers and financial journals usually list the three main stock markets: the New York Stock Exchange (NYSE), which lists the largest firms; the American Stock Exchange (AMEX), which lists smaller but nationally known firms; and the Over the Counter (OTC) market, which lists still smaller and lesser-known companies.

Next, you must locate your particular stock. Stocks are listed in alphabetical order in column #3 under the heading "Stock." Notice, for example, the stock in the Boston Celtics professional basketball team listed on the NYSE. All stocks are assumed to be common stock unless the name is followed with a "pf," indicating that it is preferred.

Columns 1 and 2 give the highest and lowest prices for the stock over the last 52 weeks. Notice that Boston Celtics stock sold for as much as $18.125 and as little as $14.50 over the last year. A downward- or upward-pointing arrow to the left of the first column indicates that a new 52-week high or low price has recently been achieved.

Column 4 gives the ticker symbol. Column 5 lists the annual dividend paid to each share of stock. Note that the Boston Celtics stock pays its holder $1.40 per share in dividends. Column 6 tells the reader the percentage return on his money that the company's dividends are currently yielding. For example, dividing the Boston Celtics stock's dividend of $1.40 by the $16.625 ($16\frac{5}{8}$) closing price tells the economist that the stock's dividend is currently 8.4% of the stock's price.

The next column provides the PE or "price to earnings" ratio. The PE ratio is a measure of the confidence that investors have in the firm. The PE ratio is the share's price divided by its earnings per share (EPS); thus, a high PE ratio indicates that people are willing to pay a higher price for a firm's per share earnings. Column 8 tells the volume, or the number of shares (in hundreds), of that particular stock that were traded that day. Note that 3,200 shares of Boston Celtics stock were traded.

Finally, columns 9, 10, and 11 provide the day's price information. Note that the highest price paid for Boston Celtics stock during the day was $17, while the lowest was $16.625. When the New York Stock Exchange closed at 4 P.M., the last trade in Boston Celtics that crossed the ticker was for $16.625. The final column indicates the difference between the closing price listed and the closing price from the previous day's newspaper. Apparently, Boston Celtics stock's closing price was $16.875 in the previous day's newspaper, since today's closing price indicates that the price fell by $.25 (-1/4).

Now that you know how to read the stock price page of the newspaper, try to answer the questions that follow the stock page information below.

52 Wks.		Stock	Sym	Div	Yld %	PE	Vol 100s	Hi	Lo	Close	Net Chg
Hi	Lo										
$18\frac{7}{8}$	$10\frac{1}{4}$	CarolFrght	CAO	.60	3.5	38	494	17	$16\frac{7}{8}$	17	. . .
49	38	CarolPwr	CPL	3.04	6.3	12	657	$48\frac{3}{8}$	48	$48\frac{1}{4}$	$+\frac{1}{8}$
$54\frac{7}{8}$	$36\frac{1}{2}$	CarpTech	CRS	2.40	5.0	14	145	$48\frac{3}{8}$	$47\frac{3}{4}$	$48\frac{3}{8}$	$+\frac{1}{4}$
$5\frac{3}{4}$	$3\frac{1}{2}$	Carriage	CGE	.10	2.2	9	18	$4\frac{3}{4}$	$4\frac{5}{8}$	$4\frac{5}{8}$	$-\frac{1}{8}$

1. What was today's closing price for Carolina Power & Light (CarolPwr) stock? **$48.25**

2. What was *yesterday's* closing share price for Carpenter Technology (CarpTech) stock? **$48.125**

   (48 3/8 – 1/4 = 48 1/8)

3. What is the symbol of Carriage Industries? **CGE**

4. Of the four stocks listed, which has the highest dividend per year? **Carolina Power & Light at $3.04**

5. Of the four stocks listed, which has the lowest dividend yield? **Carriage Industries at 2.2%**

6. In which of the four stocks listed do shareholders have the *most* confidence? **Carolina Freight**

   Corporation, since it has the highest PE ratio of 38 times earnings

7. Of the four stocks listed, which had the *least* number of shares traded during the day? How many shares were traded? **Carriage Industries with 1,800 shares**

Complete the columns below, given the following information from a financial news report: "Today, stock in the Universal Widget Corporation (UWC) experienced an unprecedented nose dive. It appears that the stock, which has sold for as much as $57.50 during the past year, fell to a new all-time low today as the price dipped 20 points below yesterday's closing price of $21.25 per share. Brokers could hardly conduct their normal business as they tried to accommodate their clients, who unloaded one million shares. Apparently, the sell-off was triggered by statements from Eugene M. Widget, president of Universal Widget. A financial journalist overheard Mr. Widget say to his vice president of finance, 'How am I supposed to tell these people that we're on the brink of bankruptcy? How am I sup-

posed to tell them that earnings per share have fallen to 25 cents and that we're cutting the dividend to 4 cents per year, huh? All because of that nuclear widget plant that almost melted down! No way! We've got to keep this under our hats!' UWC shares began trading at the previous day's closing price of $21.25, with each subsequent trade going for a lower price than the prior one. A spokesman for Universal Widget announced, 'Rumors of the firm's financial ill health are greatly exaggerated.' When asked if Mr. Widget would make a statement to the shareholders, the spokesman said, 'I am very sorry, but Mr. Widget is suffering from a severe case of laryngitis and will not be able to make a statement in the foreseeable future.' "

52 Wks.		Stock	Sym	Div	Yld %	PE	Vol 100s	Hi	Lo	Close	Net Chg
Hi	Lo										
$57\frac{1}{2}$	$1\frac{1}{4}$	UnivWidg	UWC	.04	3.2	5	10,000	$21\frac{1}{4}$	$1\frac{1}{4}$	$1\frac{1}{4}$	– 20

Students find the "Yld %" by dividing the annual dividend by the closing price: .04/1.25 = .032. The "PE" is found by dividing the closing price by the earnings per share: 1.25/.25 = 5.

Economics

Word Maze

Unravel the secret of this word maze to discover all the terms defined below. The maze begins with the boxed letter T and ends with the dot. The words in the maze are all in order; that is, the first word in the maze is described by definition #1, and so on.

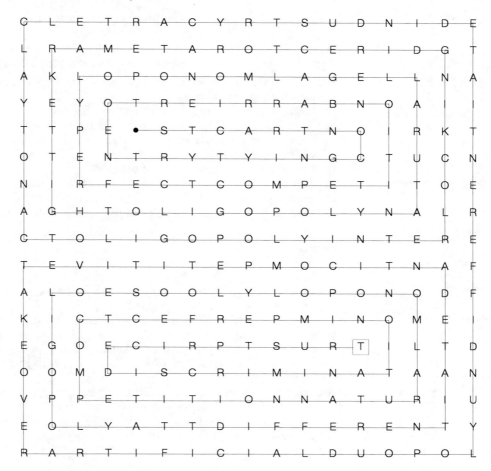

_____trust_____ 1. A business combination in which a group of companies in the same industry eliminate their competition by putting their stock into a single account and allowing a manager to look after the affairs of the group and distribute the profits

price discrimination 2. The selling of the same goods or services by a business to different buyers at different prices

imperfect competition 3. The type of market organization in which there exist many sellers of slightly differentiated goods, in which sellers and buyers are reasonably aware of market conditions, in which each seller has some control over his good's price, and in which sellers find it relatively easy to enter and exit the market

natural monopoly 4. A monopoly that exists because one firm owns or controls 100% of some resource vital to the industry

loose oligopoly 5. An oligopoly in which the top four firms account for 50% to 75% of the industry's total sales

_____ATT_____	6. The initials of the communications firm which was "broken up" by the government; also known as "Ma Bell"
_____differentiated_____	7. A term used to describe goods which are different from brand to brand
_____anticompetitive takeover_____	8. A situation that occurs when businesses buy out other firms in their industry in order to reduce or eliminate competition
_____artificial_____	9. The type of barrier to entry caused by government regulations
_____duopoly_____	10. An oligopoly which is composed of two businesses
_____undifferentiated_____	11. A term used to describe goods which are exactly alike from one firm to another
_____industry_____	12. A family of common concerns; groups of businesses that sell similar products, sell to a certain group of customers, or produce goods in a similar way
_____cartel_____	13. A group of producers who agree to control the price of their goods
_____Clayton Act_____	14. A congressional act passed in 1914 designed to enumerate and clarify certain uncompetitive practices
_____oligopoly_____	15. A market in which only a handful of firms are selling either highly differentiated or undifferentiated goods, in which sellers and buyers are not fully aware of market information, in which each seller has a great deal of control over the price, and in which sellers find it relatively difficult to enter and exit the industry
_____interlocking directorate_____	16. A situation that reduces competition in an industry by placing one or more directors of a business on the boards of competing firms
_____market_____	17. Arrangements people have developed for trading with one another
_____tight oligopoly_____	18. An oligopoly in which the top four firms account for at least 75% of the market's sales
_____natural_____	19. The type of barrier to entry that occurs when other firms own all of a vital resource
_____legal monopoly_____	20. A monopoly that exists because the government has allowed one firm the exclusive right to produce a good or service
_____perfect competition_____	21. The type of market organization in which a very large number of sellers sell an identical product, in which each seller and buyer is aware of all information about the market, in which no seller can affect the price, and in which sellers find it relatively easy to enter and exit the market
_____barrier to entry_____	22. A condition that prevents a new firm from entering an industry and competing on an equal basis with established firms
_____tying contracts_____	23. Contracts which are used by suppliers to force smaller companies into granting exclusive rights to the supplier

Skill: Recognition

Matching

To the left of each number, place the letter of the type of market competition which best corresponds to the word or phrase. *Note: Some may have more than one answer.*

a. perfect competition   d. duopoly
b. imperfect competition   e. monopoly
c. oligopoly

___E___ 1. One firm makes up the industry.

___C, D___ 2. very difficult to enter the industry

___A___ 3. undifferentiated products

___C___ 4. three competitors

___B___ 5. possesses ''reasonably complete'' information about the market

___A___ 6. very easy to enter and exit the industry

___C___ 7. may form a cartel to control price

___B___ 8. relatively easy to enter and exit the industry

___E___ 9. may be either legal or natural

Economics

Multiple Choice

Choose the response which best answers the question or completes the sentence.

_**A**_ 1. Which of the following is an example of an industry?
   A. coffee mug manufacturers
   B. Federal Communications Commission
   C. General Motors Corporation
   D. Illinois Department of Highways

_**A**_ 2. Which of the following products has the greatest potential for differentiation?
   A. jewelry
   B. milk
   C. lumber
   D. corn

_**D**_ 3. Which of the following would be considered an *artificial* barrier to entry into an industry?
   A. incompetent managers
   B. inability to raise necessary money
   C. an oligopoly
   D. government regulations

_**C**_ 4. Firms under which of the following forms of competition would most likely resort to corporate spying to gain information on competitors?
   A. perfect competition
   B. imperfect competition
   C. oligopoly
   D. monopoly

_**B**_ 5. A restaurant in Los Angeles, California, would probably be categorized under which form of competition?
   A. perfect competition
   B. imperfect competition
   C. oligopoly
   D. monopoly

_**D**_ 6. Which of the following firms enjoyed virtual monopoly power until the government forced its breakup in 1982?
   A. IBM
   B. ITT
   C. GMC
   D. ATT

_**B**_ 7. What one word is synonymous with the government's desire to minimize monopoly power and ensure competition?
   A. industry
   B. antitrust
   C. interlocking
   D. tying
   E. discrimination

Currency: Do You Really Know Your Money?

Currency in the United States has changed much since the days after the Revolutionary War. Today, as a result of the Federal Reserve Act of 1913, virtually all of the paper money in circulation in America has been created by the Federal Reserve System, and as a result those green paper bills are very familiar to us. But are they?

The most prominent characteristic of every piece of U.S. currency is the portrait of a famous American on the front of the bill and a scene or design on the back. Thanks to a government clerk by the name of Spencer Clark, portraits on the fronts of U.S. currency and stamps may only be those of individuals who are no longer living. During the Civil War, the United States began printing "fractional currency," paper money with face values of less than one dollar. The task of creating this new currency fell to Mr. Clark. When designing the first bills, Mr. Clark used the portraits of George Washington, the current secretary of the treasury, and the treasurer of the United States, men of whom the United States was justifiably proud. Mr. Clark overstepped his bounds when in 1866 he placed his own portrait on the nation's five-cent note. Many Americans joked that this new five-cent note was the only one backed by a metal—brass! (a play on the word *brazen*) Mr. Clark printed 220,000 of the five-cent notes before he was ordered to stop. Shortly thereafter Congress passed a law banning the portraits of living persons from United States currency, stamps, bonds, and other similar objects.

In the spaces provided below, see how many of the men and back designs you can match with the proper Federal Reserve Notes.

A. Abraham Lincoln
B. Andrew Jackson
C. George Washington
D. Salmon P. Chase
E. Thomas Jefferson
F. Ulysses S. Grant
G. Woodrow Wilson
H. Benjamin Franklin
I. Alexander Hamilton

J. John F. Kennedy
K. Lincoln Memorial
L. Signing of the Declaration of Independence
M. Independence Hall
N. White House
O. Great Seal of the United States
P. U.S. Treasury Building
Q. U.S. Capitol
R. Washington Monument

_C_ 1. Front of $1 bill

_O_ 2. Back of $1 bill

_E_ 3. Front of $2 bill

_L_ 4. Back of $2 bill

_A_ 5. Front of $5 bill

_K_ 6. Back of $5 bill

_I_ 7. Front of $10 bill

_P_ 8. Back of $10 bill

_B_ 9. Front of $20 bill

_N_ 10. Back of $20 bill

_F_ 11. Front of $50 bill

_Q_ 12. Back of $50 bill

_H_ 13. Front of $100 bill

_M_ 14. Back of $100 bill

You might be saying to yourself "How am I supposed to know details about $50 and $100 bills? I never see them!" Very well, let us see how much you know about the most common paper bill in the United States today—the $1 bill. Study a $1 bill for a minute or two; put it away, and then answer the questions below.

1. Under the portrait of the president pictured, is his full name given or just his last name? *Only the last name, "Washington," is given.*

2. Name the offices held by the two persons who sign the front of the bill. Which office signs on the left, and which signs on the right? *the Treasurer of the United States (signature to the left of the portrait), the Secretary of the Treasury (signature to the right of the protrait)*

3. In how many places on the bill (front and back) is the value of the bill indicated? *sixteen times— six times on the front and ten times on the back*

4. Between the green U.S. Treasury seal and the serial number is printed the name of a city. What is the city's name? *Washington, D.C.*

5. Within the green U.S. Treasury seal are two objects and a date. What are they? *a set of scales, a key, 1789*

6. Imbedded in the paper of the bill are colored threads. What are the two colors? *red, blue*

7. On the reverse side of the bill are found the front and back of the Great Seal of the United States. The front of the Great Seal is made up of the likeness of an eagle. The head of the eagle represents the executive branch of the government; the shield represents the legislative branch; and the nine tail feathers represent the nine members of the Supreme Court, the judiciary. Answer the following questions about this part of the Seal.

   • What is found in the eagle's talons? *olive branch (signifying peace), 13 arrows (signifies ability to successfully, but reluctantly, wage war)*

   • Which way is the eagle's head facing? *right (toward the olive branch of peace)*

   • In the Eagle's beak is a banner. What does it say? *E PLURIBUS UNUM ("out of many, one")*

8. The reverse of the Great Seal shows the image of a thirteen-level, incomplete pyramid which symbolizes the as yet incomplete United States.

   • On the foundation level of the pyramid is a Roman numeral. What is it? *1776*

   • Above the pyramid is a Latin phrase, "ANNUIT CŒPTIS." What is the meaning of this phrase? *He hath favored our undertakings.*

   • Beneath the pyramid is another Latin phrase, "NOVUS ORDO SECLORUM." What is the meaning of this phrase? *a new order for the ages*

Economics

Commercial Banking: Doing Your Homework Before You Open an Account

A survey was conducted recently to determine what attracted customers to their commercial banks. Was it high interest rates? No. Was it longer banking hours? Think again. How about higher credit limits? Not even close! The average person said that the primary factor affecting his decision as to which bank would handle his finances was, get ready for this, how close the bank was to his house! The second reason was even more interesting: attractive and courteous tellers. No one would expect a client to use a bank that is hundreds of miles from his home or to rely on surly and rude personnel, but such considerations should be secondary. A bank's ability to carry out its basic functions should be a potential customer's main concern. What are the basic functions of a bank? Banks exist to accept and pay interest on deposits, to act as a mechanism to help its customers pay their bills through checking accounts, to extend loans, and to offer miscellaneous services.

All right, you have decided not to be so foolish as to choose a bank just because it is next door to your home, or because the tellers have nice smiles. How, though, will you judge whether a bank is right for you? First, take a few hours to visit several banks, speaking to their customer service representatives. Avoid going on your bank safari on Mondays or Fridays, since those are usually busy days. While speaking to each banker, ask for a brochure that states the bank's services and fees. After your visits, you may not be able to remember details about each bank's services; thus, the brochures will help you remember.

An important issue to consider should be whether the bank has deposit insurance. Only a small minority of banks do not have deposit insurance, but you certainly do not want to be among the losers. Avoid uninsured banks.

Second, find out what services the bank offers. For most people, checking, NOW, and savings accounts, along with safe deposit boxes and loans, are the only services required. Other services, such as estate planning, income tax assistance and preparation, international wire transfers of money, and large denomination certificates of deposits, are needed by others. Below is a list of services that might be offered by a commercial bank.

Checking
Personal Checking
Interest Checking

Investment
Personal Savings
Super Savings Accounts
Money Market Investment Accounts
Certificates of Deposit
Individual Retirement Accounts
Purchase/Sale of Taxable and Tax-Exempt
    Securities

Money Management
Cash Key 24-Hour Banking
Banking by Mail
Traveler's Checks
Cashier's Checks
Money Orders

Bank Drafts
Collection Items
Wire Transfer Service (Domestic and
    International)
Direct Deposit
Foreign Currency Exchange
Bond Coupon Redemption

Credit
VISA
MasterCard
Check Guarantee Protection
Personal Lines of Credit
Loans

Miscellaneous
Safe Deposit Boxes
Bond Safekeeping

Third, ask about the interest rates that the banks pay on accounts. Some banks pay interest on checking accounts while others do not. Banks that offer interest on checking often require that some minimum balance be maintained in order to receive interest. Check to see if these requirements are too restrictive. Also, ask how interest is calculated on deposits. Since banks must keep around 12% of customer's deposits in a non-interest-bearing account to meet Federal Reserve Bank reserve requirements, your bank may pay interest only on a portion of your deposits since they are not able to loan your entire deposit. While such a scheme is logical, many other banks will still pay interest on 100% of your deposits. Find these banks and use them. Find out how often the bank compounds interest. As you learned in chapter 9, the more often a bank compounds interest, the faster the accounts grow. If possible, select a bank that compounds interest "daily" or "continually."

To be sure, banks exist to make profits for their owners. To make profits many banks charge fees for their services. It is imperative, therefore, for consumers to study each bank's fee schedule. Using the bank fee schedule below, answer the questions on the following page.

REGULAR CHECKING
Minimum Opening Balance	$ 100.00
Minimum Daily Balance (No Service Charge)	$ 200.00
Service Charges if minimum not maintained:	
Maintenance Charge (per month)	$ 2.50
Per Debit Charge	$ .25
Minimum Daily Balance	
if checks are not returned with statements	$ 0

INTEREST CHECKING (Personal, Sole Prop., Non-Profit)
Minimum Opening Balance	$ 100.00
Minimum Daily Balance (No Service Charge)	$ 500.00
Service Charges if minimum not maintained:	
Maintenance Charge (per month)	$ 3.00
Per Debit Charge	$ .25

BUSINESS CHECKING (Corp., Sole Prop., Non-Profit)
Minimum Opening Balance	$ 0
Interest Paid (Earnings Credit Based on Avg. Coll. Bal. X 90-day T-Bill Rate [less 12% Reserve].)	
Analysis Charges:	
Maintenance Charge (per month)	$ 4.00
Per Debit Charge	$ .15
Per Credit Charge	$ .25
Per Item Deposited Charge	$ .06
Chargeback	$ 1.50

MONEY MARKET CHECKING (Limit of 6 transfers a month, three of which may be third-party checks)
Minimum Opening Balance	$ 1000.00
Minimum Daily Collected Balance (No Service Charge)	$ 1000.00
Service Charges if minimum not maintained:	
Maintenance Charge (per month)	$ 3.00
Per Debit Charge	$ .25
Per Debit Charge over limit of 6	$ 3.00

REGULAR SAVINGS
Minimum Opening Balance	$ 50.00
Minimum Daily Balance (No Service Charge)	$ 100.00
Service Charges if minimum not maintained:	
Maintenance Charge (per month)	$ 1.00
Withdrawal Charge (per quarter after 3 withdrawals)	$ 3.00

STOP PAYMENTS (per item)	$ 10.00
COLLECTIONS (per item)	$ 8.00
RETURNS	
Returned Check (per item)	$ 18.00
Chargebacks (per item)	$ 1.50
Overdraft (per item)	$ 18.00
CUTOFF STATEMENT (without checks)	$ 2.00
(with checks)	$ 5.00
WIRES	$ 7.00
CHECK COPY	$ 3.00
RESEARCH TIME (per hour)	$ 12.50
DORMANT FEES (per month)	$ 1.00
ROLLED COIN (per roll)	$ .04
CASHIER'S CHECKS (Customers)	$ 3.00
(Non-Customers)	$ 3.00
AMEX MONEY ORDERS (Customers)	$ 1.50
(Non-Customers)	$ 3.00
TRAVELER'S CHECKS	1% of amount purchased
SAFE-DEPOSIT BOXES (per year)	
3 x 5	$ 20.00
3 x 10	$ 35.00
5 x 10	$ 45.00
10 x 10	$ 75.00
NIGHT DEPOSITORY	
First Bag	$ 10.00
Each Additional Bag	$ 5.00
Zipper Bags	$ 2.50

1. What is the fee for a 5" x 10" safe-deposit box? *$45.00 per year*

2. What would be the charge if you had the branch manager research a problem (which you caused) with your checkbook, assuming the manager spent three hours solving the problem? *$37.50 (3 hours @ $12.50 per hour)*

3. At your last bank you had a problem adding and subtracting checks in your check register, causing you to have an average of ten overdrafts (returned checks) per month. Since your previous banker was your cousin, he merely called you and told you to make deposits. It appears that this bank will not be so understanding. What will be the total of your monthly fees for bouncing ten checks per month? *$180.00 (10 overdrafts per month @ $18.00 per overdraft)*

4. What is the minimum initial deposit required to open a regular non-interest-bearing checking account? *$100.00*

5. If you maintain an average daily balance of $199.00 per month in your regular checking account and you write an average of 20 checks per month, what, if any, would be your monthly service charge (assuming you have elected to receive your cancelled checks with your monthly statement)? *$7.50 ([20 checks @ $.25] + $2.50)*

6. You are a building contractor, and your suppliers require you to pay all of your bills with cashier's checks. Assuming that you make ten such payments each month and that you will be a customer of the bank, what will be your total monthly cashier's check charges? *$30.00 (10 checks @ $3.00 each)*

7. You write a check for $5,000 to purchase a car, and on the way to the dealership you lose the check. Fearing that the finder of the check will try to cash it, you decide to issue a stop payment order to the bank. How much will the bank charge you to guarantee that the check will not be cashed? *$10.00*

8. What is the minimum initial deposit required to open a regular savings account? *$50.00*

9. Assuming that you maintain an average balance in your regular savings account of $300.00 and that you make an average of three withdrawals per month, what would be your monthly service charge? *$0 (no service charges required if a minimum balance of $100 is maintained)*

10. You go on vacation each summer, and you always purchase $750 worth of traveler's checks. What would be your traveler's check fee each summer? *$7.50 ($750.00 X 1%)*

Economics

Barter, Monetary Standards, and Relative Prices

The beauty of using a common medium of exchange such as we have in the United States is that all goods and services need carry only one price tag. Chapter 9 of the student text explains that one problem with the barter method of exchange is the overabundance of "relative prices." Under a barter system, every good must have a price tag telling its value in relation to every other good. For example, assume that you live on a small, sparsely inhabited island, and on the island there exist only four types of goods: coconuts, fish, bananas, and mangos. You grow and sell bananas. Over time you notice the following price structure: ten bananas purchase ten coconuts, five fish, or one mango. Thus, you must put the following three price tags on each banana:

1 coconut (since 10 coconuts will buy 10 bananas [10/10 = 1])

1/2 fish (since 5 fish will buy 10 bananas [5/10 = 1/2])

1/10 mango (since 1 mango will buy 10 bananas [1/10 = 1/10])

Likewise, each of your neighbor's goods will have three separate price tags. In the spaces provided, list the relative prices of each good in terms of the other three goods.

1. Each coconut will carry three price tags reading

   __1__ banana *(since 10 bananas will buy 10 coconuts [10/10 = 1])*

   __1/2__ fish *(since 5 fish will buy 10 coconuts [5/10 = 1/2])*

   __1/10__ mango *(since 1 mango will buy 10 coconuts [1/10 = 1/10])*

2. Each fish will carry three price tags reading

   __2__ bananas *(since 10 bananas will buy 5 fish [10/5 = 2])*

   __2__ coconuts *(since 10 coconuts will buy 5 fish [10/5 = 2])*

   __1/5__ mango *(since 1 mango will buy 5 fish [1/5 = 1/5])*

3. Each mango will carry three price tags reading

   __10__ bananas *(since 10 bananas will buy 1 mango [10/1 = 10])*

   __10__ coconuts *(since 10 coconuts will buy 1 mango [10/1 = 10])*

   __5__ fish *(since 5 fish will buy 1 mango [5/1 = 5])*

Are you confused yet? You should be! Your calculations revealed that six different price tags had to be printed:

1. Bananas to coconuts (or coconuts to bananas)
2. Bananas to fish (or fish to bananas)
3. Bananas to mangos (or mangos to bananas)
4. Coconuts to fish (or fish to coconuts)
5. Coconuts to mangos (or mangos to coconuts)
6. Fish to mangos (or mangos to fish)

If you thought it was difficult to calculate the relative prices for four goods, try determining relative prices for an economy with millions of goods. The price tags would weigh more than the individual products! In order to determine the number of relative prices in a larger economy, economists have developed the "relative price equation": **N(N - 1) / 2 = Number of Relative Prices.**

For our island example, the equation would be **4(4 - 1) / 2 = 6.**

Determine the number of relative prices for an economy with the following numbers of goods.

1. 50 goods   *50(50 – 1) / 2 = 1,225*

2. 100 goods   *100(100 – 1) / 2 = 4,950*

3. 1,000,0000 goods   *1,000,000(1,000,000 – 1) / 2 = 499,999,500,000*

Economics

Chapter 9   **Activity 4**

Commercial Banking: Opening a Checking or Savings Account

Opening a checking or savings account is a relatively easy procedure. The first thing a bank's customer service representative will do is find out if you are of legal age. If not, you will need to have a parent, legal guardian, or other responsible adult sign for you in order to assume full legal responsibility. In many states one must be sixteen years of age or older to open a deposit account. To open a loan account, such as overdraft protection on a checking account, one must be at least eighteen years of age and have proven credit worthiness. Second, you will be asked to complete a signature card. A signature card provides much needed personal information such as your home address, workplace, home and work telephone numbers, Social Security number, and your signature.

Requiring this information may appear intrusive at first, but it is all necessary to protect both the customer and the bank. Providing home and work addresses and telephone numbers permits the bank to mail the customer periodic statements and to make contact in case of an emergency. The bank also requires a copy of your signature in order to ensure that checks being written on your account are, indeed, being written by you. Finally, the government requires depository institutions to secure Social Security numbers in order to perform "backup withholding." In years past, many who earned interest would report their interest income at tax filing time only to discover that they did not have the money to pay the additional taxes. Others would fail to report their interest income altogether. "Backup withholding" is a procedure whereby the bank withholds income taxes on interest income much as your employer withholds taxes from your paycheck.

Below is a sample signature card. Complete it as if you were opening an individual account for interest checking with an initial deposit of $1,000 in cash. Enter all other information as accurately as possible.

ACCOUNT NAME _student's name_ _____

_____

ADDRESS _student's address_ _____

CITY, STATE, ZIP _student's city, state, and Zip_ _____

SIGNATURES: The undersigned agree(s) to the terms of this bank as provided in its disclosures. I (we) acknowledge receipt of copy of each.

ACCOUNT NUMBER: _____

NO. OF SIGNATURES REQUIRED FOR WITHDRAWAL: _1_

1. _student's signature_ _____
2. _____
3. _____
4. _____
5. _____

PERSONAL ACCOUNT
[X] Individual
[ ] Joint-Survivorship

OTHER ACCOUNTS

Interest Checking   X
Money Mkt. Checking _____
Savings _____

INITIAL DEPOSIT: $ _1,000.00_
[X] Cash   [ ] Check(s)
D.L. No.: _Answers will vary._

TELEPHONE: (HOME) _student's home #_   (BUSINESS) _student's school #_
SOCIAL SECURITY NUMBER: _student's Social Security number_
EMPLOYER: _Answers will vary._

Economics

Word Scramble

Unscramble the following words. After all words have been unscrambled, place the letters that are double underlined in the spaces provided at the bottom of this exercise and unscramble the resulting scrambled word to solve the riddle.

1. alleg __l__ __e__ __g__ __a__ __l__

2. reverse __r__ __e__ __s__ __e__ __r__ __v__ __e__

3. topside __d__ __e__ __p__ __o__ __s__ __i__ __t__

4. yemon __m__ __o__ __n__ __e__ __y__

5. fati __f__ __i__ __a__ __t__

6. nasol __l__ __o__ __a__ __n__ __s__

Riddle: After paying his taxes, the economist was happy that he had done what was legal, but his wallet was very __e__ __r__ __d__ __e__ __t__ __n__ ⇒ _____ _tender_ _____.

Matching

To the left of each number, place the letter of the function of money which best corresponds to the word or phrase.

    A. means of payment
    B. means of storing purchasing power
    C. measure of value

__A__ 1. John paid cash for his car.

__B__ 2. "I just feel a little better having a ten-dollar bill in my wallet 'just in case.' "

__A__ 3. "Joe, here is your paycheck."

__C__ 4. "That can of hair spray is $1.50."

__A__ 5. "Sold to the man in the front row!"

__C__ 6. "$80 for that old thing? No way!"

__B__ 7. "If you put it on deposit for six months, you will earn 8.5% interest."

__B__ 8. "I think we ought to save our tax refund."

__A__ 9. "I think we ought to buy a car with our tax refund."

Multiple Choice

Choose the response which best answers the question or completes the sentence.

___C___ 1. What is "legal tender"?
   A. a medium of exchange equally agreeable by both parties to a transaction
   B. money which is easily stored
   C. money which the law says must be accepted
   D. the fact that bookkeeping entries may be used as legal evidence in courts of law

___D___ 2. Which of the following was *not* listed as one of the functions of money?
   A. a means of storing purchasing power
   B. a measure of value
   C. a means of payment
   D. a measure of responsibility

___A___ 3. When too much money is placed in circulation, a type of economic spoilage results called _____.
   A. inflation
   B. recession
   C. depression
   D. monetary shrinkage

___B___ 4. Which of the following is *not* one of the money standards discussed in the text?
   A. representative money
   B. intrinsic money
   C. fiat money
   D. commodity money

___D___ 5. Of the following, which do many economists believe ought to be abolished, since it is a source of wasted time and resources?
   A. the dollar bill
   B. the dollar coin
   C. the one-half dollar coin
   D. the penny coin

___D___ 6. Which measure of the money supply accounts for the greatest amount of money?
   A. M-1
   B. M-2
   C. M-3
   D. L

___C___ 7. Which of the following financial institutions concentrate on making home loans?
   A. commercial banks
   B. credit unions
   C. savings and loan associations
   D. mutual savings banks

___B___ 8. What organization insures deposits at commercial banks?
   A. FSLIC
   B. FDIC
   C. FED
   D. FRS
   E. FIMSO

Economics

Currency: Created by Federal Reserve District Banks

Chapter 9 mentioned the fact that the Federal Reserve System produces paper currency and places it into circulation in the United States today. Within the Federal Reserve System there exist twelve Federal Reserve District Banks which produce United States currency. Each Federal Reserve District Bank identifies itself many times on the face of each Federal Reserve Note it produces, either by spelling out its name, printing its district number, or printing the letter that corresponds to its district number.

Upon examination of the face of a one-dollar Federal Reserve Note, one can find to the left of the portrait a black seal which contains the name of the Federal Reserve District Bank which produced the note along with the letter of the district. The district number is the number that corresponds to the letter (A = 1; B = 2; etc.). Where and how many times does a Federal Reserve District Bank identify itself on the face of a one-dollar Federal Reserve Note?

You may wish to try to find a federal reserve note from each of the twelve districts for distribution or framing in your classroom.

Eight times: (1) name within the black seal to the left of the portrait; (2) district number in the center of the black seal; (3) district number in the lower left corner; (4) district number in the upper left corner; (5) district number in the upper right corner; (6) district number in the lower right corner; (7) district letter at the beginning of the lower left serial number; (8) district letter at the beginning of the upper right serial number

Identification of the Federal Reserve Districts

On the map provided, write the name and identifying letter of the Federal Reserve District Bank which serves the district indicated. After completing the map, answer the following questions.

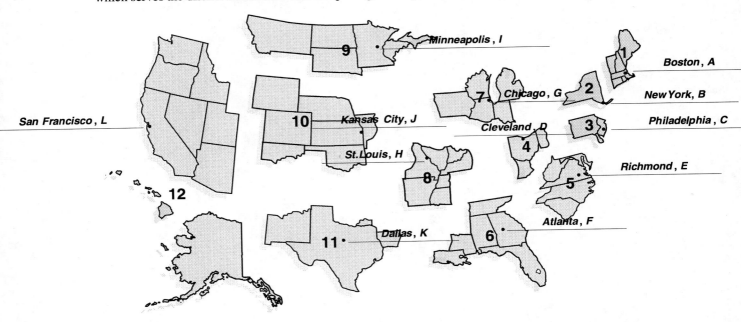

1. How many Federal Reserve District Banks exist? *twelve* _____

2. Within which Federal Reserve District do you live? *Answers will vary.* _____

3. Where does the Fed's Board of Governors convene? *Washington, D.C.* _____

4. Within which Federal Reserve District are securities purchased and sold for the FOMC?

   the New York Federal Reserve District (2, B) _____

Economics

The Money Multiplier:
How the Fed and Commercial Banks Work Together to Create Money

Obviously the United States has more money in circulation today than it had in the early 1800s. Equally obvious is the fact that as a result of a larger population, a more educated work force, and more productive capital equipment, there are more goods and services being produced today than in the past. As a nation's quantity of goods and services grows, the quantity of money in circulation should grow at roughly the same rate in order to keep prices relatively constant. The Federal Reserve Bank is the agency designated by Congress to monitor and control the quantity of money in circulation and to make adjustments in order to help the nation reach its economic goals.

Before you read Chapter 10, you may have thought that the government created money by printing currency; however, you soon learned that currency makes up a relatively small part of the total money supply. Most money is created through the lending process via a phenomenon called the money multiplier. When a loan is made between friends, no new money is created. That is, if Joe lends Bob $100, Joe relinquishes ownership of the $100 to Bob. When a loan is made from a financial institution, however, new money is created because the concept of money ownership is blurred. When Joe deposits a $100 bill into his checking account, the money remains his property. When Joe made the deposit, the bank gave him a receipt stating that he was no longer holder of a $100 bill, but rather the holder of a $100 demand deposit. Joe's bank then lent $90 of Joe's deposit ($100 less 10% reserve) to Bob. Who now "owns" the money? Joe or Bob? Both! Joe can still write checks based on his $100 deposit while at the same time Bob is free to spend his borrowed $90. Thus, the bank, in concert with the Fed's required reserve ratio, increased the money supply by $90.

You read in Chapter 10 (page 156) that the money multiplier is actually much lower than it could be, thus preventing the money supply from expanding to its full potential. Two reasons exist for this phenomenon. First, not all deposited money is lent. That is, many commercial banks maintain a small amount of excess reserves above what is required. Second, some people choose to hold their money in the form of cash. Thus, not all money is deposited and placed in the lending stream. The Fed could control this situation by instituting a cashless financial system.

The table on the next page (similar to the table found on page 156 of your text) illustrates the money multiplication process. The columns are labeled "Bank," "Amount Deposited," "Amount Held on Reserve," "Amount Lent," and "Money Supply." As you may recall, the money multiplication process begins with an initial entry in the money supply column. This entry represents the "monetary base" or the "seed money" from which all money in the United States originates. The monetary base consists of all currency and coin in circulation plus all money held on reserve in the Fed. The monetary base is deposited in the nation's financial institutions (column #2). After funds are deposited, a percentage (specified by the Fed) is deducted to satisfy the Fed's reserve requirement (column #3). For our example we will assume that there exists a uniform 20% required reserve ratio for all institutions. The amount remaining (column #4) represents the excess reserves that may be lent (and entered into column #2 and added to the total money supply in column #5).

Beginning with a monetary base of $100, complete the table on the next page through "Bank Z." What is the total money supply by the end of the process? After completing the table, answer the questions that follow.

	Money Multiplier (Assuming a 20% Required Reserve Ratio)			
Bank	Amount Deposited	Amount Held on Reserve	Amount Lent (Excess Reserves)	Money Supply
MONETARY BASE				$100.00
A	$100.00	$20.00	$80.00	$180.00
B	80.00	16.00	64.00	244.00
C	64.00	12.80	51.20	295.20
D	51.20	10.24	40.96	336.16
E	40.96	8.19	32.77	368.93
F	32.77	6.55	26.22	395.15
G	26.22	5.24	20.98	416.13
H	20.98	4.20	16.78	432.91
I	16.78	3.36	13.42	446.33
J	13.42	2.68	10.74	457.07
K	10.74	2.15	8.59	465.66
L	8.59	1.72	6.87	472.53
M	6.87	1.37	5.50	478.03
N	5.50	1.10	4.40	482.43
O	4.40	.88	3.52	485.95
P	3.52	.70	2.82	488.77
Q	2.82	.56	2.26	491.03
R	2.26	.45	1.81	492.84
S	1.81	.36	1.45	494.29
T	1.45	.29	1.16	495.45
U	1.16	.23	.93	496.38
V	.93	.19	.74	497.12
W	.74	.15	.59	497.71
X	.59	.12	.47	498.18
Y	.47	.09	.38	498.56
Z	.38	.08	.30	498.86

1. What is the total money supply after a loan is provided by Bank Z? *$498.86*

2. If you used the money multiplier formula (text p. 156), what would be the potential money supply?
   $500.00: $100.00 X (1 / .20)

3. Why is the potential money supply in question #2 greater than the potential money supply in question #1? *In question 1 we did not follow through each possible permutation; we multiplied only through Bank Z.*

4. By how much would the potential money supply change if the Fed changed the required reserve ratio to 10%? *The potential money supply would double to $1,000.00: $100.00 X (1 / .10).*

5. What would be the total potential money supply and money multiplier if the one who borrowed from Bank O decided to hold his borrowed funds in cash? *The money multiplication process would immediately cease with Bank O; therefore, the total potential money supply would be only $485.95. The money multiplier would be, therefore, 485.95/100 = 4.8595 times.*

Economics

Matching

To the left of each number, place the letter of the result which best corresponds to the item.

A. decreases the money supply
B. has no effect on the money supply
C. increases the money supply

__A__ 1. FOMC sells $3 billion in securities.

__A__ 2. Fed raises the discount rate.

__C__ 3. Fed lowers the required reserve ratio from 12% to 3%.

__B__ 4. Fed accepts a $1 billion deposit from the federal government.

__C__ 5. FOMC buys $8 billion in securities.

__B__ 6. Fed clears $100 million in checks.

__A__ 7. A commercial bank pays off a loan which it received from the Fed.

__B__ 8. Fed shreds $1 billion worth of worn-out currency and replaces them with new bills.

__C__ 9. Fed lowers the discount rate.

Computations

Given each scenario, compute the total dollar potential increase or decrease in the money supply.

1. The Fed sells $100 million in securities on the open market. (The required reserve ratio is 7%.)
   Total potential decrease would be $1,428,571,428.57: $100 million X (1 / .07) = $1,428,571,428.57.

2. The Fed lowers the discount rate from 8% to 6%, causing commercial banks to borrow an additional $1.5 billion. (The required reserve ratio is 10%.) *increase of $15 billion*

3. The Fed raises the required reserve ratio from 5% to 10%. (The total money supply was $1 trillion when the required reserve ratio was 5%.) *decrease of $500 billion*

4. The Fed raises the discount rate from 8% to 12%, causing commercial banks to pay back $900 million in loans. (The required reserve ratio is 5%.) *decrease of $18 billion*

5. The Fed buys $200 million in securities on the open market. (The required reserve ratio is 9%.)
   increase of $2,222,222,222.22; $200 million X (1 / .09) = $2,222,222,222.22

Economics

Crossword Puzzle

Fill in the blanks on the crossword puzzle with the words which best correspond to the definitions or statements provided.

ACROSS

1. The _____ requirement forces commercial banks to hold a specified percentage of each deposit.
5. number of years that constitute a term for a member of the Federal Reserve Board
8. initials of the Fed organization that buys and sells securities
9. Money is said to be _____ if its supply has the ability to expand and contract.
11. One method of clearing checks is _____ banking.
13. number of members of the Federal Reserve Board
16. number of members on the Federal Open Market Committee
17. The Fed buys and sells securities in the _____ market.
18. The Fed is controlled by a Board of _____.
19. Congress has granted this to the Fed, allowing it to be run with no outside control and little supervision.

DOWN

2. The Fed may attempt to keep the money supply growing at the same rate as the growth of the nation's production of goods and services in order to promote price _____.
3. city in which the main office of the Fed bank of the first Federal Reserve District is located
4. The Fed controls the money supply in part to control the _____ rate.
6. By taking deposits from and making loans to commercial banks, the Fed has come to be known as the _____ bank.
7. the interest rate the Fed charges banks on loans
10. Checks may be cleared through a local _____.
12. The _____ effect is the phenomenon of a deposit's being lent, deposited, and relent, causing the money supply to grow.
14. He wrote *Human Action.*
15. The Fed is said to be "the lender of last _____."

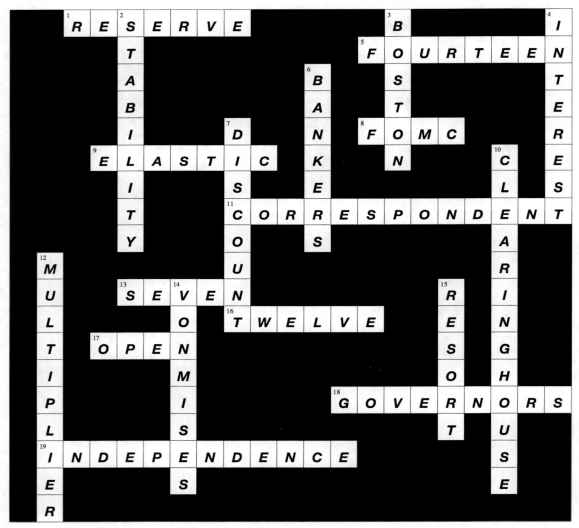

Economics

Multiple Choice

Choose the response which best answers the question or completes the sentence.

__D__ 1. Which of the following is *not* a creator of money in the United States today?
A. commercial banks
B. the Federal Reserve System
C. the United States Treasury
D. All of the above are creators of money in the United States today.

__C__ 2. Which of the following is a function of a central bank?
A. provision of a means of efficiently collecting taxes
B. to act in the place of a commercial bank
C. provision of a national check-clearing system
D. to act as a lender of last resort for businesses

__B__ 3. In what year was the Federal Reserve System created?
A. 1875
B. 1913
C. 1929
D. 1933

__C__ 4. Which of the following is responsible for increasing and decreasing the supply of money through the purchasing and selling of securities?
A. Federal Reserve Board of Governors
B. Federal Advisory Council
C. Federal Open Market Committee
D. Quadriad

__A__ 5. Which of the following would serve on a Federal Reserve District bank's board of directors?
A. bankers
B. members of the United States House of Representatives
C. members of the United States Senate
D. members of the Federal Reserve's Board of Governors

__B__ 6. How many persons serve on the Federal Reserve's Board of Governors?
A. 3
B. 7
C. 12
D. 14

__A__ 7. The interest rate a commercial bank would pay the Federal Reserve on borrowed funds is the
A. discount rate.
B. Fed funds rate.
C. reserve rate.
D. prime rate.

__D__ 8. Which of the following is one of the Fed's sources of operating funds?
A. the federal budget
B. the Fed funds trust fund
C. fees received from Congress for the creation of new currency
D. fees charged commercial banks for services rendered by the Fed

_**D**_ 9. Which of the following is *not* one of the major economic services provided by the Federal Reserve?
   A. provision of a uniform currency
   B. provision of an elastic currency
   C. regulation of state member banks
   D. All of the above are major economic services provided by the Fed.

_**C**_ 10. Which of the following would be one of the Fed's duties as fiscal agent?
   A. provision of a uniform currency
   B. clearance of checks
   C. holding the federal government's checking account
   D. placing coin into circulation

Economics

Name _____

Chapter 11   **Activity 1**

Calculation of Nominal GNP

Use the following information to complete the second table in order to calculate gross national product. (Warning: Not all of the figures will be used!)

Category	Amount (in billions)
Federal government purchases of goods and services	$ 463.3
Consumer nondurable goods	1,287.1
Payments for imported goods	774.1
Indirect business taxes	14.2
Transfer payments to individuals	227.0
Change in business inventories	33.7
Consumer durable goods	543.0
Contributions to social insurance	333.7
Sales of exported goods	715.9
Consumer services	2,148.7
Retained corporate profits	733.6
Corporation profit taxes	401.3
Fixed business investment	857.3
State and local government purchases of goods and services	725.1

Gross National Product		
Personal consumption expenditures (dollars in billions)		
Consumer durable goods	$ 543.0	
Consumer nondurable goods	1,287.1	
Consumer services	2,148.7	
Total personal consumption expenditures		$ 3,978.8
Gross private domestic investment		
Fixed business investment	$ 857.3	
Change in business inventories	33.7	
Total gross private domestic investment		891.0
Government purchases of goods and services		
Federal government purchases of goods and services	$ 463.3	
State and local government purchases of goods and services	725.1	
Total government purchases of goods and services		1,188.4
Net exports of goods and services		
Sales of exported goods	$ 715.9	
Payments for imported goods	− 774.1	
Total net exports of goods and services		− 58.2
Total Nominal Gross National Product		6,000.0

Enrichment: Section I   **Skill: Application**   **89**

Comparing Nominal and Real Gross National Product

Government leaders use the economic information generated by economists to make decisions about taxation, spending, and social welfare policies. Therefore, it is imperative that the information be accurate. The table below gives nominal and real gross national product statistics along with growth rates for several years. Complete the graph below the table by plotting the nominal GNP growth rates in one color and the real GNP growth rates in another color. In the space provided after the graph, comment on the differences you found in the plotted growth rates.

Nominal and Real Gross National Product for Selected Years				
Year	Nominal GNP ($ Bil.)	Nominal GNP Growth During the Five-Year Period	Real GNP (1982=100)	Real GNP Growth During the Five-Year Period
1939	$ 91.3		$ 716.6	
1944	211.4	131.54%	1,380.6	92.66%
1949	260.4	23.18%	1,109.0	-19.67%
1954	372.5	43.05%	1,416.2	27.70%
1959	495.8	33.10%	1,629.1	15.03%
1964	649.8	31.06%	1,973.3	21.13%
1969	963.9	48.34%	2,423.3	22.80%
1974	1,472.8	52.80%	2,729.3	12.63%
1979	2,508.2	70.30%	3,192.4	16.97%
1984	3,772.2	50.39%	3,501.4	9.68%
1989	5,233.2	38.73%	4,142.6	18.31%

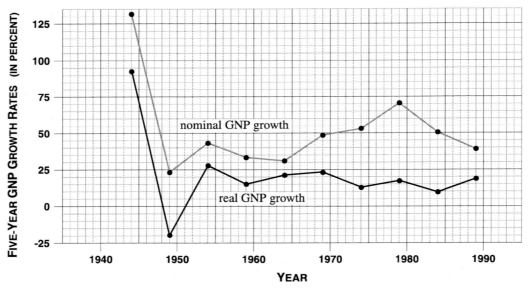

Comments: _Students should note two important observations. First, in most cases when nominal GNP rises, real GNP likewise rises, and vice versa. In several instances, however, nominal and real GNP growth do not rise or fall at the same rate. For example, between 1969 and 1974, nominal GNP rose at a rate of 52.80%. Doubtless, this kind of growth would cause economists much glee. When we look at real GNP, however, we see that the rate of economic growth was in fact only 12.63%. Second, nominal and real GNP growths occasionally go in opposite directions, sending policy makers mixed signals. For example, in the five-year period between 1944 and 1949, nominal GNP grew by 23.18% while real GNP fell by 19.67%._

Economics

Gross National Product: A Barometer of Industrial Health

As you have seen, gross national product statistics can be an invaluable aid to economists and government leaders in determining the relative health of the U.S. economy in general and of the four GNP categories in particular. When broken down still further by industrial groups, gross national product figures also provide some startling revelations about the growth of those industries. The table below has broken down the GNP for selected years by the industries which contributed to it. After examining the table, answer the questions that follow.

Real Gross National Product by Selected Industries (Rounded Billions of 1982 Dollars)										
Year	GNP	Agriculture	Mining	Construction	Manufacturing	Transportation	Wholesale & Retail Trades	Finance & Real Estate	Services	Government
1950	1,204	64	73	100	258	95	182	120	134	169
1955	1,495	69	92	133	328	112	215	160	153	223
1960	1,665	68	94	163	339	128	245	207	190	240
1965	2,088	67	109	194	463	162	310	260	240	284
1970	2,416	69	135	168	507	204	368	321	296	340
1975	2,695	73	126	149	548	246	433	388	352	355
1980	3,187	76	136	162	665	293	500	464	443	383
1985	3,619	94	130	165	787	326	610	524	546	401
Growth Rate		46.88%	78.08%	65.00%	205.04%	243.16%	235.16%	336.67%	307.46%	137.28%

1. Which industry contributed the most to the nation's GNP in 1950? in 1970? in 1985?

   Manufacturing contributed the most to the nation's GNP for all three periods.

2. Which industry contributed the least to the nation's GNP in 1950? in 1970? in 1985?

   Agriculture contributed the least to the nation's GNP for all three periods.

3. Fill in the last row of the chart above where it asks for the industry's growth rate. To calculate percentage growth rates, use the following formula: ([1985 GNP – 1950 GNP]/1950 GNP) × 100.

   a. Which industry grew the most between 1950 and 1985? *finance and real estate (9.62% per year)*

   b. Which industry grew the least between 1950 and 1985? *agriculture (1.34% per year)*

4. How could such information help economists? *By examining growth rates of industries' contributions to the nation's GNP, economists are able to tell which industries have been experiencing economic distress. More importantly, economists are able to predict which industries are likely to need assistance in the future. Economists will be able to predict which areas of the country will experience economic prosperity and which will be experiencing economic decline.*

Multiple Choice

Choose the response which best answers the question or completes the sentence.

___D___ 1. The gross national product is the total dollar value of all _____ goods and services produced in one year.
   A. intermediate
   B. domestic
   C. household consumption
   D. final

___D___ 2. Your neighbor just purchased a new Italian sports car for his personal use. Under which GNP category would the purchase be listed?
   A. consumer durables
   B. consumer nondurables
   C. business investment
   D. net exports

___A___ 3. During World War II which GNP category saw a dramatic increase?
   A. government spending
   B. consumer nondurables
   C. business investment
   D. consumer durables

___C___ 4. In some cases a foreign product is cheaper than the same domestically produced product because it is subsidized. Who (or what) ultimately pays the subsidy?
   A. the foreign government
   B. foreign business firms
   C. foreign taxpayers
   D. domestic consumers

___A___ 5. Americans who advocate free trade would probably argue for which of the following?
   A. reducing import taxes
   B. imposing import quotas
   C. subsidizing American-made products sold to foreign countries
   D. imposing limits on the quantity of goods American manufacturers can produce

Modified True/False

If the statement is true, write the word *true* in the blank. If it is false, change the underlined word(s) to make the statement true. Write the correct word(s) in the blank.

___sold or left in inventory___ 1. The value of goods which are used in the production of other goods are counted as part of GNP at the time they are <u>purchased by the manufacturer.</u>

___True___ 2. A <u>consumer durable good</u> is one which has a life expectancy greater than one year.

___Consumption spending___ 3. <u>Government spending</u> is the largest of the four GNP categories.

___inflation___ 4. Real GNP is GNP that has been adjusted to take <u>government spending</u> into account.

___True___ 5. A negative balance of trade is said to exist when a nation is running a <u>trade deficit.</u>

___True___ 6. <u>Protectionists</u> believe that restrictions on imported goods will preserve domestic jobs.

___1987___ 7. The United States' negative balance of trade grew each year between 1983 and <u>1989.</u>

Economics

Understanding Foreign Exchange Rates

Imagine an Italian man coming into an American store to purchase some coffee and handing the clerk a handful of Italian lira! The clerk would probably swallow hard and call the manager. The manager could graciously tell the shopper that his currency was not acceptable and tell him to go to a bank to convert it to U.S. currency, or he could accept the lira and convert it himself. In a sense, this is what happens every time you purchase a foreign-made good. You purchase the good with American dollars, and the seller converts the dollars into the currency of the nation from which he purchased the goods and sends it to the foreign manufacturer. So, why is all of this "behind the scenes" activity important to you? It is important to you because it has a very real impact on the prices you pay for foreign-produced goods.

Let us use a very simple example. Let us assume that on Friday, July 19, 1991, Greg Fastlane was in the market to purchase a sports car, and he decided to purchase a German model which he was told cost $45,000. (No one said that cars in examples have to be cheap!) When he heard the price, he cleared his throat and said that he would be back on Friday, December 27, 1991, when his end-of-the-year bonus check would come in. The anxiously awaited day arrived, and Greg indeed did receive an end-of-the-year bonus of exactly $45,000. He immediately rushed to the dealership and told the salesperson that he now had the money and wished to buy the car. "Sorry, sir," the salesperson exclaimed. "That vehicle now costs $51,788.54." "What!" he exclaimed with a little more desperation in his voice than he wished to betray. "What could possibly make the price of the same car go up 15.09% in just over five months?"

What, indeed, could have caused the price of the car to rise so dramatically? The answer: a change in what is known as the exchange rate. On July 19, 1991, the financial newspapers carried the following information.

Exchange Rates Friday, July 19, 1991		
Country	U.S. $ equivalent	Currency per U.S. $
Argentina (Austral)	.0001010	9902.00
Britain (Pound)	1.6925	.5908
China (Renmimbi)	.186567	5.36
France (Franc)	.16846	5.9360
Germany (Mark)	.5724	1.7470
Israel (Shekel)	.4276	2.3384

On any given day you can exchange your American currency for almost any other currency in the world market, and the price (or value) of it in terms of dollars will be published in the financial publications such as the *Wall Street Journal* and *Barrons*. The above table contains actual exchange rate information. The first column gives the exchange rate from an American's perspective; it tells the reader that on Friday, July 19, 1991, one German mark was worth $ .5724. The second column gives the rate of exchange from the foreigner's perspective; that is, one American dollar was worth 1.7470 marks ($1 /.5724 = 1.747). Thus, when the car dealer told Greg that the car he wanted cost $45,000, he really meant that it cost 78,615 German marks (78,615 marks / 1.747 marks per dollar = $45,000).

Greg was unaware that almost every day the price of each currency changes because of changing supply-and-demand conditions. On the supply side, if the United States government creates money faster than the Germans, it will take more dollars to buy the same number of marks as before. On the demand side, if everyone in the world starts buying a lot of German goods, there will be a high demand for marks as people convert their currencies so that marks may be used to purchase the German goods. The increase in demand for marks will cause the price of marks to rise. On Friday, December 29, 1991, however, the exchange rate information had changed. The 78,615 German marks that the German manufacturer demanded of the American dealership now cost $51,788.54 (78,615 marks / 1.518 marks per dollar). The new table looked like the following.

Exchange Rates Friday, December 27, 1991		
Country	**U.S. $ equivalent**	**Currency per U.S. $**
Argentina (Austral)	.0001010	9905.01
Britain (Pound)	1.8750	.5333
China (Renmimbi)	.185185	5.4000
France (Franc)	.19290	5.1840
Germany (Mark)	.6588	1.5180
Israel (Shekel)	.4478	2.2329

Now that you know about exchange rates, let us see how well you can complete a few exercises. Below is an incomplete exchange rate table. Fill in the missing values and then answer the questions which follow. Round your answers to four decimal places. (Note: Some of the countries' monetary unit titles have been left off; see if you can figure them out too!)

Exchange Rates		
Country	**U.S. $ equivalent**	**Currency per U.S. $**
Australia *(Dollar)*	*(1 / 1.3132) = .7615*	1.3132
Canada (Dollar)	.8617	*(1 / .8617) = 1.1605*
Japan *(Yen)*	.007949	*(1 /.007949) = 125.8020*
Poland (Zloty)	*(1 / 11,000.00) = .0001*	11,000.0000
Saudi Arabia *(Riyal)*	.26667	*(1 /.26667) = 3.7500*
Switzerland (Franc)	*(1 / 1.3504) = .7405*	1.3504

1. If you were planning to go on vacation to Canada and you took $547 in U.S. currency to your bank to exchange for Canadian dollars, how many could you buy (ignore bank service charges)?
   634.79 Canadian dollars (547 U.S. dollars X 1.1605 Canadian dollars per U.S. dollar)

2. You returned from your Canadian vacation with 22.50 Canadian dollars in your pocket. Assuming the exchange rate stayed the same, how many U.S. dollars did your banker give you in exchange? *$19.39 in U.S. dollars (22.50 Canadian dollars X .8617 U.S. dollars per Canadian dollar)*

3. On a mission trip to Poland you were on your way to an official exchange station to convert $127 into zlotys when you were stopped by a street vendor who offered to convert your U.S. dollars. He offered you 2,286,000 zlotys. Assuming this is a legal transaction and no fraud is involved, would it be wise on your part to convert your dollars with the street vendor or to proceed to the official currency exchange station? Why? *You should convert your U.S. dollars into zlotys with the street vendor. At the official exchange station you will receive only 1,397,000 zlotys ($127 X 11,000 zlotys per U.S. dollar). Even if you were not planning to convert your U.S. dollars into zlotys, you should do so with the street vendor. You could exchange your $127 for 2,286,000 zlotys and then proceed to the official exchange station, where you could re-exchange them for $207.82 (2,286,000 zlotys / 11,000 zlotys per U.S. dollar = $207.82).*

Economics

Word Scramble

Unscramble the following words. After all of the words have been unscrambled, place the letters that are double underlined in the spaces provided at the bottom of this exercise and unscramble them to solve the riddle.

1. moneynetplum   u n e m p l o y m e n t
2. descudirago   d i s c o u r a g e d
3. clecy   c y c l e
4. niceroses   r e c e s s i o n
5. kape   p e a k

Riddle: How the economist felt after having a stack of unemployment statistics fall on him at the library.

e p d s d e r s e ⇒

_____depressed_____.

Characteristics of Business Cycle Phases

Write the letter of the phase of the business cycle with which each of the following phenomena is identified.

A. expansion phase   C. recessionary phase
B. peak phase   D. trough phase

   C   1. The cost of labor and raw materials is falling.

   B   2. The economic expansion reaches the high point.

   A   3. Demand is on the increase for practically all goods and services.

   D   4. Consumer pessimism has reached rock bottom.

   D   5. If it is bad enough, this is called a depression.

   C   6. Real gross national product is falling.

   A   7. The unemployment rate is falling.

   B   8. The unemployment rate reaches its lowest point.

Economics

Identifying Phases in the Business Cycle

On the graph below, plot the hypothetical quarterly GNP information given in the table and then answer the questions after plotting your graph.

	Hypothetical Quarterly Gross National Product (Billions of Real Dollars)			
Year	**First Quarter**	**Second Quarter**	**Third Quarter**	**Fourth Quarter**
19X1	3,300	3,500	3,600	3,700
19X2	3,600	3,400	3,300	3,300
19X3	3,300	3,600	3,800	4,000
19X4	3,900	3,600	3,300	3,500
19X5	3,700	3,700	3,800	4,000
19X6	4,200	4,300	4,300	4,200
19X7	4,100	4,000	3,600	3,900

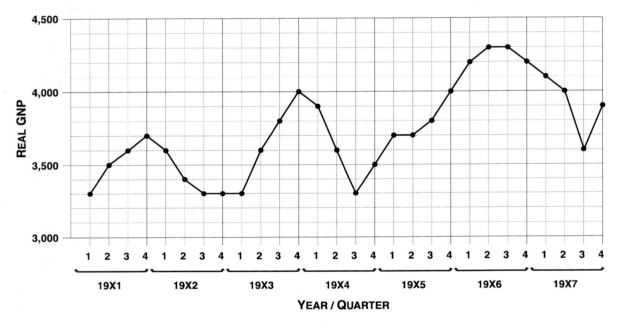

1. A recession is officially defined as two consecutive quarters of declining GNP. In your hypothetical example, how many recessions were experienced? _____ *three* _____

2. At what point was the first recession declared? *after the second quarter statistics were reported in 19X2*

3. List the years and quarters when peak and trough phases began.

Peak Phases		**Trough Phases**	
Year	**Quarter**	**Year**	**Quarter**
19X1	*4*	*19X2*	*3*
19X3	*4*	*19X4*	*3*
19X6	*2*	*19X7*	*3*

Economics

Understanding the Dow Jones Industrial Average

Why is the "business" cycle not called the "economic" cycle? Or better yet, the "GNP" cycle? It is called the business cycle because it represents the periodic economic ups and downs experienced by businesses, and what is experienced by businesses is experienced by all Americans. If, as President Calvin Coolidge once observed, "the business of America is business," we should see if there is some index which connects the business cycle to business. In 1884 a man named Charles Dow created such an index and later began printing it on a daily basis in the financial newspaper called the *Wall Street Journal,* which he created with his partner Edward Jones.

Mr. Dow created a list of eleven companies which he believed were representative of all American businesses. His original list comprised the following:

Chicago & North Western   Union Pacific
Delaware Lackawanna & Western   Missouri Pacific
Lake Shore Line   Louisville & Nashville
New York Central   Pacific Mail
St. Paul   Western Union
Northern Pacific

At the end of each business day, Dow and Jones would add the final selling prices of each of the stocks in their list and would publish the result in the *Wall Street Journal* the next day. Soon business people were noticing a correlation between business activity and the Dow & Jones list. Over the years the list was refined. Today business activity is reflected in *three* lists: the Dow Jones Industrial Average, the Dow Jones Transportation Average, and the Dow Jones Utility Average. The Transportation Average averages the share prices of the top twenty firms in the railroad, trucking, and airline industries. The Utility Average averages the share prices of fifteen of the leading gas and electricity businesses. By far the most popular, however, is the Dow Jones Industrial Average, an average of the share prices of thirty industrial companies which are believed to be representative of American business.

In the spaces below, write the names of ten of what you believe to be the top businesses in the United States. Compare your list with the answers, which are upside down at the bottom of the page. How many did you get correct?

_____   _____

_____   _____

_____   _____

_____   _____

_____   _____

As of January 1, 1992, the Dow Jones 30 Industrials were Alcoa, Allied Signal, American Express, AT&T, Bethlehem Steel, Boeing, Caterpillar, Chevron, Coca Cola, Disney, Dupont, Eastman Kodak, Exxon, General Electric, General Motors, Goodyear, IBM, International Paper, McDonald's, Merck, Minnesota Mining & Manufacturing (3M), Morgan JP, Philip Morris, Proctor & Gamble, Sears, Texaco, Union Carbide, United Technologies, Westinghouse, and Woolworth. *The thirty firms that make up the DJIA change very infrequently; however, to see if this list is current, you could check a recent copy of the Wall Street Journal.* A box containing a complete listing is found on page C3 within the DJIA graph.

Generally speaking, prices of stock in the stock market tend to rise and fall in tandem with increases and decreases in the general economy. The table below provides some historical Dow Jones Industrial Average information. Plot the information on the graph which follows. Note that the graph already has real GNP plotted.

Year	DJIA	Year	DJIA
1953	276	1971	885
1954	334	1972	951
1955	443	1973	924
1956	493	1974	759
1957	476	1975	802
1958	492	1976	975
1959	632	1977	895
1960	618	1978	820
1961	692	1979	844
1962	640	1980	891
1963	715	1981	933
1964	834	1982	884
1965	911	1983	1,190
1966	874	1984	1,178
1967	879	1985	1,328
1968	906	1986	1,793
1969	877	1987	2,276
1970	753	1988	2,061

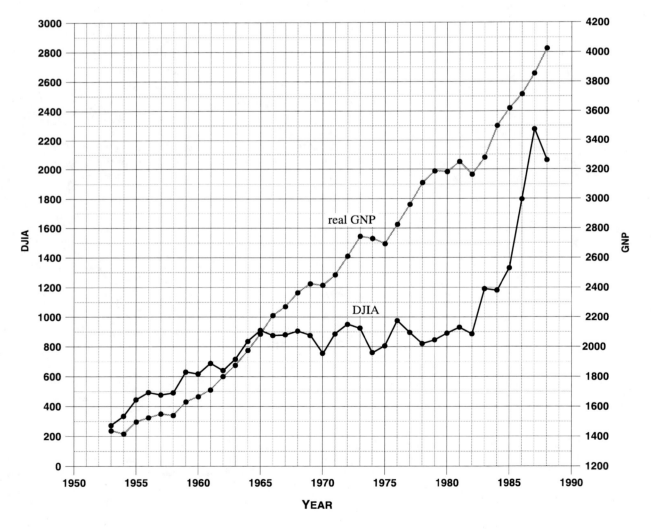

Economics

Calculating the Unemployment Rate

Given the following information, fill in the spaces in the blank table which follows and calculate the unemployment rate.

Total population	239,279,000
Children under 16 years of age	55,695,000
Discouraged workers (those who have not found employment after six months of searching)	11,288,000
Institutionalized persons	3,672,000
Members of the armed services	1,706,000
Employed persons	107,150,000
Those who have chosen not to participate in the labor force	22,917,000
Adults over 64 years of age	28,540,000

Calculation of the 19X5 Unemployment Rate	
Category	**Quantity**
Total Population	*239,279,000*
Less: Persons younger than age 16	*– 55,695,000*
Less: Persons over age 64	*– 28,540,000*
Less: Members of the armed services	*– 1,706,000*
Less: Institutionalized persons	*– 3,672,000*
Equals	*149,666,000*
Less: Those who have chosen not to participate in the labor force	*– 22,917,000*
Less: Discouraged workers	*– 11,288,000*
Equals: Labor force	*115,461,000*
Less: Employed persons	*– 107,150,000*
Equals: Unemployed persons	*8,311,000*
Unemployment Rate (unemployed / labor force)	*7.2%*

Answer the following questions. Unless otherwise indicated, each question refers to the original scenario shown above.

1. What would happen to the unemployment rate if on one given day American business firms simultaneously announced layoffs totalling five million workers? *The unemployment rate would rise to 11.5%: [(8,311,000 + 5,000,000) / 115,461,000] x 100.*

2. What would happen to the unemployment rate if three million of those who had chosen not to participate in the labor force suddenly decided to look for jobs? *The unemployment rate would rise to 9.5%: [(8,311,000 + 3,000,000) / (115,461,000 + 3,000,000)] x 100.*

3. What would happen to the unemployment rate if two million of the three million entrants into the work force in question #2 were successful in finding jobs? *The unemployment rate would fall to 7.9%: [(11,311,000 - 2,000,000) / 118,461,000] x 100.*

4. What would happen to the unemployment rate in the original scenario if two million of those un-employed members of the labor force passed their six-month anniversaries of being out of work without yet finding jobs? *The unemployment rate would fall to 5.5%: [(8,311,000 - 2,000,000) / 115,461,000] x 100.*

5. What would happen to the unemployment rate in the original scenario if two million of those un-employed members of the labor force were able to find employment while, at the same time, two million employed persons became unemployed? *The unemployment rate would remain at its original 7.2%: [(8,311,000 - 2,000,000 + 2,000,000) / 115,461,000] x 100.*

6. What would happen to the unemployment rate in the original scenario if all employers (1) cut their employees' working hours by 75%, from forty hours per week to ten hours per week and (2) cut each employee's wages from $25 per hour to $5 per hour. Assume that the disgruntled employees remain in their jobs. *The unemployment rate would remain at the original 7.2% because there would be no change either in the number of those unemployed or in the labor force. The definition of an employed person is one who is working at least one hour per week for pay.*

Employment-Population Ratio

Using all of the information from the six questions under ''Calculating the Unemployment Rate,'' calculate the employment-population ratio for each of the previous problems' questions.

1. *If the Dow Jones thirty industrial firms had layoffs totaling five million, the employment-population ratio would fall to 68.3%: [(107,150,000 - 5,000,000) / 149,666,000] x 100.*

2. *If three million of those who had chosen not to participate in the labor force suddenly decided to look for jobs, the employment-population ratio would remain at 71.6%, since neither the number employed nor the number of the adult, civilian, noninstitutionalized population would change: (107,150,000 / 149,666,000) x 100.*

3. *If two million of the three million of those in question #2 were successful in finding jobs, the employment-population ratio would rise to 72.9%: [(107,150,000 + 2,000,000) / 149,666,000] x 100.*

4. *The employment-population ratio would remain unchanged at 71.6%. The employment-population ratio changes only when the number of those employed and/or the number of those in the adult, civilian, noninstitutionalized population changes: (107,150,000 / 149,666,000) x 100.*

5. *If two million unemployed people found employment while at the same time two million employed persons became unemployed, the employment-population ratio would remain unchanged at 71.6%: [(107,150,000 - 2,000,000 + 2,000,000) / 149,666,000] x 100.*

6. *If all employers cut their employees' working hours by 75% from forty hours per week to ten hours per week while at the same time cutting each employee's wages from $25 per hour to $5 per hour, the employment-population ratio would remain unchanged at 71.6%.*

Economics

Duration of Unemployment

Imagine a bathtub that has water flowing in at a rate of twenty gallons per minute. If you close the drain, the water level will begin to rise. If you later open the drain (which drains at the rate of twenty gallons per minute), the water level will remain constant as the quantity entering the bathtub exactly equals the quantity leaving. If something clogs the drain allowing it to drain at a rate of only fifteen gallons per minute, the results will be as predictable as they will be disastrous: the bathtub will eventually fill to overflowing. Likewise, in our economy today, there is a constant flow of people into and out of the ranks of the unemployed. If there is a reduction in the number of those leaving the ranks of the unemployed relative to the numbers of those newly entering the ranks of the unemployed, the duration of unemployment (the length of time the average unemployed person remains unemployed) will rise. Economists realize that this increase in the duration of unemployment will be accompanied by an increase in the unemployment rate and are eager to remove things that obstruct the flow of the unemployed into the ranks of the employed.

To better understand the concept of the duration of unemployment, economists have created a graph. The vertical axis of the graph is labeled "Wages;" the horizontal axis is labeled "Weeks Unemployed." The first curve to be placed on the graph is called the wage-offer curve. The graph below shows that the wage-offer curve slopes upward until it flattens out, demonstrating that as an unemployed person searches for work, he can find firms willing to offer higher wages up to a point beyond which no firm will pay more. For example, if an executive of a manufacturing firm were laid off, he could probably immediately find a job that would pay the federal minimum wage of around $4 per hour, but he knows that well-paying jobs take time both to find and then to secure. As the graph shows, by week four of his job search, he will find a job that pays $9.50 per hour, and by week twelve he will be able to secure a job paying the maximum (for him) of $20.50 per hour.

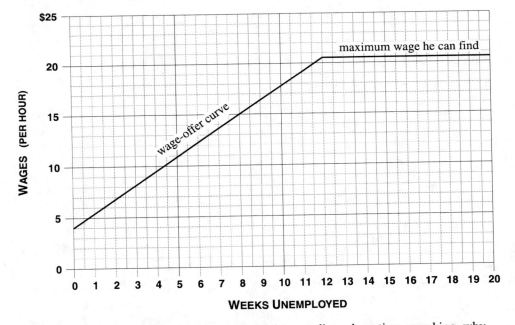

If an unemployed person can find a high-paying job by spending a long time searching, why does not every unemployed person spend a long time on unemployment? The answer is found in the reservation-wage curve. The reservation-wage curve is downward sloping, revealing that as time progresses and financial pressures mount, unemployed persons will have fewer "reservations" about taking lower-paying jobs. At first, our unemployed executive believed that he deserved to be paid $23 per hour, but as time progressed and his savings began to run out, he became willing to settle for lower wages. After being unemployed for four weeks, he became willing to settle for a job which paid $18 per hour.

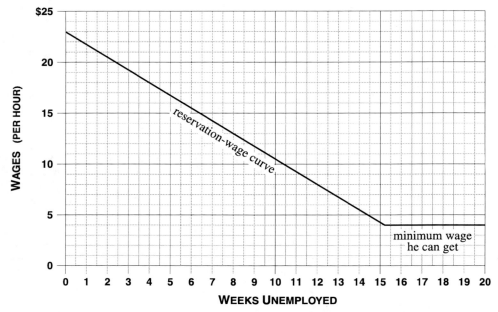

When the wage-offer curve and the reservation-wage curve are combined, we notice an interesting phenomenon: as time progresses, potential employers become willing to pay higher wages. During the same time period, however, potential employees adjust their wage expectations downward. At the point where the wages expected match the wages offered, a job is filled and one person leaves the ranks of the unemployed. In our example, the business executive will be unemployed for slightly longer than seven weeks, the time it takes for him to secure a job paying $14 per hour.

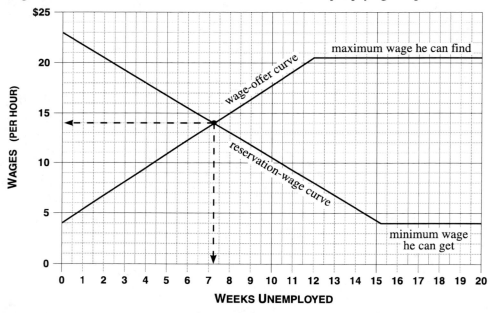

Now let us create an example you can work with. Fred, a worker on an automotive assembly line in Detroit, Michigan, was earning $18 per hour before the recession hit automotive sales. After the recession hit, Fred lost his job. Scouring the newspapers, he immediately located a job at the minimum wage of about $4 per hour, but that was far lower than his expectation of $18 per hour. Because of his skill level and persistent searching, Fred began to receive job offers each week that were $1 per hour higher than the offers he received the week before. His friends told him that the highest-paying jobs around were paying $18 per hour but that it takes time to find them and to go through the interviewing process.

Fred's family spends $1,600 per month to meet basic expenses such as food, shelter, gas and electricity, the monthly car payment, and the credit card bills. Because he was laid off, Fred was eligible for approximately $800 per month in unemployment compensation (at the time of this writing,

unemployment compensation pays a maximum of $207 per week for 26 weeks). Because of the difference between his expenses and what the state employment security commission was paying, he will have to dip into the savings account $800 per month (or $200 per week). With the savings account balance at $2,400, Fred and his wife estimate that they could hold out for twelve-weeks, after which point he will have to take any job, even one paying the minimum wage.

1. By drawing Fred's wage-offer curve and his reservation-wage curve on the blank graph below, calculate the duration of his unemployment and the hourly wage he will earn from the job he selects. Assume that Fred's reservation-wage curve falls steadily from $18 per hour to $4 per hour over the twelve-week period that his savings account holds out.

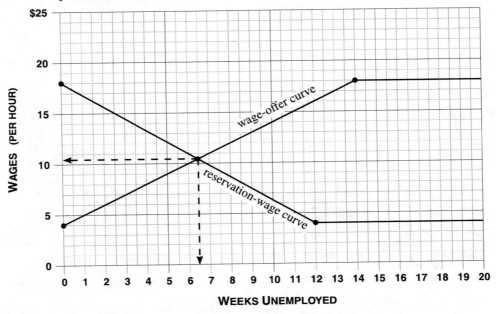

Fred will be unemployed slightly less than 6 1/2 weeks. According to the graph, he will probably agree to a job Tuesday or Wednesday of week six. The job to which Fred agrees will pay slightly less than $10.50 an hour.

2. Explain what would happen if, because of state and federal budget crises, unemployment compensation benefits fell to $400 per month.

Because of the difference between Fred's financial need of $400 per week and his unemployment benefits of $100 per week, he will need to take $300 per week from his savings account. At that rate, his savings account will last eight weeks. Fred's reservation-wage curve will shift to the left. Beginning at $18 per hour and ending at $4 per hour eight weeks later, his reservation-wage curve will intersect the wage-offer curve at a point of unemployment duration of slightly over five weeks and with a wage of slightly over $9 per hour. (Point out that while most people applaud the assistance unemployment compensation provides, it has the unforeseen consequence of prolonging unemployment. In Fred's case, the lower the unemployment compensation, the sooner he is forced to take a job.)

3. Explain what would happen if, out of a sense of compassion, the government boosted Fred's unemployment compensation benefits to $1,200 per month.

The increase in unemployment compensation would mean that Fred would need to draw only $100 per week from his savings account, giving him twenty-four weeks before his savings account would fall to a zero balance.

Fred's reservation-wage curve would shift to the right. With the reservation-wage curve beginning at $18 per hour and ending at $4 per hour twenty-four weeks later, Fred's reservation-wage curve will intersect his wage- offer curve at a point of unemployment duration of over 8 1/2 weeks and with a wage of around $12.75 per hour.

Short Answer

Answer the following questions in the spaces provided.

1. List the four phases of the business cycle.

   expansion phase

   peak phase

   recession phase

   trough phase

2. What are the characteristics of the expansion phase of the business cycle? *The nation's gross national product rises, the number of available jobs grows, the unemployment rate falls, national income expands, and there is an increase in credit purchases.*

3. Who developed the sunspot theory of the business cycle? *William Jevons*

4. How was it believed that sunspots caused a change in business activity on earth? *It was believed that sunspots caused a change in agricultural yields as a result of alterations of the earth's weather patterns.*

5. How is it that "easy money" causes a temporary expansion in business activity? *As the growth of the money supply outstrips the growth of the nation's production of goods and services, prices rise as products are rationed by the market. Since demand for goods is increasing, business firms seek to satisfy the demand by hiring new workers, purchasing new factories and equipment, and buying more raw materials.*

6. What is the "unemployment rate"? *the number of unemployed people divided by the total labor force*

7. What are the four flaws in the unemployment statistics?

   Many people work but are not counted as being employed. (e.g., 15-year-olds and military personnel)

   Some people do not work and are not included in the unemployment statistics. (e.g., discouraged workers)

   Some people are counted as being employed but are actually underemployed.

   Some who are counted as unemployed do have jobs. (e.g., those temporarily laid off)

8. Of the four types of unemployment mentioned in your text, which do many consider to be a "beneficial" type of unemployment? Why? *Many economists consider frictional unemployment to be beneficial because it is evidence of the fact that workers have the freedom to quit jobs with which they are dissatisfied and seek better employment. It also evidences the fact that employers are free to replace unproductive employees with more productive workers.*

9. What was the name of the act in which Congress first declared that the federal government's number one priority was maximum employment? *the Employment Act of 1946*

Economics

How Inflation Affects You

"Who cares if prices go up a little bit each year?" "A little inflation is good for an economy!" Economists and business people often hear questions and statements like these. We should all care if prices go up a little bit each year. A little inflation is not good for an economy, as the following exercise demonstrates. In the following table, insert the annual prices of a $100 good at various rates of inflation. Note the column illustrating 2% inflation. In year 1 the good has a price of $100; year 2, $102 ($100 × 1.02); year 3, $104.04 ($102 × 1.02); etc.

Year	2% Inflation	5% Inflation	10% Inflation	20% Inflation	50% Inflation	100% Inflation
0	$100.00	$100.00	$100.00	$100.00	$100.00	$100.00
1	102.00	105.00	110.00	120.00	150.00	200.00
2	104.04	110.25	121.00	144.00	225.00	400.00
3	106.12	115.76	133.10	172.80	337.50	800.00
4	108.24	121.55	146.41	207.36	506.25	1,600.00
5	110.41	127.63	161.05	248.83	759.38	3,200.00
6	112.62	134.01	177.16	298.60	1,139.06	6,400.00

1. If you were elderly and living on a fixed income of $10,000 per year and that amount was able exactly to meet your expenses in year 0, by how much would your expenses exceed your income in year 5 if over that period inflation was at 5%? (Note: For this and the following problems you will need to convert amounts in the table above to factors of 100.) *$2,763*

2. In real terms, how much is your $10,000 worth at the end of year 5 with 5% inflation? (Hint: To calculate real value, progressively subtract the percentage. For example, at 2% inflation the value of $100 falls to $98.00 in year 1 (100 - 2%); $96.04 in year 2 ($98.00 - 2%); $94.12 in year 3 ($96.04 - 2%); etc.) *$7,737.81*

3. Imagine you have $10,000 on deposit at a bank which pays you 5% interest per year. How much money would you lose if you kept your money on deposit from year 0 through year 6 while the inflation rate was 10%? Round to the nearest dollar. *$4,315 (17,716 – 13,401)*

4. Some countries, notably Third-World nations in South America, suffer from tremendous rates of inflation because of politicians' attempts to create money to pay the nation's expenses. At one point in Bolivia in the mid-1980s, the nation suffered an inflation rate of around 115,000% per year! The loss of value to the citizens' currency was tremendous. A nation's inflation rate, however, need not be at Third-World levels to seriously harm its citizens' standard of living. Using the formula in question 2 for calculating the loss of value of money during inflation, calculate the loss of value for a family that has an income of $37,000 (1992's median income) over a 10-year period at an inflation rate of 3% (what many politicians and economists would have us believe is an acceptable inflation rate). Round to the nearest dollar. *$9,715 loss*

Economics

Creating Your Own CPI

How is the consumer price index calculated? In Chapter 13 of your text, you discovered that the CPI measures the changes in prices of a market basket of goods purchased by the average urban household. But what are the mechanics involved in calculating the CPI? First, government economists survey 57,000 households in 85 urban areas of the nation to determine what they buy each year and in what quantities. Next, the price of each of the goods in the "market basket" is determined by sending surveyors out to 19,000 retail establishments—department stores, supermarkets, hospitals, gasoline stations, and service establishments. The price of each good is multiplied by the quantity of the good represented in the market basket and a total value of the basket is calculated. The first total is used as a standard against which future basket totals are compared; hence, the first year is called the "base year." In the years which follow, government surveyors determine the new prices of each of the goods in order to calculate a new total value for the basket. The new total is divided by the old total, and the result is the consumer price index. Economists have a formula for this process:

$$\frac{\text{Quantity}_{\text{Base Year}} \times \text{Price}_{\text{Current Year}}}{\text{Quantity}_{\text{Base Year}} \times \text{Price}_{\text{Base Year}}}$$

Thus, if the market basket costs $8,000 in the first year, then its CPI would be as follows:

($8,000 / $8,000) × 100 = $100.00

If the market basket should cost $8,400 the next year, the CPI would be as follows:

($8,400 / $8,000) × 100 = $105.00

Now that you know how a price index is computed, we will create one of our own. The following example involves a market basket consisting of goods purchased by the average urban child. Below is a theoretical list of the quantities of goods and their prices in 1975 and 1980. Fill in the blanks to determine the $\text{CPI}_{\text{children}}$.

Children's Consumer Price Index (CCPI)					
Item	Quantity Purchased Each Year	Price in 1975	Total Purchased in 1975	Price in 1980	Total Purchased in 1980
Baseball game ticket (general admission)	6	$2.00	*$12.00*	$3.00	*$18.00*
Regular Frisbee	2	.97	*1.94*	1.29	*2.58*
Soft drink (12 oz. from vending machine)	26	.20	*5.20*	.40	*10.40*
Chewing gum (7-stick pack)	35	.15	*5.25*	.25	*8.75*
Hamburger, small French fries, 12-oz. soft drink	18	.80	*14.40*	1.39	*25.02*
Crayons (package of eight)	4	.25	*1.00*	.45	*1.80*
TOTAL	*95*		*$39.79*		*$66.55*
PRICE INDEX (1975=100)			*100.00*		*167.25*

Economics

Changes in the Price Level Versus Changes in Prices of Classes of Goods

Inflation is often defined as a rise in the *general* price level, but the prices of all goods do not rise at the same rate. Some goods experience price increases that are greater than the general price level while others rise more slowly. Some prices actually decline over the same time period. The table below gives the consumer price index for the overall economy ("All Items") and for certain selected categories of goods. Use the information to answer the questions or perform the exercises that follow the table.

Consumer Price Indexes by Major Expenditure Classifications 1981-1993 (1982-1984 = 100)					
Year	All Items	Food	Shelter	Medical Care	Motor Fuel
1981	90.0	93.6	90.5	82.9	108.5
1982	96.5	97.4	96.9	92.5	102.8
1983	99.6	99.4	99.1	100.6	99.4
1984	103.9	103.2	104.0	106.8	97.9
1985	107.6	105.6	109.8	113.5	98.7
1986	109.6	109.0	115.8	122.0	77.1
1987	113.6	113.5	121.3	130.1	80.2
1988	118.3	118.2	127.1	138.6	80.9
1989	124.0	125.1	132.8	149.3	88.5
1990	130.7	132.1	140.0	163.8	101.2
1991	136.2	136.8	146.3	177.0	99.4
1992	140.3	138.7	151.2	190.1	99.0
1993	144.5	141.6	155.7	201.4	98.0

1. Unlike the gross national product statistics which have a base year (in our exercises, the base year was 1982), the consumer price index statistics use an average of prices surveyed as a base. As the title of the above table implies when it reads "1982-1984 = 100," the base "year" for the CPI is an average of the prices surveyed in the years 1982, 1983, and 1984. Although you do not have access to all of the prices which the government used in computing the CPI, you can prove that the three-year period is, indeed, the base against which prices for past and future years are compared. In the spaces provided below insert the appropriate CPI figures, add them, and divide by three. What answers do you get?

Year	All Items	Food	Shelter
1982	96.5	97.4	96.9
1983	99.6	99.4	99.1
1984	103.9	103.2	104.0
Total	300.0	300.0	300.0
Total ÷ 3	100.0	100.0	100.0

2. On the blank graph provided below, plot the consumer price indexes for the categories found on the original table (food, shelter, medical care, and motor fuel), using a different colored pencil for each class of goods. After creating your graph, answer the questions which follow the graph.

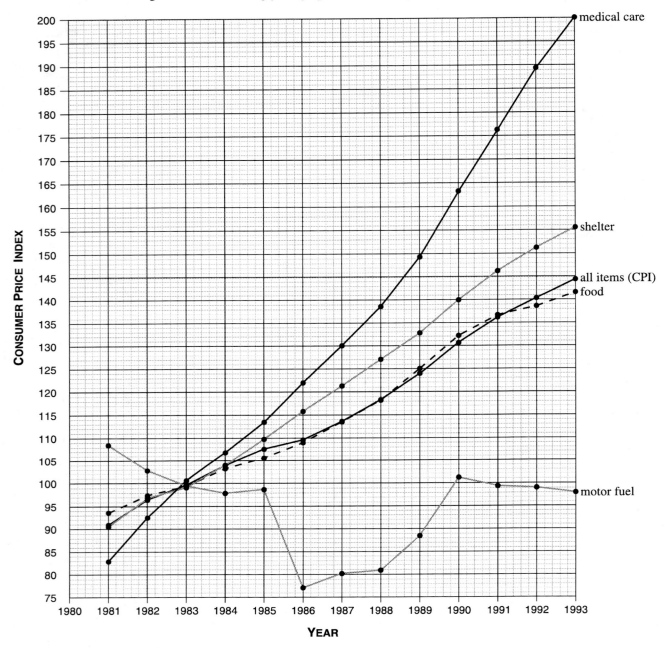

- According to the graph, which categories of expenditures have price indexes consistently above the CPI? *shelter and medical care*

- Which category has experienced the greatest price increase? *medical care*

- Which category of goods or services had the highest price level in 1981? *motor fuel*

- Which good or service actually had a lower real cost in 1993 than it did in 1981? *motor fuel*

- Which category of goods or services had a price level that moved very consistently with the general consumer price index? *food*

Economics

The CPI Versus the Inflation Rate

It is a common error for students to confuse the consumer price index with the inflation rate. Most people believe that both measures do the same thing. In reality, each has a separate purpose. The purpose of the consumer price index is to inform the reader of the current overall price level relative to the base period. Thus, a CPI of 144.5 in 1993 tells the analyst that prices in 1993 were 44.5% higher than those in the base period. The inflation rate, on the other hand, tells the analyst the rate of change between periods with differing CPIs. The method of computing the inflation rate for any given year is to use the following formula:

$$\frac{\text{Recent CPI} - \text{Earlier CPI}}{\text{Earlier CPI}}$$

An "inflation rate" is nothing more than a measure of a change in the price level between two intervals. Usually economists consider the inflation rate the change in the price level from year to year, but the inflation rate formula is really quite flexible and can be used to calculate the rate of change in price levels over longer intervals as well. Given the following table and the inflation rate formula, perform the calculations which follow the table.

Consumer Price Indexes 1972-1993 (1982-1984 = 100)			
YEAR	CPI	YEAR	CPI
1972	41.8	1983	99.6
1973	44.4	1984	103.9
1974	49.3	1985	107.6
1975	53.8	1986	109.6
1976	56.9	1987	113.6
1977	60.6	1988	118.3
1978	65.2	1989	124.0
1979	72.6	1990	130.7
1980	82.4	1991	136.2
1981	90.9	1992	140.3
1982	96.5	1993	144.5

A. Calculate the inflation rate for the one-year period between 1972 and 1973.

$$\frac{44.4 - 41.8}{41.8} = 6.22\%$$

B. Calculate the inflation rate for the five-year period between 1977 and 1982.

$$\frac{96.5 - 60.6}{60.6} = 59.24\%$$

C. Calculate the inflation rate for the three-year period between 1990 and 1993.

$$\frac{144.5 - 130.7}{130.7} = 10.56\%$$

Economics

The Misery Index

When he was running for the presidency against Gerald Ford in 1976, Jimmy Carter asked the voters a simple question: "Are you economically better off now than you were before the last election?" To help the voters answer the question, he created a new indicator which he dubbed the "misery index." The misery index was the sum of the rate of the year's inflation and the unemployment rate. Complete the table below by calculating the misery index for each year. Then transfer your results to the blank graph and answer the questions.

Misery Index 1974-1993							
Year	Inflation Rate	Unemployment Rate	Misery Index	Year	Inflation Rate	Unemployment Rate	Misery Index
1974	11.0	5.6	*16.6*	1984	4.3	7.5	*11.8*
1975	9.1	8.5	*17.6*	1985	3.6	7.2	*10.8*
1976	5.8	7.7	*13.5*	1986	1.9	7.0	*8.9*
1977	6.5	7.1	*13.6*	1987	3.7	6.2	*9.9*
1978	7.6	6.1	*13.7*	1988	4.1	5.5	*9.6*
1979	11.4	5.8	*17.2*	1989	4.8	5.3	*10.1*
1980	13.5	7.1	*20.6*	1990	5.4	5.5	*10.9*
1981	10.3	7.6	*17.9*	1991	4.2	6.7	*10.9*
1982	6.2	9.7	*15.9*	1992	3.0	7.4	*10.4*
1983	3.2	9.6	*12.8*	1993	2.3	6.8	*9.1*

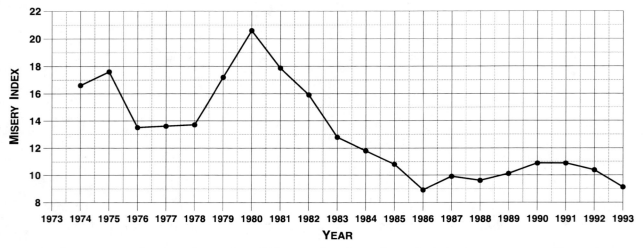

1. On your completed graph, use four different colored pencils to shade in the years covered by each of the four presidents' administrations included in the graph (Gerald Ford—1974 to 1977; Jimmy Carter—1977 to 1981; Ronald Reagan—1981 to 1989; George Bush—1989 to 1993).

2. What was the level of the misery index when presidential candidate Jimmy Carter developed it in 1976? *13.5* _____

3. In what year and at what level was the misery index at its highest point? Who was president?
   1980, 20.6; Jimmy Carter _____

4. What was the misery index when Ronald Reagan began his bid for the presidency in 1980? *20.6*

5. In what year and at what level was the misery index at its lowest point? *1986; 8.9* _____

6. What can we learn from this study of the misery index? *Possible answers include the following: the president cannot control the economy. We should be careful of what we accuse others; it may be used against us later.*

Economics

Multiple Choice

Choose the response which best answers the question or completes the sentence.

__C__ 1. Inflation is a sustained _____ in the general _____ level.
- A. rise, wage
- B. decline, price
- C. rise, price
- D. decline, GNP

__A__ 2. Which of the following is not hurt by inflation?
- A. borrowers
- B. those who are living on fixed incomes
- C. savers
- D. creditors

__C__ 3. The cost-push theory of inflation defines inflation as a shift of the _____ curve to the _____.
- A. total demand, right
- B. total supply, right
- C. total supply, left
- D. total demand, left

__C__ 4. A period of very rapid inflation such as was experienced in post–World War I Germany is commonly referred to as
- A. demand-pull inflation.
- B. cost-push inflation.
- C. hyperinflation.
- D. money growth inflation.

__B__ 5. What does COLA stand for?
- A. Coordinated Operational Loan Authority
- B. Cost of Living Adjustment
- C. Consumer Liquidity Appreciation
- D. Coordinated Lending Authority

__B__ 6. The measure of inflation that best indicates changes in the prices consumers pay is the
- A. PPI.
- B. CPI.
- C. GNPIPD.
- D. WPI.

Modified True/False

If the statement is true, write true in the blank. If it is false, change the underlined words to make the statement true. Write the correct word(s) in the blank.

___cost-push___ 1. In their attempts to discredit labor unions, many managers accuse unions of causing demand-pull inflation through constant demands for higher wages.

___True___ 2. The U.S. has experienced some degree of inflation each year since 1961.

___True___ 3. Inflation is sustained by a sustained increase in the money supply.

___are not___ 4. Wage-price controls are usually successful in curing inflation in cases where the government continues to expand the money supply.

___since the base year___ 5. If a nation had a CPI of 154.0 at the end of 1995 (base year = 1990), we can conclude that it experienced an inflation rate of 54% in 1995.

___True___ 6. The nation's price level is found graphically at the intersection point of the total demand and total supply curves.

Economics

The Phillips Curve: A Look at an Either/Or Fallacy

1. Fiscal policy is the ability of the government to control the inflation and unemployment rates by changing its methods of spending, taxing, and borrowing. In the late 1950s, an obscure economist named A.W.H. Phillips had an article published in *Economica*. He suggested that a connection existed between the inflation rate, the unemployment rate, and fiscal policy. Economists of the day argued that there was a tradeoff between the two rates. They argued that "free spending" Democrats, in their quest to shrink the unemployment rate, would inflate the currency to achieve their goal. The "rich" Republicans, however, seeking to protect themselves and their fortunes, would reduce the growth of government spending and money creation, which would lead to a growing unemployment rate. Thus, the nation could have a tradeoff between the two rates. The Phillips Curve was the result of this hypothesis. The table below gives inflation and unemployment rates for the years 1961 to 1969. Plot the data on the graph on the next page and put the dates next to the data points. Answer the questions that follow the graph.

Inflation and Unemployment Rates		
Year	Inflation Rate	Unemployment Rate
1961	1.0	6.7
1962	1.0	5.5
1963	1.3	5.7
1964	1.3	5.2
1965	1.6	4.5
1966	2.9	3.8
1967	3.1	3.8
1968	4.2	3.6
1969	5.5	3.5

Source: President's Council of Economic Advisors, *Economic Report of the President, 1994* (Washington, D.C.: Government Printing Office, 1994), Tables B-40 and B-59. Civilian unemployment rate and changes in average annual CPI (year to year)

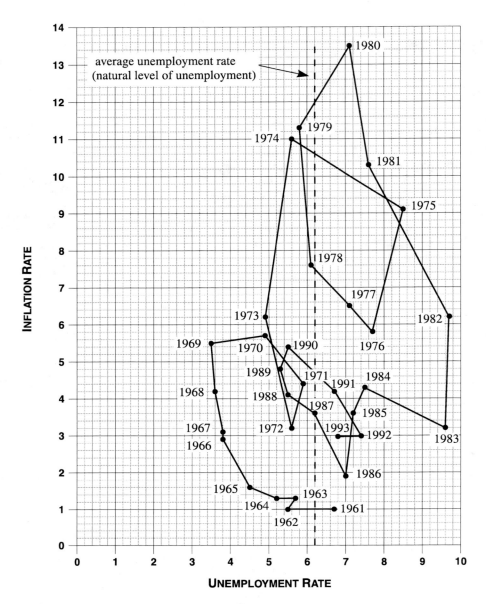

2. Between 1961 and 1969 how well did the Phillips Curve conform to the inflation-rate/unemployment-rate tradeoff hypothesis? *very well; notice the negatively sloped curve suggesting that an increase in one of the factors was associated with a decrease in the other.*

3. On the next page is a table containing inflation-rate and unemployment-rate data for the period 1970-1989. Plot this new data on your graph using a different colored pencil.

Inflation and Unemployment Rates (1970-1989)		
Year	Inflation Rate (Given in %)	Unemployment Rate (Given in %)
1970	5.7	4.9
1971	4.4	5.9
1972	3.2	5.6
1973	6.2	4.9
1974	11.0	5.6
1975	9.1	8.5
1976	5.8	7.7
1977	6.5	7.1
1978	7.6	6.1
1979	11.3	5.8
1980	13.5	7.1
1981	10.3	7.6
1982	6.2	9.7
1983	3.2	9.6
1984	4.3	7.5
1985	3.6	7.2
1986	1.9	7.0
1987	3.6	6.2
1988	4.1	5.5
1989	4.8	5.3
1990	5.4	5.5
1991	4.2	6.7
1992	3.0	7.4
1993	3.0	6.8

Source: President's Council of Economic Advisors, Economic Report of the President, 1994 (Washington, D.C.: Government Printing Office, 1994), Tables B-40 and B-59. Civilian unemployment rate and changes in average annual CPI (year to year)

4. Comment on the conformation of 1970-1993's inflation and unemployment data to the inflation-rate/unemployment-rate hypothesis. *The data did not conform well at all to the hypothesis. Indeed, during some periods both rates rose at the same time.*

5. After nearly thirty years of plotting the Phillips Curve, economists noticed that no matter how much the government inflated the nation's money in order to lower the unemployment rate, the economy always tended to "spring back" to an average unemployment rate. Economists call this rate the "natural level of unemployment." The natural level of unemployment is the sum of the nation's frictional, seasonal, and structural unemployment. The economy rises above or falls below this natural level according to the phases of the business cycle. Many economists believe that the economy naturally tends to this rate of unemployment no matter what policymakers do to try to lower unemployment. By their inflationary fiscal policy measures, Congress can lower the unemployment rate *for a short time*. The unemployment rate will eventually spring back toward the natural level of unemployment *while the economy remains at the higher rate of inflation*. The only way for Congress to lower the unemployment rate is to inflate the currency again.

   Find the average unemployment rate between 1961 and 1993. Insert your answer in the space provided and plot a vertical line on your graph representing that average unemployment rate. (Don't forget to include the rates for 1961-1969 found on page 113.) *6.2%*

Economics

The National Debt: Who Holds It?

One argument used by those who favor massive government deficit spending is that deficits do not matter since they are "intrafamily debt"—that is, the American government owes it to American citizens. Just as a son should not be overly concerned about a debt owed to his parents, the government need not be concerned about a debt owed to its own people. Although this argument may have been applicable several decades ago, it is no longer valid.

The table below provides the total national debt and the amount held by foreign investors. Fill in the third column and then plot these points on the blank graph that follows.

National Debt Held by Foreigners			
Year	Total National Debt ($ in Billions)	National Debt Held by Foreigners ($ in Billions)	Percentage of National Debt Held by Foreigners
1976	$ 409.5	$ 78.1	19.0%
1977	461.3	109.6	23.8
1978	508.6	133.1	26.2
1979	540.5	119.0	22.0
1980	616.4	129.7	21.0
1981	694.5	136.6	19.7
1982	848.4	149.5	17.6
1983	1,022.6	166.3	16.3
1984	1,212.5	192.9	15.9
1985	1,417.2	224.8	15.9
1986	1,602.0	263.4	16.4
1987	1,745.2	299.7	17.2
1988	1,852.8	362.1	19.5
1989	1,954.6	393.5	20.1
1990	2288.3	458.4	20.0
1991	2563.2	491.7	19.2
1992	2839.9	549.7	19.4
1993*	2983.0	592.3	19.9

*January-September 1993

Source: President's Council of Economic Advisors, Economic Report of the President (Washington, D.C.: Government Printing Office, 1994), Table B-87.

116   **Enrichment: Section I**   **Skill: Graphs**

Economics

The Federal Personal Income Tax: Proportional, Progressive, or Regressive?

Use the tax tables on pages 123-28 to determine the total tax the person must pay and the percentage he is paying in taxes.

Tax Liability and Percentage of Income		
Taxable Income	Tax from Tax Tables (Filing as a Single)	Percentage of Taxable Income
$9,001	$ 1,354	15.04%
19,001	2,854	15.02
29,001	5,254	18.1
39,001	8,054	20.7
49,001	10,854	22.2

Given the above exercise, is the United States federal personal income tax a proportional tax, a progressive tax, or a regressive tax? *The United States federal personal income tax is a progressive*

income tax, since it takes a greater percentage of one's income as the income goes up.

Modified True/False

If the statement is true, write the word *true* in the blank. If it is false, change the underlined word(s) to make the statement true. Write the correct word(s) in the blank.

John Maynard Keynes 1. <u>Adam Smith</u> developed the basic idea of modern fiscal policy in his book *The General Theory of Employment, Interest, and Money.*

46% 2. During World War II government purchases of goods and services reached a peak of <u>86%</u> of gross national product.

True 3. Everything else being constant, if everyone in the nation spent more of each dollar of his income, the expenditure multiplier would <u>increase</u>.

decrease, increase 4. If the government wished to smooth the economy via fiscal policy, it would <u>increase</u> its spending during an expansionary phase of the business cycle and would <u>decrease</u> its spending during a recessionary phase.

True 5. The <u>Federal Insurance Contribution Act</u> (FICA) requires the payment of Social Security taxes.

Progressive taxes 6. <u>Regressive taxes</u> are based on the ability-to-pay principle.

Economics

Taxes and Incentive to Work: The Laffer Curve

When tax rates rise, tax revenues to the government increase, right? Maybe not! Congress believes that if tax rates are constantly increased, they will constantly receive higher revenues, but what does common sense tell us? If the income tax rate were 0%, the government would receive no tax revenues. On the other hand, if the government were to impose a 100% income tax, that is, every dollar earned would go to the government, again, the government would receive nothing. If the government were to impose a 100% tax rate, it would receive 100% of people's incomes, but people would refuse to work. Arthur Laffer, a professor of economics, illustrated this with a graph. Although each individual's work ethic is different, causing his personal sensitivity to tax rates to vary from all others, we will generalize and, for the sake of example, create a hypothetical Laffer Curve for the entire economy. Given the information in the table below, plot the information on the blank graph.

Hypothetical Tax Data	
Tax Rate (In %)	**Tax Revenues (Billions of Dollars)**
0	$0
14	450
30	850
46	1,000
52	1,000
68	850
84	450
100	0

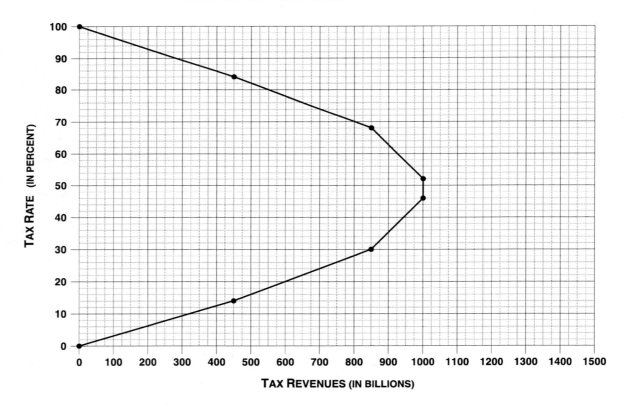

Economics

Personal Income Taxes: A Hands-on Problem

Perhaps one of the most dreaded tasks every American must perform is the yearly filing of income tax returns. During the course of the year at the end of every pay period, virtually every employer withholds income taxes from each employee's paycheck. At the end of the year, each employee is responsible to tabulate the total income tax that *should have* been paid. If the amount withheld is greater than the amount of the computed tax, the person is due a refund. If the amount withheld is less than the total tax, the person must pay the difference.

In order to inform each employee of important tax information, employers must furnish them with what is known as a W-2 form. Below is a blank W-2 form and some hypothetical tax information. Complete the W-2 with the information provided.

Employer's name:	General Computer Corporation
Employer's address:	801 North Farnsworth Avenue Greenville, SC 29616-5010
Employer's ID number (federal and state):	34-0000000
Date W-2 issued:	January 1, 1994
Your name and address:	John Q. Taxpayer 1040 Iris Drive Greenville, SC 29600-0000
Your Social Security number:	559-10-0000
Your wages for 1993 (for both federal and state income taxes):	$38,446.32
Federal income tax withheld:	$3,149.43
Social Security tax withheld:	$2,883.47
State income tax withheld:	$1,577.70

Employer's name, address, and Zip Code: **General Computer Corporation** **801 North Farnsworth Avenue** **Greenville, SC 29616-5010**	Issue Date: **01/01/94**	**Copy B to be filed with employee's FEDERAL tax return**
	Employer's identification number: **34-0000000**	Employer's state identification number: **34-0000000**
Employee's Social Security number: **559-10-0000** Total federal income tax withheld: **$3,149.43**	Wages, tips, other compensation: **$38,446.32**	Social Security tax withheld: **$2,883.47**
Employee's name, address, and Zip Code: **John Q. Taxpayer** **1040 Iris Drive** **Greenville, SC 29600-0000**	Social Security wages: **$38,446.32**	Social Security tips: **$ 0.00**
	State income tax wages: **$38,446.32**	State income tax withheld: **$1,577.70**

After an employee receives his W-2 form from his employer, he is responsible to calculate his income tax liability. Given the following information, complete the Internal Revenue Service form 1040A that follows. (If no information is provided, leave the space blank.)

STEP 1

Spouse's name: Jane B. Taxpayer (Mrs. Taxpayer does not work outside the home.)

Spouse's Social Security number: 262-19-0000

Neither John nor his wife wishes to have $3 go to the Presidential Election Campaign Fund.

STEP 2

John wishes to file a joint return with his wife.

STEP 3

Children: Lila M. Taxpayer
                              Age: 7
                              SS#: 123-45-6789
                              Lived with parents all year

STEPS 4 & 5

Wages, salaries, tips, etc.:   From W-2 form

Income other than John's: $350.00 taxable interest income

No dividends, IRA transactions, unemployment benefits, or Social Security income.

STEP 6

John and Jane are both 35 years old.

Claim the standard deduction for being married and filing jointly.

STEP 7

Taxes owed: From tax table

Taxes withheld: From W-2 form

STEP 8

Determine whether John and Jane will need to pay extra taxes or whether they will be receiving a refund.

Department of the Treasury—Internal Revenue Service

U.S. Individual Income Tax Return (L)   1993

IRS Use Only—Do not write or staple in this space.

OMB No. 1545-0085

Label
(See page 15.)

Use the IRS label. Otherwise, please print or type.

Your first name and initial	Last name	Your social security number
John Q.	Taxpayer	559 : 10 : 0000

If a joint return, spouse's first name and initial	Last name	Spouse's social security number
Jane B.	Taxpayer	262 : 19 : 0000

Home address (number and street). If you have a P.O. box, see page 16. **1040 Iris Drive**   Apt. no.

City, town or post office, state, and ZIP code. If you have a foreign address, see page 16. **Greenville, SC 29600-0000**

For Privacy Act and Paperwork Reduction Act Notice, see page 4.

Presidential Election Campaign Fund (See page 16.)

Do you want $3 to go to this fund? . . . .   Yes No [X]

If a joint return, does your spouse want $3 to go to this fund?   [X]

Note: *Checking "Yes" will not change your tax or reduce your refund.*

Check the box for your filing status
(See page 16.)

Check only one box.

1 ☐ Single
2 ☒ Married filing joint return (even if only one had income)
3 ☐ Married filing separate return. Enter spouse's social security number above and full name here. ▶ _____
4 ☐ Head of household (with qualifying person). (See page 17.) If the qualifying person is a child but not your dependent, enter this child's name here. ▶ _____
5 ☐ Qualifying widow(er) with dependent child (year spouse died ▶ 19 ___). (See page 18.)

Figure your exemptions
(See page 19.)

If more than seven dependents, see page 22.

6a ☒ **Yourself.** If your parent (or someone else) can claim you as a dependent on his or her tax return, **do not** check box 6a. But be sure to check the box on line 18b on page 2.

b ☒ **Spouse**

c **Dependents:** (1) Name (first, initial, and last name)	(2) Check if under age 1	(3) If age 1 or older, dependent's social security number	(4) Dependent's relationship to you	(5) No. of months lived in your home in 1993
Lila M. Taxpayer		123 : 45 : 6789	Daughter	12

No. of boxes checked on 6a and 6b   **2**

No. of your children on 6c who:

• lived with you   **1**

• didn't live with you due to divorce or separation (see page 22)   ___

Dependents on 6c not entered above   ___

d If your child didn't live with you but is claimed as your dependent under a pre-1985 agreement, check here . . . . ▶ ☐

e Total number of exemptions claimed.

Add numbers entered on lines above   **3**

Figure your total income

Attach Copy B of your Forms W-2 and 1099-R here.

If you didn't get a W-2, see page 24.

If you are attaching a check or money order, put it on top of any Forms W-2 or 1099-R.

7	Wages, salaries, tips, etc. This should be shown in box 1 of your W-2 form(s). Attach Form(s) W-2.	7	38,446	32
8a	**Taxable** interest income (see page 25). If over $400, also complete and attach Schedule 1, Part I.	8a	350	00
b	Tax-exempt interest. DO NOT include on line 8a. 8b			
9	Dividends. If over $400, also complete and attach Schedule 1, Part II.	9	—	
10a	Total IRA distributions. 10a	10b Taxable amount (see page 26).	10b	—	
11a	Total pensions and annuities. 11a	11b Taxable amount (see page 26).	11b	—	
12	Unemployment compensation (see page 30).	12	—	
13a	Social security benefits. 13a	13b Taxable amount (see page 30).	13b	—	
14	Add lines 7 through 13b (far right column). This is your **total income.** ▶	14	38,796	32

Figure your adjusted gross income

15a	Your IRA deduction (see page 32). 15a			
b	Spouse's IRA deduction (see page 32). 15b			
c	Add lines 15a and 15b. These are your **total adjustments.**	15c		
16	Subtract line 15c from line 14. This is your **adjusted gross income.** If less than $23,050 and a child lived with you, see page 63 to find out if you can claim the "Earned income credit" on line 28c. ▶	16	38,796	32

1993 Form 1040A page 1

Name(s) shown on page 1	Your social security number
John Q. Taxpayer, Jane B. Taxpayer	559 10 0000

Figure your standard deduction, exemption amount, and taxable income

17	Enter the amount from line 16.	17	**38,796** 32

18a Check if: ☐ You were 65 or older ☐ Blind | Enter number of boxes checked ▶ 18a ☐
☐ Spouse was 65 or older ☐ Blind |

b If your parent (or someone else) can claim you as a dependent, check here . . . . ▶ 18b ☐

c If you are married filing separately and your spouse files Form 1040 and itemizes deductions, see page 36 and check here ▶ 18c ☐

19 Enter the **standard deduction** shown below for your filing status. **But if you checked any box on line 18a or b,** go to page 36 to find your standard deduction. **If you checked box 18c,** enter -0-.
- Single—$3,700   • Head of household—$5,450
- Married filing jointly or Qualifying widow(er)—$6,200
- Married filing separately—$3,100

		19	**6,200** 00
20	Subtract line 19 from line 17. If line 19 is more than line 17, enter -0-.	20	**32,596** 32
21	Multiply $2,350 by the total number of exemptions claimed on line 6e.	21	**7,050** 00
22	Subtract line 21 from line 20. If line 21 is more than line 20, enter -0-. This is your **taxable income.** ▶	22	**25,546** 32

Figure your tax, credits, and payments

If you want the IRS to figure your tax, see the instructions for line 22 on page 37.

23	Find the tax on the amount on line 22. Check if from: ☒ Tax Table (pages 37–42) or ☐ Form 8615 (see page 38).	23	**3,829** 00

24a Credit for child and dependent care expenses. Complete and attach Schedule 2. 24a

b Credit for the elderly or the disabled. Complete and attach Schedule 3. 24b

c	Add lines 24a and 24b. These are your **total credits.**	24c	**0** 00
25	Subtract line 24c from line 23. If line 24c is more than line 23, enter -0-.	25	**3,829** 00
26	Advance earned income credit payments from Form W-2.	26	—
27	Add lines 25 and 26. This is your **total tax.** ▶	27	**3,829** 00

28a Total Federal income tax withheld. If any tax is from Form(s) 1099, check here. ▶ ☐ | 28a **3,149** 43

b 1993 estimated tax payments and amount applied from 1992 return. 28b

c **Earned income credit.** Complete and attach Schedule EIC. 28c

d	Add lines 28a, 28b, and 28c. These are your **total payments.** ▶	28d	**3,149** 43

Figure your refund or amount you owe

29	If line 28d is more than line 27, subtract line 27 from line 28d. This is the amount you **overpaid.**	29	
30	Amount of line 29 you want **refunded to you.**	30	
31	Amount of line 29 you want **applied to your 1994 estimated tax.** 31		
32	If line 27 is more than line 28d, subtract line 28d from line 27. This is the **amount you owe.** For details on how to pay, including what to write on your payment, see page 42.	32	**679** 57
33	Estimated tax penalty (see page 43). Also, include on line 32. 33		

Sign your return

Keep a copy of this return for your records.

Under penalties of perjury, I declare that I have examined this return and accompanying schedules and statements, and to the best of my knowledge and belief, they are true, correct, and accurately list all amounts and sources of income I received during the tax year. Declaration of preparer (other than the taxpayer) is based on all information of which the preparer has any knowledge.

Your signature	Date	Your occupation
John Q. Taxpayer		
Spouse's signature. If joint return, BOTH must sign.	Date	Spouse's occupation
Jane B. Taxpayer		

Paid preparer's use only

Preparer's signature ▶	Date	Check if self-employed ☐	Preparer's social security no.
Firm's name (or yours if self-employed) and address ▶		E.I. No.	
		ZIP code	

Section 7.

1993 Tax Table

Use if your taxable income is less than $100,000.
If $100,000 or more, use the Tax Rate Schedules.

Example. Mr. and Mrs. Brown are filing a joint return. Their taxable income on line 37 of Form 1040 is $25,300. First, they find the $25,300–25,350 income line. Next, they find the column for married filing jointly and read down the column. The amount shown where the income line and filing status column meet is $3,799. This is the tax amount they must enter on line 38 of their Form 1040.

Sample Table

At least	But less than	Single	Married filing jointly *	Married filing separately	Head of a house-hold
			Your tax is—		
25,200	25,250	4,190	3,784	4,665	3,784
25,250	25,300	4,204	3,791	4,679	3,791
25,300	25,350	4,218	(3,799)	4,693	3,799
25,350	25,400	4,232	3,806	4,707	3,806

If line 37 (taxable income) is— At least	But less than	Single	Married filing jointly *	Married filing separately	Head of a house-hold
			Your tax is—		
0	5	0	0	0	0
5	15	2	2	2	2
15	25	3	3	3	3
25	50	6	6	6	6
50	75	9	9	9	9
75	100	13	13	13	13
100	125	17	17	17	17
125	150	21	21	21	21
150	175	24	24	24	24
175	200	28	28	28	28
200	225	32	32	32	32
225	250	36	36	36	36
250	275	39	39	39	39
275	300	43	43	43	43
300	325	47	47	47	47
325	350	51	51	51	51
350	375	54	54	54	54
375	400	58	58	58	58
400	425	62	62	62	62
425	450	66	66	66	66
450	475	69	69	69	69
475	500	73	73	73	73
500	525	77	77	77	77
525	550	81	81	81	81
550	575	84	84	84	84
575	600	88	88	88	88
600	625	92	92	92	92
625	650	96	96	96	96
650	675	99	99	99	99
675	700	103	103	103	103
700	725	107	107	107	107
725	750	111	111	111	111
750	775	114	114	114	114
775	800	118	118	118	118
800	825	122	122	122	122
825	850	126	126	126	126
850	875	129	129	129	129
875	900	133	133	133	133
900	925	137	137	137	137
925	950	141	141	141	141
950	975	144	144	144	144
975	1,000	148	148	148	148

1,000

At least	But less than	Single	Married filing jointly *	Married filing separately	Head of a house-hold
1,000	1,025	152	152	152	152
1,025	1,050	156	156	156	156
1,050	1,075	159	159	159	159
1,075	1,100	163	163	163	163
1,100	1,125	167	167	167	167
1,125	1,150	171	171	171	171
1,150	1,175	174	174	174	174
1,175	1,200	178	178	178	178
1,200	1,225	182	182	182	182
1,225	1,250	186	186	186	186
1,250	1,275	189	189	189	189
1,275	1,300	193	193	193	193

If line 37 (taxable income) is— At least	But less than	Single	Married filing jointly *	Married filing separately	Head of a house-hold
			Your tax is—		
1,300	1,325	197	197	197	197
1,325	1,350	201	201	201	201
1,350	1,375	204	204	204	204
1,375	1,400	208	208	208	208
1,400	1,425	212	212	212	212
1,425	1,450	216	216	216	216
1,450	1,475	219	219	219	219
1,475	1,500	223	223	223	223
1,500	1,525	227	227	227	227
1,525	1,550	231	231	231	231
1,550	1,575	234	234	234	234
1,575	1,600	238	238	238	238
1,600	1,625	242	242	242	242
1,625	1,650	246	246	246	246
1,650	1,675	249	249	249	249
1,675	1,700	253	253	253	253
1,700	1,725	257	257	257	257
1,725	1,750	261	261	261	261
1,750	1,775	264	264	264	264
1,775	1,800	268	268	268	268
1,800	1,825	272	272	272	272
1,825	1,850	276	276	276	276
1,850	1,875	279	279	279	279
1,875	1,900	283	283	283	283
1,900	1,925	287	287	287	287
1,925	1,950	291	291	291	291
1,950	1,975	294	294	294	294
1,975	2,000	298	298	298	298

2,000

At least	But less than	Single	Married filing jointly *	Married filing separately	Head of a house-hold
2,000	2,025	302	302	302	302
2,025	2,050	306	306	306	306
2,050	2,075	309	309	309	309
2,075	2,100	313	313	313	313
2,100	2,125	317	317	317	317
2,125	2,150	321	321	321	321
2,150	2,175	324	324	324	324
2,175	2,200	328	328	328	328
2,200	2,225	332	332	332	332
2,225	2,250	336	336	336	336
2,250	2,275	339	339	339	339
2,275	2,300	343	343	343	343
2,300	2,325	347	347	347	347
2,325	2,350	351	351	351	351
2,350	2,375	354	354	354	354
2,375	2,400	358	358	358	358
2,400	2,425	362	362	362	362
2,425	2,450	366	366	366	366
2,450	2,475	369	369	369	369
2,475	2,500	373	373	373	373
2,500	2,525	377	377	377	377
2,525	2,550	381	381	381	381
2,550	2,575	384	384	384	384
2,575	2,600	388	388	388	388
2,600	2,625	392	392	392	392
2,625	2,650	396	396	396	396
2,650	2,675	399	399	399	399
2,675	2,700	403	403	403	403

If line 37 (taxable income) is— At least	But less than	Single	Married filing jointly *	Married filing separately	Head of a house-hold
			Your tax is—		
2,700	2,725	407	407	407	407
2,725	2,750	411	411	411	411
2,750	2,775	414	414	414	414
2,775	2,800	418	418	418	418
2,800	2,825	422	422	422	422
2,825	2,850	426	426	426	426
2,850	2,875	429	429	429	429
2,875	2,900	433	433	433	433
2,900	2,925	437	437	437	437
2,925	2,950	441	441	441	441
2,950	2,975	444	444	444	444
2,975	3,000	448	448	448	448

3,000

At least	But less than	Single	Married filing jointly *	Married filing separately	Head of a house-hold
3,000	3,050	454	454	454	454
3,050	3,100	461	461	461	461
3,100	3,150	469	469	469	469
3,150	3,200	476	476	476	476
3,200	3,250	484	484	484	484
3,250	3,300	491	491	491	491
3,300	3,350	499	499	499	499
3,350	3,400	506	506	506	506
3,400	3,450	514	514	514	514
3,450	3,500	521	521	521	521
3,500	3,550	529	529	529	529
3,550	3,600	536	536	536	536
3,600	3,650	544	544	544	544
3,650	3,700	551	551	551	551
3,700	3,750	559	559	559	559
3,750	3,800	566	566	566	566
3,800	3,850	574	574	574	574
3,850	3,900	581	581	581	581
3,900	3,950	589	589	589	589
3,950	4,000	596	596	596	596

4,000

At least	But less than	Single	Married filing jointly *	Married filing separately	Head of a house-hold
4,000	4,050	604	604	604	604
4,050	4,100	611	611	611	611
4,100	4,150	619	619	619	619
4,150	4,200	626	626	626	626
4,200	4,250	634	634	634	634
4,250	4,300	641	641	641	641
4,300	4,350	649	649	649	649
4,350	4,400	656	656	656	656
4,400	4,450	664	664	664	664
4,450	4,500	671	671	671	671
4,500	4,550	679	679	679	679
4,550	4,600	686	686	686	686
4,600	4,650	694	694	694	694
4,650	4,700	701	701	701	701
4,700	4,750	709	709	709	709
4,750	4,800	716	716	716	716
4,800	4,850	724	724	724	724
4,850	4,900	731	731	731	731
4,900	4,950	739	739	739	739
4,950	5,000	746	746	746	746

Continued on next page

* This column must also be used by a qualifying widow(er).

If line 37 (taxable income) is—		And you are—				If line 37 (taxable income) is—		And you are—				If line 37 (taxable income) is—		And you are—			
At least	But less than	Single	Married filing jointly *	Married filing separately	Head of a household	At least	But less than	Single	Married filing jointly *	Married filing separately	Head of a household	At least	But less than	Single	Married filing jointly *	Married filing separately	Head of a household
		Your tax is—						Your tax is—						Your tax is—			
5,000						**8,000**						**11,000**					
5,000	5,050	754	754	754	754	8,000	8,050	1,204	1,204	1,204	1,204	11,000	11,050	1,654	1,654	1,654	1,654
5,050	5,100	761	761	761	761	8,050	8,100	1,211	1,211	1,211	1,211	11,050	11,100	1,661	1,661	1,661	1,661
5,100	5,150	769	769	769	769	8,100	8,150	1,219	1,219	1,219	1,219	11,100	11,150	1,669	1,669	1,669	1,669
5,150	5,200	776	776	776	776	8,150	8,200	1,226	1,226	1,226	1,226	11,150	11,200	1,676	1,676	1,676	1,676
5,200	5,250	784	784	784	784	8,200	8,250	1,234	1,234	1,234	1,234	11,200	11,250	1,684	1,684	1,684	1,684
5,250	5,300	791	791	791	791	8,250	8,300	1,241	1,241	1,241	1,241	11,250	11,300	1,691	1,691	1,691	1,691
5,300	5,350	799	799	799	799	8,300	8,350	1,249	1,249	1,249	1,249	11,300	11,350	1,699	1,699	1,699	1,699
5,350	5,400	806	806	806	806	8,350	8,400	1,256	1,256	1,256	1,256	11,350	11,400	1,706	1,706	1,706	1,706
5,400	5,450	814	814	814	814	8,400	8,450	1,264	1,264	1,264	1,264	11,400	11,450	1,714	1,714	1,714	1,714
5,450	5,500	821	821	821	821	8,450	8,500	1,271	1,271	1,271	1,271	11,450	11,500	1,721	1,721	1,721	1,721
5,500	5,550	829	829	829	829	8,500	8,550	1,279	1,279	1,279	1,279	11,500	11,550	1,729	1,729	1,729	1,729
5,550	5,600	836	836	836	836	8,550	8,600	1,286	1,286	1,286	1,286	11,550	11,600	1,736	1,736	1,736	1,736
5,600	5,650	844	844	844	844	8,600	8,650	1,294	1,294	1,294	1,294	11,600	11,650	1,744	1,744	1,744	1,744
5,650	5,700	851	851	851	851	8,650	8,700	1,301	1,301	1,301	1,301	11,650	11,700	1,751	1,751	1,751	1,751
5,700	5,750	859	859	859	859	8,700	8,750	1,309	1,309	1,309	1,309	11,700	11,750	1,759	1,759	1,759	1,759
5,750	5,800	866	866	866	866	8,750	8,800	1,316	1,316	1,316	1,316	11,750	11,800	1,766	1,766	1,766	1,766
5,800	5,850	874	874	874	874	8,800	8,850	1,324	1,324	1,324	1,324	11,800	11,850	1,774	1,774	1,774	1,774
5,850	5,900	881	881	881	881	8,850	8,900	1,331	1,331	1,331	1,331	11,850	11,900	1,781	1,781	1,781	1,781
5,900	5,950	889	889	889	889	8,900	8,950	1,339	1,339	1,339	1,339	11,900	11,950	1,789	1,789	1,789	1,789
5,950	6,000	896	896	896	896	8,950	9,000	1,346	1,346	1,346	1,346	11,950	12,000	1,796	1,796	1,796	1,796
6,000						**9,000**						**12,000**					
6,000	6,050	904	904	904	904	9,000	9,050	1,354	1,354	1,354	1,354	12,000	12,050	1,804	1,804	1,804	1,804
6,050	6,100	911	911	911	911	9,050	9,100	1,361	1,361	1,361	1,361	12,050	12,100	1,811	1,811	1,811	1,811
6,100	6,150	919	919	919	919	9,100	9,150	1,369	1,369	1,369	1,369	12,100	12,150	1,819	1,819	1,819	1,819
6,150	6,200	926	926	926	926	9,150	9,200	1,376	1,376	1,376	1,376	12,150	12,200	1,826	1,826	1,826	1,826
6,200	6,250	934	934	934	934	9,200	9,250	1,384	1,384	1,384	1,384	12,200	12,250	1,834	1,834	1,834	1,834
6,250	6,300	941	941	941	941	9,250	9,300	1,391	1,391	1,391	1,391	12,250	12,300	1,841	1,841	1,841	1,841
6,300	6,350	949	949	949	949	9,300	9,350	1,399	1,399	1,399	1,399	12,300	12,350	1,849	1,849	1,849	1,849
6,350	6,400	956	956	956	956	9,350	9,400	1,406	1,406	1,406	1,406	12,350	12,400	1,856	1,856	1,856	1,856
6,400	6,450	964	964	964	964	9,400	9,450	1,414	1,414	1,414	1,414	12,400	12,450	1,864	1,864	1,864	1,864
6,450	6,500	971	971	971	971	9,450	9,500	1,421	1,421	1,421	1,421	12,450	12,500	1,871	1,871	1,871	1,871
6,500	6,550	979	979	979	979	9,500	9,550	1,429	1,429	1,429	1,429	12,500	12,550	1,879	1,879	1,879	1,879
6,550	6,600	986	986	986	986	9,550	9,600	1,436	1,436	1,436	1,436	12,550	12,600	1,886	1,886	1,886	1,886
6,600	6,650	994	994	994	994	9,600	9,650	1,444	1,444	1,444	1,444	12,600	12,650	1,894	1,894	1,894	1,894
6,650	6,700	1,001	1,001	1,001	1,001	9,650	9,700	1,451	1,451	1,451	1,451	12,650	12,700	1,901	1,901	1,901	1,901
6,700	6,750	1,009	1,009	1,009	1,009	9,700	9,750	1,459	1,459	1,459	1,459	12,700	12,750	1,909	1,909	1,909	1,909
6,750	6,800	1,016	1,016	1,016	1,016	9,750	9,800	1,466	1,466	1,466	1,466	12,750	12,800	1,916	1,916	1,916	1,916
6,800	6,850	1,024	1,024	1,024	1,024	9,800	9,850	1,474	1,474	1,474	1,474	12,800	12,850	1,924	1,924	1,924	1,924
6,850	6,900	1,031	1,031	1,031	1,031	9,850	9,900	1,481	1,481	1,481	1,481	12,850	12,900	1,931	1,931	1,931	1,931
6,900	6,950	1,039	1,039	1,039	1,039	9,900	9,950	1,489	1,489	1,489	1,489	12,900	12,950	1,939	1,939	1,939	1,939
6,950	7,000	1,046	1,046	1,046	1,046	9,950	10,000	1,496	1,496	1,496	1,496	12,950	13,000	1,946	1,946	1,946	1,946
7,000						**10,000**						**13,000**					
7,000	7,050	1,054	1,054	1,054	1,054	10,000	10,050	1,504	1,504	1,504	1,504	13,000	13,050	1,954	1,954	1,954	1,954
7,050	7,100	1,061	1,061	1,061	1,061	10,050	10,100	1,511	1,511	1,511	1,511	13,050	13,100	1,961	1,961	1,961	1,961
7,100	7,150	1,069	1,069	1,069	1,069	10,100	10,150	1,519	1,519	1,519	1,519	13,100	13,150	1,969	1,969	1,969	1,969
7,150	7,200	1,076	1,076	1,076	1,076	10,150	10,200	1,526	1,526	1,526	1,526	13,150	13,200	1,976	1,976	1,976	1,976
7,200	7,250	1,084	1,084	1,084	1,084	10,200	10,250	1,534	1,534	1,534	1,534	13,200	13,250	1,984	1,984	1,984	1,984
7,250	7,300	1,091	1,091	1,091	1,091	10,250	10,300	1,541	1,541	1,541	1,541	13,250	13,300	1,991	1,991	1,991	1,991
7,300	7,350	1,099	1,099	1,099	1,099	10,300	10,350	1,549	1,549	1,549	1,549	13,300	13,350	1,999	1,999	1,999	1,999
7,350	7,400	1,106	1,106	1,106	1,106	10,350	10,400	1,556	1,556	1,556	1,556	13,350	13,400	2,006	2,006	2,006	2,006
7,400	7,450	1,114	1,114	1,114	1,114	10,400	10,450	1,564	1,564	1,564	1,564	13,400	13,450	2,014	2,014	2,014	2,014
7,450	7,500	1,121	1,121	1,121	1,121	10,450	10,500	1,571	1,571	1,571	1,571	13,450	13,500	2,021	2,021	2,021	2,021
7,500	7,550	1,129	1,129	1,129	1,129	10,500	10,550	1,579	1,579	1,579	1,579	13,500	13,550	2,029	2,029	2,029	2,029
7,550	7,600	1,136	1,136	1,136	1,136	10,550	10,600	1,586	1,586	1,586	1,586	13,550	13,600	2,036	2,036	2,036	2,036
7,600	7,650	1,144	1,144	1,144	1,144	10,600	10,650	1,594	1,594	1,594	1,594	13,600	13,650	2,044	2,044	2,044	2,044
7,650	7,700	1,151	1,151	1,151	1,151	10,650	10,700	1,601	1,601	1,601	1,601	13,650	13,700	2,051	2,051	2,051	2,051
7,700	7,750	1,159	1,159	1,159	1,159	10,700	10,750	1,609	1,609	1,609	1,609	13,700	13,750	2,059	2,059	2,059	2,059
7,750	7,800	1,166	1,166	1,166	1,166	10,750	10,800	1,616	1,616	1,616	1,616	13,750	13,800	2,066	2,066	2,066	2,066
7,800	7,850	1,174	1,174	1,174	1,174	10,800	10,850	1,624	1,624	1,624	1,624	13,800	13,850	2,074	2,074	2,074	2,074
7,850	7,900	1,181	1,181	1,181	1,181	10,850	10,900	1,631	1,631	1,631	1,631	13,850	13,900	2,081	2,081	2,081	2,081
7,900	7,950	1,189	1,189	1,189	1,189	10,900	10,950	1,639	1,639	1,639	1,639	13,900	13,950	2,089	2,089	2,089	2,089
7,950	8,000	1,196	1,196	1,196	1,196	10,950	11,000	1,646	1,646	1,646	1,646	13,950	14,000	2,096	2,096	2,096	2,096

* This column must also be used by a qualifying widow(er).

Continued on next page

If line 37 (taxable income) is—		And you are—			
At least	But less than	Single	Married filing jointly *	Married filing separately	Head of a household
		Your tax is—			
14,000					
14,000	14,050	2,104	2,104	2,104	2,104
14,050	14,100	2,111	2,111	2,111	2,111
14,100	14,150	2,119	2,119	2,119	2,119
14,150	14,200	2,126	2,126	2,126	2,126
14,200	14,250	2,134	2,134	2,134	2,134
14,250	14,300	2,141	2,141	2,141	2,141
14,300	14,350	2,149	2,149	2,149	2,149
14,350	14,400	2,156	2,156	2,156	2,156
14,400	14,450	2,164	2,164	2,164	2,164
14,450	14,500	2,171	2,171	2,171	2,171
14,500	14,550	2,179	2,179	2,179	2,179
14,550	14,600	2,186	2,186	2,186	2,186
14,600	14,650	2,194	2,194	2,194	2,194
14,650	14,700	2,201	2,201	2,201	2,201
14,700	14,750	2,209	2,209	2,209	2,209
14,750	14,800	2,216	2,216	2,216	2,216
14,800	14,850	2,224	2,224	2,224	2,224
14,850	14,900	2,231	2,231	2,231	2,231
14,900	14,950	2,239	2,239	2,239	2,239
14,950	15,000	2,246	2,246	2,246	2,246
15,000					
15,000	15,050	2,254	2,254	2,254	2,254
15,050	15,100	2,261	2,261	2,261	2,261
15,100	15,150	2,269	2,269	2,269	2,269
15,150	15,200	2,276	2,276	2,276	2,276
15,200	15,250	2,284	2,284	2,284	2,284
15,250	15,300	2,291	2,291	2,291	2,291
15,300	15,350	2,299	2,299	2,299	2,299
15,350	15,400	2,306	2,306	2,306	2,306
15,400	15,450	2,314	2,314	2,314	2,314
15,450	15,500	2,321	2,321	2,321	2,321
15,500	15,550	2,329	2,329	2,329	2,329
15,550	15,600	2,336	2,336	2,336	2,336
15,600	15,650	2,344	2,344	2,344	2,344
15,650	15,700	2,351	2,351	2,351	2,351
15,700	15,750	2,359	2,359	2,359	2,359
15,750	15,800	2,366	2,366	2,366	2,366
15,800	15,850	2,374	2,374	2,374	2,374
15,850	15,900	2,381	2,381	2,381	2,381
15,900	15,950	2,389	2,389	2,389	2,389
15,950	16,000	2,396	2,396	2,396	2,396
16,000					
16,000	16,050	2,404	2,404	2,404	2,404
16,050	16,100	2,411	2,411	2,411	2,411
16,100	16,150	2,419	2,419	2,419	2,419
16,150	16,200	2,426	2,426	2,426	2,426
16,200	16,250	2,434	2,434	2,434	2,434
16,250	16,300	2,441	2,441	2,441	2,441
16,300	16,350	2,449	2,449	2,449	2,449
16,350	16,400	2,456	2,456	2,456	2,456
16,400	16,450	2,464	2,464	2,464	2,464
16,450	16,500	2,471	2,471	2,471	2,471
16,500	16,550	2,479	2,479	2,479	2,479
16,550	16,600	2,486	2,486	2,486	2,486
16,600	16,650	2,494	2,494	2,494	2,494
16,650	16,700	2,501	2,501	2,501	2,501
16,700	16,750	2,509	2,509	2,509	2,509
16,750	16,800	2,516	2,516	2,516	2,516
16,800	16,850	2,524	2,524	2,524	2,524
16,850	16,900	2,531	2,531	2,531	2,531
16,900	16,950	2,539	2,539	2,539	2,539
16,950	17,000	2,546	2,546	2,546	2,546

If line 37 (taxable income) is—		And you are—			
At least	But less than	Single	Married filing jointly *	Married filing separately	Head of a household
		Your tax is—			
17,000					
17,000	17,050	2,554	2,554	2,554	2,554
17,050	17,100	2,561	2,561	2,561	2,561
17,100	17,150	2,569	2,569	2,569	2,569
17,150	17,200	2,576	2,576	2,576	2,576
17,200	17,250	2,584	2,584	2,584	2,584
17,250	17,300	2,591	2,591	2,591	2,591
17,300	17,350	2,599	2,599	2,599	2,599
17,350	17,400	2,606	2,606	2,606	2,606
17,400	17,450	2,614	2,614	2,614	2,614
17,450	17,500	2,621	2,621	2,621	2,621
17,500	17,550	2,629	2,629	2,629	2,629
17,550	17,600	2,636	2,636	2,636	2,636
17,600	17,650	2,644	2,644	2,644	2,644
17,650	17,700	2,651	2,651	2,651	2,651
17,700	17,750	2,659	2,659	2,659	2,659
17,750	17,800	2,666	2,666	2,666	2,666
17,800	17,850	2,674	2,674	2,674	2,674
17,850	17,900	2,681	2,681	2,681	2,681
17,900	17,950	2,689	2,689	2,689	2,689
17,950	18,000	2,696	2,696	2,696	2,696
18,000					
18,000	18,050	2,704	2,704	2,704	2,704
18,050	18,100	2,711	2,711	2,711	2,711
18,100	18,150	2,719	2,719	2,719	2,719
18,150	18,200	2,726	2,726	2,726	2,726
18,200	18,250	2,734	2,734	2,734	2,734
18,250	18,300	2,741	2,741	2,741	2,741
18,300	18,350	2,749	2,749	2,749	2,749
18,350	18,400	2,756	2,756	2,756	2,756
18,400	18,450	2,764	2,764	2,764	2,764
18,450	18,500	2,771	2,771	2,775	2,771
18,500	18,550	2,779	2,779	2,789	2,779
18,550	18,600	2,786	2,786	2,803	2,786
18,600	18,650	2,794	2,794	2,817	2,794
18,650	18,700	2,801	2,801	2,831	2,801
18,700	18,750	2,809	2,809	2,845	2,809
18,750	18,800	2,816	2,816	2,859	2,816
18,800	18,850	2,824	2,824	2,873	2,824
18,850	18,900	2,831	2,831	2,887	2,831
18,900	18,950	2,839	2,839	2,901	2,839
18,950	19,000	2,846	2,846	2,915	2,846
19,000					
19,000	19,050	2,854	2,854	2,929	2,854
19,050	19,100	2,861	2,861	2,943	2,861
19,100	19,150	2,869	2,869	2,957	2,869
19,150	19,200	2,876	2,876	2,971	2,876
19,200	19,250	2,884	2,884	2,985	2,884
19,250	19,300	2,891	2,891	2,999	2,891
19,300	19,350	2,899	2,899	3,013	2,899
19,350	19,400	2,906	2,906	3,027	2,906
19,400	19,450	2,914	2,914	3,041	2,914
19,450	19,500	2,921	2,921	3,055	2,921
19,500	19,550	2,929	2,929	3,069	2,929
19,550	19,600	2,936	2,936	3,083	2,936
19,600	19,650	2,944	2,944	3,097	2,944
19,650	19,700	2,951	2,951	3,111	2,951
19,700	19,750	2,959	2,959	3,125	2,959
19,750	19,800	2,966	2,966	3,139	2,966
19,800	19,850	2,974	2,974	3,153	2,974
19,850	19,900	2,981	2,981	3,167	2,981
19,900	19,950	2,989	2,989	3,181	2,989
19,950	20,000	2,996	2,996	3,195	2,996

If line 37 (taxable income) is—		And you are—			
At least	But less than	Single	Married filing jointly *	Married filing separately	Head of a household
		Your tax is—			
20,000					
20,000	20,050	3,004	3,004	3,209	3,004
20,050	20,100	3,011	3,011	3,223	3,011
20,100	20,150	3,019	3,019	3,237	3,019
20,150	20,200	3,026	3,026	3,251	3,026
20,200	20,250	3,034	3,034	3,265	3,034
20,250	20,300	3,041	3,041	3,279	3,041
20,300	20,350	3,049	3,049	3,293	3,049
20,350	20,400	3,056	3,056	3,307	3,056
20,400	20,450	3,064	3,064	3,321	3,064
20,450	20,500	3,071	3,071	3,335	3,071
20,500	20,550	3,079	3,079	3,349	3,079
20,550	20,600	3,086	3,086	3,363	3,086
20,600	20,650	3,094	3,094	3,377	3,094
20,650	20,700	3,101	3,101	3,391	3,101
20,700	20,750	3,109	3,109	3,405	3,109
20,750	20,800	3,116	3,116	3,419	3,116
20,800	20,850	3,124	3,124	3,433	3,124
20,850	20,900	3,131	3,131	3,447	3,131
20,900	20,950	3,139	3,139	3,461	3,139
20,950	21,000	3,146	3,146	3,475	3,146
21,000					
21,000	21,050	3,154	3,154	3,489	3,154
21,050	21,100	3,161	3,161	3,503	3,161
21,100	21,150	3,169	3,169	3,517	3,169
21,150	21,200	3,176	3,176	3,531	3,176
21,200	21,250	3,184	3,184	3,545	3,184
21,250	21,300	3,191	3,191	3,559	3,191
21,300	21,350	3,199	3,199	3,573	3,199
21,350	21,400	3,206	3,206	3,587	3,206
21,400	21,450	3,214	3,214	3,601	3,214
21,450	21,500	3,221	3,221	3,615	3,221
21,500	21,550	3,229	3,229	3,629	3,229
21,550	21,600	3,236	3,236	3,643	3,236
21,600	21,650	3,244	3,244	3,657	3,244
21,650	21,700	3,251	3,251	3,671	3,251
21,700	21,750	3,259	3,259	3,685	3,259
21,750	21,800	3,266	3,266	3,699	3,266
21,800	21,850	3,274	3,274	3,713	3,274
21,850	21,900	3,281	3,281	3,727	3,281
21,900	21,950	3,289	3,289	3,741	3,289
21,950	22,000	3,296	3,296	3,755	3,296
22,000					
22,000	22,050	3,304	3,304	3,769	3,304
22,050	22,100	3,311	3,311	3,783	3,311
22,100	22,150	3,322	3,319	3,797	3,319
22,150	22,200	3,336	3,326	3,811	3,326
22,200	22,250	3,350	3,334	3,825	3,334
22,250	22,300	3,364	3,341	3,839	3,341
22,300	22,350	3,378	3,349	3,853	3,349
22,350	22,400	3,392	3,356	3,867	3,356
22,400	22,450	3,406	3,364	3,881	3,364
22,450	22,500	3,420	3,371	3,895	3,371
22,500	22,550	3,434	3,379	3,909	3,379
22,550	22,600	3,448	3,386	3,923	3,386
22,600	22,650	3,462	3,394	3,937	3,394
22,650	22,700	3,476	3,401	3,951	3,401
22,700	22,750	3,490	3,409	3,965	3,409
22,750	22,800	3,504	3,416	3,979	3,416
22,800	22,850	3,518	3,424	3,993	3,424
22,850	22,900	3,532	3,431	4,007	3,431
22,900	22,950	3,546	3,439	4,021	3,439
22,950	23,000	3,560	3,446	4,035	3,446

* This column must also be used by a qualifying widow(er).

Continued on next page

If line 37 (taxable income) is— / And you are—

Columns: At least | But less than | Single | Married filing jointly * | Married filing separately | Head of a household — Your tax is—

23,000

At least	But less than	Single	Married filing jointly	Married filing separately	Head of a household
23,000	23,050	3,574	3,454	4,049	3,454
23,050	23,100	3,588	3,461	4,063	3,461
23,100	23,150	3,602	3,469	4,077	3,469
23,150	23,200	3,616	3,476	4,091	3,476
23,200	23,250	3,630	3,484	4,105	3,484
23,250	23,300	3,644	3,491	4,119	3,491
23,300	23,350	3,658	3,499	4,133	3,499
23,350	23,400	3,672	3,506	4,147	3,506
23,400	23,450	3,686	3,514	4,161	3,514
23,450	23,500	3,700	3,521	4,175	3,521
23,500	23,550	3,714	3,529	4,189	3,529
23,550	23,600	3,728	3,536	4,203	3,536
23,600	23,650	3,742	3,544	4,217	3,544
23,650	23,700	3,756	3,551	4,231	3,551
23,700	23,750	3,770	3,559	4,245	3,559
23,750	23,800	3,784	3,566	4,259	3,566
23,800	23,850	3,798	3,574	4,273	3,574
23,850	23,900	3,812	3,581	4,287	3,581
23,900	23,950	3,826	3,589	4,301	3,589
23,950	24,000	3,840	3,596	4,315	3,596

24,000

At least	But less than	Single	Married filing jointly	Married filing separately	Head of a household
24,000	24,050	3,854	3,604	4,329	3,604
24,050	24,100	3,868	3,611	4,343	3,611
24,100	24,150	3,882	3,619	4,357	3,619
24,150	24,200	3,896	3,626	4,371	3,626
24,200	24,250	3,910	3,634	4,385	3,634
24,250	24,300	3,924	3,641	4,399	3,641
24,300	24,350	3,938	3,649	4,413	3,649
24,350	24,400	3,952	3,656	4,427	3,656
24,400	24,450	3,966	3,664	4,441	3,664
24,450	24,500	3,980	3,671	4,455	3,671
24,500	24,550	3,994	3,679	4,469	3,679
24,550	24,600	4,008	3,686	4,483	3,686
24,600	24,650	4,022	3,694	4,497	3,694
24,650	24,700	4,036	3,701	4,511	3,701
24,700	24,750	4,050	3,709	4,525	3,709
24,750	24,800	4,064	3,716	4,539	3,716
24,800	24,850	4,078	3,724	4,553	3,724
24,850	24,900	4,092	3,731	4,567	3,731
24,900	24,950	4,106	3,739	4,581	3,739
24,950	25,000	4,120	3,746	4,595	3,746

25,000

At least	But less than	Single	Married filing jointly	Married filing separately	Head of a household
25,000	25,050	4,134	3,754	4,609	3,754
25,050	25,100	4,148	3,761	4,623	3,761
25,100	25,150	4,162	3,769	4,637	3,769
25,150	25,200	4,176	3,776	4,651	3,776
25,200	25,250	4,190	3,784	4,665	3,784
25,250	25,300	4,204	3,791	4,679	3,791
25,300	25,350	4,218	3,799	4,693	3,799
25,350	25,400	4,232	3,806	4,707	3,806
25,400	25,450	4,246	3,814	4,721	3,814
25,450	25,500	4,260	3,821	4,735	3,821
25,500	25,550	4,274	3,829	4,749	3,829
25,550	25,600	4,288	3,836	4,763	3,836
25,600	25,650	4,302	3,844	4,777	3,844
25,650	25,700	4,316	3,851	4,791	3,851
25,700	25,750	4,330	3,859	4,805	3,859
25,750	25,800	4,344	3,866	4,819	3,866
25,800	25,850	4,358	3,874	4,833	3,874
25,850	25,900	4,372	3,881	4,847	3,881
25,900	25,950	4,386	3,889	4,861	3,889
25,950	26,000	4,400	3,896	4,875	3,896

26,000

At least	But less than	Single	Married filing jointly	Married filing separately	Head of a household
26,000	26,050	4,414	3,904	4,889	3,904
26,050	26,100	4,428	3,911	4,903	3,911
26,100	26,150	4,442	3,919	4,917	3,919
26,150	26,200	4,456	3,926	4,931	3,926
26,200	26,250	4,470	3,934	4,945	3,934
26,250	26,300	4,484	3,941	4,959	3,941
26,300	26,350	4,498	3,949	4,973	3,949
26,350	26,400	4,512	3,956	4,987	3,956
26,400	26,450	4,526	3,964	5,001	3,964
26,450	26,500	4,540	3,971	5,015	3,971
26,500	26,550	4,554	3,979	5,029	3,979
26,550	26,600	4,568	3,986	5,043	3,986
26,600	26,650	4,582	3,994	5,057	3,994
26,650	26,700	4,596	4,001	5,071	4,001
26,700	26,750	4,610	4,009	5,085	4,009
26,750	26,800	4,624	4,016	5,099	4,016
26,800	26,850	4,638	4,024	5,113	4,024
26,850	26,900	4,652	4,031	5,127	4,031
26,900	26,950	4,666	4,039	5,141	4,039
26,950	27,000	4,680	4,046	5,155	4,046

27,000

At least	But less than	Single	Married filing jointly	Married filing separately	Head of a household
27,000	27,050	4,694	4,054	5,169	4,054
27,050	27,100	4,708	4,061	5,183	4,061
27,100	27,150	4,722	4,069	5,197	4,069
27,150	27,200	4,736	4,076	5,211	4,076
27,200	27,250	4,750	4,084	5,225	4,084
27,250	27,300	4,764	4,091	5,239	4,091
27,300	27,350	4,778	4,099	5,253	4,099
27,350	27,400	4,792	4,106	5,267	4,106
27,400	27,450	4,806	4,114	5,281	4,114
27,450	27,500	4,820	4,121	5,295	4,121
27,500	27,550	4,834	4,129	5,309	4,129
27,550	27,600	4,848	4,136	5,323	4,136
27,600	27,650	4,862	4,144	5,337	4,144
27,650	27,700	4,876	4,151	5,351	4,151
27,700	27,750	4,890	4,159	5,365	4,159
27,750	27,800	4,904	4,166	5,379	4,166
27,800	27,850	4,918	4,174	5,393	4,174
27,850	27,900	4,932	4,181	5,407	4,181
27,900	27,950	4,946	4,189	5,421	4,189
27,950	28,000	4,960	4,196	5,435	4,196

28,000

At least	But less than	Single	Married filing jointly	Married filing separately	Head of a household
28,000	28,050	4,974	4,204	5,449	4,204
28,050	28,100	4,988	4,211	5,463	4,211
28,100	28,150	5,002	4,219	5,477	4,219
28,150	28,200	5,016	4,226	5,491	4,226
28,200	28,250	5,030	4,234	5,505	4,234
28,250	28,300	5,044	4,241	5,519	4,241
28,300	28,350	5,058	4,249	5,533	4,249
28,350	28,400	5,072	4,256	5,547	4,256
28,400	28,450	5,086	4,264	5,561	4,264
28,450	28,500	5,100	4,271	5,575	4,271
28,500	28,550	5,114	4,279	5,589	4,279
28,550	28,600	5,128	4,286	5,603	4,286
28,600	28,650	5,142	4,294	5,617	4,294
28,650	28,700	5,156	4,301	5,631	4,301
28,700	28,750	5,170	4,309	5,645	4,309
28,750	28,800	5,184	4,316	5,659	4,316
28,800	28,850	5,198	4,324	5,673	4,324
28,850	28,900	5,212	4,331	5,687	4,331
28,900	28,950	5,226	4,339	5,701	4,339
28,950	29,000	5,240	4,346	5,715	4,346

29,000

At least	But less than	Single	Married filing jointly	Married filing separately	Head of a household
29,000	29,050	5,254	4,354	5,729	4,354
29,050	29,100	5,268	4,361	5,743	4,361
29,100	29,150	5,282	4,369	5,757	4,369
29,150	29,200	5,296	4,376	5,771	4,376
29,200	29,250	5,310	4,384	5,785	4,384
29,250	29,300	5,324	4,391	5,799	4,391
29,300	29,350	5,338	4,399	5,813	4,399
29,350	29,400	5,352	4,406	5,827	4,406
29,400	29,450	5,366	4,414	5,841	4,414
29,450	29,500	5,380	4,421	5,855	4,421
29,500	29,550	5,394	4,429	5,869	4,429
29,550	29,600	5,408	4,436	5,883	4,436
29,600	29,650	5,422	4,444	5,897	4,447
29,650	29,700	5,436	4,451	5,911	4,461
29,700	29,750	5,450	4,459	5,925	4,475
29,750	29,800	5,464	4,466	5,939	4,489
29,800	29,850	5,478	4,474	5,953	4,503
29,850	29,900	5,492	4,481	5,967	4,517
29,900	29,950	5,506	4,489	5,981	4,531
29,950	30,000	5,520	4,496	5,995	4,545

30,000

At least	But less than	Single	Married filing jointly	Married filing separately	Head of a household
30,000	30,050	5,534	4,504	6,009	4,559
30,050	30,100	5,548	4,511	6,023	4,573
30,100	30,150	5,562	4,519	6,037	4,587
30,150	30,200	5,576	4,526	6,051	4,601
30,200	30,250	5,590	4,534	6,065	4,615
30,250	30,300	5,604	4,541	6,079	4,629
30,300	30,350	5,618	4,549	6,093	4,643
30,350	30,400	5,632	4,556	6,107	4,657
30,400	30,450	5,646	4,564	6,121	4,671
30,450	30,500	5,660	4,571	6,135	4,685
30,500	30,550	5,674	4,579	6,149	4,699
30,550	30,600	5,688	4,586	6,163	4,713
30,600	30,650	5,702	4,594	6,177	4,727
30,650	30,700	5,716	4,601	6,191	4,741
30,700	30,750	5,730	4,609	6,205	4,755
30,750	30,800	5,744	4,616	6,219	4,769
30,800	30,850	5,758	4,624	6,233	4,783
30,850	30,900	5,772	4,631	6,247	4,797
30,900	30,950	5,786	4,639	6,261	4,811
30,950	31,000	5,800	4,646	6,275	4,825

31,000

At least	But less than	Single	Married filing jointly	Married filing separately	Head of a household
31,000	31,050	5,814	4,654	6,289	4,839
31,050	31,100	5,828	4,661	6,303	4,853
31,100	31,150	5,842	4,669	6,317	4,867
31,150	31,200	5,856	4,676	6,331	4,881
31,200	31,250	5,870	4,684	6,345	4,895
31,250	31,300	5,884	4,691	6,359	4,909
31,300	31,350	5,898	4,699	6,373	4,923
31,350	31,400	5,912	4,706	6,387	4,937
31,400	31,450	5,926	4,714	6,401	4,951
31,450	31,500	5,940	4,721	6,415	4,965
31,500	31,550	5,954	4,729	6,429	4,979
31,550	31,600	5,968	4,736	6,443	4,993
31,600	31,650	5,982	4,744	6,457	5,007
31,650	31,700	5,996	4,751	6,471	5,021
31,700	31,750	6,010	4,759	6,485	5,035
31,750	31,800	6,024	4,766	6,499	5,049
31,800	31,850	6,038	4,774	6,513	5,063
31,850	31,900	6,052	4,781	6,527	5,077
31,900	31,950	6,066	4,789	6,541	5,091
31,950	32,000	6,080	4,796	6,555	5,105

* This column must also be used by a qualifying widow(er).

Continued on next page

If line 37 (taxable income) is—		And you are—				If line 37 (taxable income) is—		And you are—				If line 37 (taxable income) is—		And you are—			
At least	But less than	Single	Married filing jointly *	Married filing sepa-rately	Head of a house-hold	At least	But less than	Single	Married filing jointly *	Married filing sepa-rately	Head of a house-hold	At least	But less than	Single	Married filing jointly *	Married filing sepa-rately	Head of a house-hold
		Your tax is—						Your tax is—						Your tax is—			
32,000						**35,000**						**38,000**					
32,000	32,050	6,094	4,804	6,569	5,119	35,000	35,050	6,934	5,254	7,409	5,959	38,000	38,050	7,774	5,850	8,249	6,799
32,050	32,100	6,108	4,811	6,583	5,133	35,050	35,100	6,948	5,261	7,423	5,973	38,050	38,100	7,788	5,864	8,263	6,813
32,100	32,150	6,122	4,819	6,597	5,147	35,100	35,150	6,962	5,269	7,437	5,987	38,100	38,150	7,802	5,878	8,277	6,827
32,150	32,200	6,136	4,826	6,611	5,161	35,150	35,200	6,976	5,276	7,451	6,001	38,150	38,200	7,816	5,892	8,291	6,841
32,200	32,250	6,150	4,834	6,625	5,175	35,200	35,250	6,990	5,284	7,465	6,015	38,200	38,250	7,830	5,906	8,305	6,855
32,250	32,300	6,164	4,841	6,639	5,189	35,250	35,300	7,004	5,291	7,479	6,029	38,250	38,300	7,844	5,920	8,319	6,869
32,300	32,350	6,178	4,849	6,653	5,203	35,300	35,350	7,018	5,299	7,493	6,043	38,300	38,350	7,858	5,934	8,333	6,883
32,350	32,400	6,192	4,856	6,667	5,217	35,350	35,400	7,032	5,306	7,507	6,057	38,350	38,400	7,872	5,948	8,347	6,897
32,400	32,450	6,206	4,864	6,681	5,231	35,400	35,450	7,046	5,314	7,521	6,071	38,400	38,450	7,886	5,962	8,361	6,911
32,450	32,500	6,220	4,871	6,695	5,245	35,450	35,500	7,060	5,321	7,535	6,085	38,450	38,500	7,900	5,976	8,375	6,925
32,500	32,550	6,234	4,879	6,709	5,259	35,500	35,550	7,074	5,329	7,549	6,099	38,500	38,550	7,914	5,990	8,389	6,939
32,550	32,600	6,248	4,886	6,723	5,273	35,550	35,600	7,088	5,336	7,563	6,113	38,550	38,600	7,928	6,004	8,403	6,953
32,600	32,650	6,262	4,894	6,737	5,287	35,600	35,650	7,102	5,344	7,577	6,127	38,600	38,650	7,942	6,018	8,417	6,967
32,650	32,700	6,276	4,901	6,751	5,301	35,650	35,700	7,116	5,351	7,591	6,141	38,650	38,700	7,956	6,032	8,431	6,981
32,700	32,750	6,290	4,909	6,765	5,315	35,700	35,750	7,130	5,359	7,605	6,155	38,700	38,750	7,970	6,046	8,445	6,995
32,750	32,800	6,304	4,916	6,779	5,329	35,750	35,800	7,144	5,366	7,619	6,169	38,750	38,800	7,984	6,060	8,459	7,009
32,800	32,850	6,318	4,924	6,793	5,343	35,800	35,850	7,158	5,374	7,633	6,183	38,800	38,850	7,998	6,074	8,473	7,023
32,850	32,900	6,332	4,931	6,807	5,357	35,850	35,900	7,172	5,381	7,647	6,197	38,850	38,900	8,012	6,088	8,487	7,037
32,900	32,950	6,346	4,939	6,821	5,371	35,900	35,950	7,186	5,389	7,661	6,211	38,900	38,950	8,026	6,102	8,501	7,051
32,950	33,000	6,360	4,946	6,835	5,385	35,950	36,000	7,200	5,396	7,675	6,225	38,950	39,000	8,040	6,116	8,515	7,065
33,000						**36,000**						**39,000**					
33,000	33,050	6,374	4,954	6,849	5,399	36,000	36,050	7,214	5,404	7,689	6,239	39,000	39,050	8,054	6,130	8,529	7,079
33,050	33,100	6,388	4,961	6,863	5,413	36,050	36,100	7,228	5,411	7,703	6,253	39,050	39,100	8,068	6,144	8,543	7,093
33,100	33,150	6,402	4,969	6,877	5,427	36,100	36,150	7,242	5,419	7,717	6,267	39,100	39,150	8,082	6,158	8,557	7,107
33,150	33,200	6,416	4,976	6,891	5,441	36,150	36,200	7,256	5,426	7,731	6,281	39,150	39,200	8,096	6,172	8,571	7,121
33,200	33,250	6,430	4,984	6,905	5,455	36,200	36,250	7,270	5,434	7,745	6,295	39,200	39,250	8,110	6,186	8,585	7,135
33,250	33,300	6,444	4,991	6,919	5,469	36,250	36,300	7,284	5,441	7,759	6,309	39,250	39,300	8,124	6,200	8,599	7,149
33,300	33,350	6,458	4,999	6,933	5,483	36,300	36,350	7,298	5,449	7,773	6,323	39,300	39,350	8,138	6,214	8,613	7,163
33,350	33,400	6,472	5,006	6,947	5,497	36,350	36,400	7,312	5,456	7,787	6,337	39,350	39,400	8,152	6,228	8,627	7,177
33,400	33,450	6,486	5,014	6,961	5,511	36,400	36,450	7,326	5,464	7,801	6,351	39,400	39,450	8,166	6,242	8,641	7,191
33,450	33,500	6,500	5,021	6,975	5,525	36,450	36,500	7,340	5,471	7,815	6,365	39,450	39,500	8,180	6,256	8,655	7,205
33,500	33,550	6,514	5,029	6,989	5,539	36,500	36,550	7,354	5,479	7,829	6,379	39,500	39,550	8,194	6,270	8,669	7,219
33,550	33,600	6,528	5,036	7,003	5,553	36,550	36,600	7,368	5,486	7,843	6,393	39,550	39,600	8,208	6,284	8,683	7,233
33,600	33,650	6,542	5,044	7,017	5,567	36,600	36,650	7,382	5,494	7,857	6,407	39,600	39,650	8,222	6,298	8,697	7,247
33,650	33,700	6,556	5,051	7,031	5,581	36,650	36,700	7,396	5,501	7,871	6,421	39,650	39,700	8,236	6,312	8,711	7,261
33,700	33,750	6,570	5,059	7,045	5,595	36,700	36,750	7,410	5,509	7,885	6,435	39,700	39,750	8,250	6,326	8,725	7,275
33,750	33,800	6,584	5,066	7,059	5,609	36,750	36,800	7,424	5,516	7,899	6,449	39,750	39,800	8,264	6,340	8,739	7,289
33,800	33,850	6,598	5,074	7,073	5,623	36,800	36,850	7,438	5,524	7,913	6,463	39,800	39,850	8,278	6,354	8,753	7,303
33,850	33,900	6,612	5,081	7,087	5,637	36,850	36,900	7,452	5,531	7,927	6,477	39,850	39,900	8,292	6,368	8,767	7,317
33,900	33,950	6,626	5,089	7,101	5,651	36,900	36,950	7,466	5,542	7,941	6,491	39,900	39,950	8,306	6,382	8,781	7,331
33,950	34,000	6,640	5,096	7,115	5,665	36,950	37,000	7,480	5,556	7,955	6,505	39,950	40,000	8,320	6,396	8,795	7,345
34,000						**37,000**						**40,000**					
34,000	34,050	6,654	5,104	7,129	5,679	37,000	37,050	7,494	5,570	7,969	6,519	40,000	40,050	8,334	6,410	8,809	7,359
34,050	34,100	6,668	5,111	7,143	5,693	37,050	37,100	7,508	5,584	7,983	6,533	40,050	40,100	8,348	6,424	8,823	7,373
34,100	34,150	6,682	5,119	7,157	5,707	37,100	37,150	7,522	5,598	7,997	6,547	40,100	40,150	8,362	6,438	8,837	7,387
34,150	34,200	6,696	5,126	7,171	5,721	37,150	37,200	7,536	5,612	8,011	6,561	40,150	40,200	8,376	6,452	8,851	7,401
34,200	34,250	6,710	5,134	7,185	5,735	37,200	37,250	7,550	5,626	8,025	6,575	40,200	40,250	8,390	6,466	8,865	7,415
34,250	34,300	6,724	5,141	7,199	5,749	37,250	37,300	7,564	5,640	8,039	6,589	40,250	40,300	8,404	6,480	8,879	7,429
34,300	34,350	6,738	5,149	7,213	5,763	37,300	37,350	7,578	5,654	8,053	6,603	40,300	40,350	8,418	6,494	8,893	7,443
34,350	34,400	6,752	5,156	7,227	5,777	37,350	37,400	7,592	5,668	8,067	6,617	40,350	40,400	8,432	6,508	8,907	7,457
34,400	34,450	6,766	5,164	7,241	5,791	37,400	37,450	7,606	5,682	8,081	6,631	40,400	40,450	8,446	6,522	8,921	7,471
34,450	34,500	6,780	5,171	7,255	5,805	37,450	37,500	7,620	5,696	8,095	6,645	40,450	40,500	8,460	6,536	8,935	7,485
34,500	34,550	6,794	5,179	7,269	5,819	37,500	37,550	7,634	5,710	8,109	6,659	40,500	40,550	8,474	6,550	8,949	7,499
34,550	34,600	6,808	5,186	7,283	5,833	37,550	37,600	7,648	5,724	8,123	6,673	40,550	40,600	8,488	6,564	8,963	7,513
34,600	34,650	6,822	5,194	7,297	5,847	37,600	37,650	7,662	5,738	8,137	6,687	40,600	40,650	8,502	6,578	8,977	7,527
34,650	34,700	6,836	5,201	7,311	5,861	37,650	37,700	7,676	5,752	8,151	6,701	40,650	40,700	8,516	6,592	8,991	7,541
34,700	34,750	6,850	5,209	7,325	5,875	37,700	37,750	7,690	5,766	8,165	6,715	40,700	40,750	8,530	6,606	9,005	7,555
34,750	34,800	6,864	5,216	7,339	5,889	37,750	37,800	7,704	5,780	8,179	6,729	40,750	40,800	8,544	6,620	9,019	7,569
34,800	34,850	6,878	5,224	7,353	5,903	37,800	37,850	7,718	5,794	8,193	6,743	40,800	40,850	8,558	6,634	9,033	7,583
34,850	34,900	6,892	5,231	7,367	5,917	37,850	37,900	7,732	5,808	8,207	6,757	40,850	40,900	8,572	6,648	9,047	7,597
34,900	34,950	6,906	5,239	7,381	5,931	37,900	37,950	7,746	5,822	8,221	6,771	40,900	40,950	8,586	6,662	9,061	7,611
34,950	35,000	6,920	5,246	7,395	5,945	37,950	38,000	7,760	5,836	8,235	6,785	40,950	41,000	8,600	6,676	9,075	7,625

* This column must also be used by a qualifying widow(er).

Continued on next page

- 41 -

If line 37 (taxable income) is— / And you are—

At least	But less than	Single	Married filing jointly *	Married filing separately	Head of a household

41,000

At least	But less than	Single	Married filing jointly *	Married filing separately	Head of a household
41,000	41,050	8,614	6,690	9,089	7,639
41,050	41,100	8,628	6,704	9,103	7,653
41,100	41,150	8,642	6,718	9,117	7,667
41,150	41,200	8,656	6,732	9,131	7,681
41,200	41,250	8,670	6,746	9,145	7,695
41,250	41,300	8,684	6,760	9,159	7,709
41,300	41,350	8,698	6,774	9,173	7,723
41,350	41,400	8,712	6,788	9,187	7,737
41,400	41,450	8,726	6,802	9,201	7,751
41,450	41,500	8,740	6,816	9,215	7,765
41,500	41,550	8,754	6,830	9,229	7,779
41,550	41,600	8,768	6,844	9,243	7,793
41,600	41,650	8,782	6,858	9,257	7,807
41,650	41,700	8,796	6,872	9,271	7,821
41,700	41,750	8,810	6,886	9,285	7,835
41,750	41,800	8,824	6,900	9,299	7,849
41,800	41,850	8,838	6,914	9,313	7,863
41,850	41,900	8,852	6,928	9,327	7,877
41,900	41,950	8,866	6,942	9,341	7,891
41,950	42,000	8,880	6,956	9,355	7,905

42,000

At least	But less than	Single	Married filing jointly *	Married filing separately	Head of a household
42,000	42,050	8,894	6,970	9,369	7,919
42,050	42,100	8,908	6,984	9,383	7,933
42,100	42,150	8,922	6,998	9,397	7,947
42,150	42,200	8,936	7,012	9,411	7,961
42,200	42,250	8,950	7,026	9,425	7,975
42,250	42,300	8,964	7,040	9,439	7,989
42,300	42,350	8,978	7,054	9,453	8,003
42,350	42,400	8,992	7,068	9,467	8,017
42,400	42,450	9,006	7,082	9,481	8,031
42,450	42,500	9,020	7,096	9,495	8,045
42,500	42,550	9,034	7,110	9,509	8,059
42,550	42,600	9,048	7,124	9,523	8,073
42,600	42,650	9,062	7,138	9,537	8,087
42,650	42,700	9,076	7,152	9,551	8,101
42,700	42,750	9,090	7,166	9,565	8,115
42,750	42,800	9,104	7,180	9,579	8,129
42,800	42,850	9,118	7,194	9,593	8,143
42,850	42,900	9,132	7,208	9,607	8,157
42,900	42,950	9,146	7,222	9,621	8,171
42,950	43,000	9,160	7,236	9,635	8,185

43,000

At least	But less than	Single	Married filing jointly *	Married filing separately	Head of a household
43,000	43,050	9,174	7,250	9,649	8,199
43,050	43,100	9,188	7,264	9,663	8,213
43,100	43,150	9,202	7,278	9,677	8,227
43,150	43,200	9,216	7,292	9,691	8,241
43,200	43,250	9,230	7,306	9,705	8,255
43,250	43,300	9,244	7,320	9,719	8,269
43,300	43,350	9,258	7,334	9,733	8,283
43,350	43,400	9,272	7,348	9,747	8,297
43,400	43,450	9,286	7,362	9,761	8,311
43,450	43,500	9,300	7,376	9,775	8,325
43,500	43,550	9,314	7,390	9,789	8,339
43,550	43,600	9,328	7,404	9,803	8,353
43,600	43,650	9,342	7,418	9,817	8,367
43,650	43,700	9,356	7,432	9,831	8,381
43,700	43,750	9,370	7,446	9,845	8,395
43,750	43,800	9,384	7,460	9,859	8,409
43,800	43,850	9,398	7,474	9,873	8,423
43,850	43,900	9,412	7,488	9,887	8,437
43,900	43,950	9,426	7,502	9,901	8,451
43,950	44,000	9,440	7,516	9,915	8,465

44,000

At least	But less than	Single	Married filing jointly *	Married filing separately	Head of a household
44,000	44,050	9,454	7,530	9,929	8,479
44,050	44,100	9,468	7,544	9,943	8,493
44,100	44,150	9,482	7,558	9,957	8,507
44,150	44,200	9,496	7,572	9,971	8,521
44,200	44,250	9,510	7,586	9,985	8,535
44,250	44,300	9,524	7,600	9,999	8,549
44,300	44,350	9,538	7,614	10,013	8,563
44,350	44,400	9,552	7,628	10,027	8,577
44,400	44,450	9,566	7,642	10,041	8,591
44,450	44,500	9,580	7,656	10,055	8,605
44,500	44,550	9,594	7,670	10,069	8,619
44,550	44,600	9,608	7,684	10,083	8,633
44,600	44,650	9,622	7,698	10,098	8,647
44,650	44,700	9,636	7,712	10,114	8,661
44,700	44,750	9,650	7,726	10,129	8,675
44,750	44,800	9,664	7,740	10,145	8,689
44,800	44,850	9,678	7,754	10,160	8,703
44,850	44,900	9,692	7,768	10,176	8,717
44,900	44,950	9,706	7,782	10,191	8,731
44,950	45,000	9,720	7,796	10,207	8,745

45,000

At least	But less than	Single	Married filing jointly *	Married filing separately	Head of a household
45,000	45,050	9,734	7,810	10,222	8,759
45,050	45,100	9,748	7,824	10,238	8,773
45,100	45,150	9,762	7,838	10,253	8,787
45,150	45,200	9,776	7,852	10,269	8,801
45,200	45,250	9,790	7,866	10,284	8,815
45,250	45,300	9,804	7,880	10,300	8,829
45,300	45,350	9,818	7,894	10,315	8,843
45,350	45,400	9,832	7,908	10,331	8,857
45,400	45,450	9,846	7,922	10,346	8,871
45,450	45,500	9,860	7,936	10,362	8,885
45,500	45,550	9,874	7,950	10,377	8,899
45,550	45,600	9,888	7,964	10,393	8,913
45,600	45,650	9,902	7,978	10,408	8,927
45,650	45,700	9,916	7,992	10,424	8,941
45,700	45,750	9,930	8,006	10,439	8,955
45,750	45,800	9,944	8,020	10,455	8,969
45,800	45,850	9,958	8,034	10,470	8,983
45,850	45,900	9,972	8,048	10,486	8,997
45,900	45,950	9,986	8,062	10,501	9,011
45,950	46,000	10,000	8,076	10,517	9,025

46,000

At least	But less than	Single	Married filing jointly *	Married filing separately	Head of a household
46,000	46,050	10,014	8,090	10,532	9,039
46,050	46,100	10,028	8,104	10,548	9,053
46,100	46,150	10,042	8,118	10,563	9,067
46,150	46,200	10,056	8,132	10,579	9,081
46,200	46,250	10,070	8,146	10,594	9,095
46,250	46,300	10,084	8,160	10,610	9,109
46,300	46,350	10,098	8,174	10,625	9,123
46,350	46,400	10,112	8,188	10,641	9,137
46,400	46,450	10,126	8,202	10,656	9,151
46,450	46,500	10,140	8,216	10,672	9,165
46,500	46,550	10,154	8,230	10,687	9,179
46,550	46,600	10,168	8,244	10,703	9,193
46,600	46,650	10,182	8,258	10,718	9,207
46,650	46,700	10,196	8,272	10,734	9,221
46,700	46,750	10,210	8,286	10,749	9,235
46,750	46,800	10,224	8,300	10,765	9,249
46,800	46,850	10,238	8,314	10,780	9,263
46,850	46,900	10,252	8,328	10,796	9,277
46,900	46,950	10,266	8,342	10,811	9,291
46,950	47,000	10,280	8,356	10,827	9,305

47,000

At least	But less than	Single	Married filing jointly *	Married filing separately	Head of a household
47,000	47,050	10,294	8,370	10,842	9,319
47,050	47,100	10,308	8,384	10,858	9,333
47,100	47,150	10,322	8,398	10,873	9,347
47,150	47,200	10,336	8,412	10,889	9,361
47,200	47,250	10,350	8,426	10,904	9,375
47,250	47,300	10,364	8,440	10,920	9,389
47,300	47,350	10,378	8,454	10,935	9,403
47,350	47,400	10,392	8,468	10,951	9,417
47,400	47,450	10,406	8,482	10,966	9,431
47,450	47,500	10,420	8,496	10,982	9,445
47,500	47,550	10,434	8,510	10,997	9,459
47,550	47,600	10,448	8,524	11,013	9,473
47,600	47,650	10,462	8,538	11,028	9,487
47,650	47,700	10,476	8,552	11,044	9,501
47,700	47,750	10,490	8,566	11,059	9,515
47,750	47,800	10,504	8,580	11,075	9,529
47,800	47,850	10,518	8,594	11,090	9,543
47,850	47,900	10,532	8,608	11,106	9,557
47,900	47,950	10,546	8,622	11,121	9,571
47,950	48,000	10,560	8,636	11,137	9,585

48,000

At least	But less than	Single	Married filing jointly *	Married filing separately	Head of a household
48,000	48,050	10,574	8,650	11,152	9,599
48,050	48,100	10,588	8,664	11,168	9,613
48,100	48,150	10,602	8,678	11,183	9,627
48,150	48,200	10,616	8,692	11,199	9,641
48,200	48,250	10,630	8,706	11,214	9,655
48,250	48,300	10,644	8,720	11,230	9,669
48,300	48,350	10,658	8,734	11,245	9,683
48,350	48,400	10,672	8,748	11,261	9,697
48,400	48,450	10,686	8,762	11,276	9,711
48,450	48,500	10,700	8,776	11,292	9,725
48,500	48,550	10,714	8,790	11,307	9,739
48,550	48,600	10,728	8,804	11,323	9,753
48,600	48,650	10,742	8,818	11,338	9,767
48,650	48,700	10,756	8,832	11,354	9,781
48,700	48,750	10,770	8,846	11,369	9,795
48,750	48,800	10,784	8,860	11,385	9,809
48,800	48,850	10,798	8,874	11,400	9,823
48,850	48,900	10,812	8,888	11,416	9,837
48,900	48,950	10,826	8,902	11,431	9,851
48,950	49,000	10,840	8,916	11,447	9,865

49,000

At least	But less than	Single	Married filing jointly *	Married filing separately	Head of a household
49,000	49,050	10,854	8,930	11,462	9,879
49,050	49,100	10,868	8,944	11,478	9,893
49,100	49,150	10,882	8,958	11,493	9,907
49,150	49,200	10,896	8,972	11,509	9,921
49,200	49,250	10,910	8,986	11,524	9,935
49,250	49,300	10,924	9,000	11,540	9,949
49,300	49,350	10,938	9,014	11,555	9,963
49,350	49,400	10,952	9,028	11,571	9,977
49,400	49,450	10,966	9,042	11,586	9,991
49,450	49,500	10,980	9,056	11,602	10,005
49,500	49,550	10,994	9,070	11,617	10,019
49,550	49,600	11,008	9,084	11,633	10,033
49,600	49,650	11,022	9,098	11,648	10,047
49,650	49,700	11,036	9,112	11,664	10,061
49,700	49,750	11,050	9,126	11,679	10,075
49,750	49,800	11,064	9,140	11,695	10,089
49,800	49,850	11,078	9,154	11,710	10,103
49,850	49,900	11,092	9,168	11,726	10,117
49,900	49,950	11,106	9,182	11,741	10,131
49,950	50,000	11,120	9,196	11,757	10,145

* This column must also be used by a qualifying widow(er).

Continued on next page

Economics

Word Search

Search the word puzzle for the following words and then connect the letters vertically, horizontally, diagonally, backwards, or forwards. Multiple word combinations have no space separating the words.

fiscal	multiplier
general theory	lags
John Maynard Keynes	Hungary
government spending	taxation
budget	FICA
marginal	proportional
propensity	progressive
consume	regressive
save	pump priming

```
T  C  T  Q  P  O  Y  S  H  L  M  U  K  M  N  O  A  C  I  F
A  S  G  R  E  G  R  E  S  S  I  V  E  A  R  N  D  A  G  G
V  X  T  V  V  I  A  D  I  A  O  L  E  R  N  U  E  Y  N  N
E  E  R  T  A  O  G  K  S  O  I  P  B  G  S  C  G  N  I  A
C  H  A  B  S  P  N  C  Y  B  U  S  E  I  O  K  I  E  D  E
A  G  C  D  A  T  U  F  O  M  C  N  N  N  A  U  B  R  N  H
E  T  I  S  T  O  H  N  P  N  E  O  L  A  C  A  L  T  E  O
P  R  F  I  S  C  A  P  A  R  S  C  M  L  A  G  S  J  P  C
P  P  N  A  N  T  R  J  A  A  M  U  R  P  R  O  B  N  S  T
R  E  I  L  P  I  T  L  U  M  X  L  M  D  N  Q  E  S  T  O
O  N  E  N  M  N  T  R  O  J  I  Y  A  E  E  J  K  T  N  L
G  P  N  I  T  H  H  N  E  C  T  A  X  A  T  I  O  N  E  S
R  I  N  T  E  G  D  U  B  I  N  F  N  I  A  S  I  T  M  H
E  G  N  O  E  A  L  A  S  U  N  A  I  U  M  O  N  C  N  S
S  O  R  V  S  I  A  N  A  M  N  R  X  S  N  R  E  P  R  R
S  Y  F  O  F  N  E  A  L  D  O  S  P  N  C  T  O  I  E  P
I  X  C  A  Y  P  R  O  P  O  R  T  I  O  N  A  L  O  V  C
V  G  V  T  O  O  L  D  N  D  I  E  G  T  E  L  F  O  O
E  O  H  R  P  N  M  E  O  G  N  O  F  O  R  L  A  L  G  Y
G  U  P  S  E  N  Y  E  K  D  R  A  N  Y  A  M  N  H  O  J
X  N  E  P  X  E  O  T  L  I  N  D  P  O  L  S  F  T  X  L
```

Multiple Choice

Choose the response which best answers the question or completes the sentence.

___D___ 1. The current emphasis on fiscal policy actions stems back to the 1930s and the work of
   A. Eugene Dolan.
   B. Arthur Okun.
   C. Karl Marx.
   D. John Maynard Keynes.

___A___ 2. Nearly $____ out of every $5.00 of GNP is spent by government.
   A. 1.00
   B. 1.50
   C. 2.00
   D. 2.25

___D___ 3. The largest category of federal government spending in 1989 was
   A. health and medical care.
   B. savings and loan association bailouts.
   C. national defense.
   D. income security.

___A___ 4. The formula for the expenditure multiplier is $1 / (1 - ___)$.
   A. MPC
   B. APC
   C. MPS
   D. SGLI

___D___ 5. If a person's tax bill is $250 on $1,000 of income and $500 on $2,000 of income, he is paying a _____ tax.
   A. progressive
   B. regressive
   C. restrictive
   D. proportional

___C___ 6. Which of the following terms best describes what government officials believe they are doing by spending borrowed money?
   A. ''logrolling''
   B. ''pork barreling''
   C. ''pump priming''
   D. ''recycling''

Economics

Setting Up a Family Budget

Creating a family budget is not as difficult a task as one might imagine. Before one can properly begin the budgeting process, one must outline what spending has gone on in the past. Below is listed income and expense information for a family of four for a one-month period. Assume that the month is an accurate representation of all other months. Using the worksheet provided on the following page, enter the information in the proper categories. Indicate whether each expense is fixed or variable. That is, if the expense remains constant as income rises (and it cannot be reduced at will), it is fixed. If, on the other hand, the expense rises or falls as income rises or falls (and it can be reduced at will), it is a variable expense. Note that some expenses have fixed *and* variable elements. In such cases, if the majority of the amount is fixed, then call it "mostly fixed," and vice versa. After you have completed a current income/expense budget, comment (in the space provided) on those expenses which to you appear frivolous and which could be reduced and/or eliminated. Also comment on those expenses which could be increased.

Income

Husband's monthly net income	$1,700
Wife's monthly net income	1,330
Total monthly net income	$3,030

Expenses

Mortgage payment	$600
Water	35
Property insurance	50
Cable television	55
Groceries	700
Automobile insurance, registration, and taxes	50
Church giving	100
Payment on automobile #1	300
Payment on automobile #2	150
Gasoline	175
Clothing	45
Electricity	150
Credit card payment	40
Telephone	50
Life insurance	25
Medical expenses	75
Eating out	100
Heart fund contribution	5
Property taxes	50
Savings	110
Health insurance	165
Total expenses	$3,030

CONTRIBUTIONS:		
Church giving	100	Variable (should be increased to at least 10% of income—$303)
Heart fund contribution	5	Variable (could be reduced)
SAVINGS:	110	Variable (should be increased)
FOOD:		
Groceries	700	Mostly fixed (could be reduced)
Eating out	100	Variable (could be reduced or eliminated)
HOUSING:		
Mortgage payment	600	Fixed
Property insurance	50	Fixed
Property taxes	50	Fixed
UTILITIES:		
Water	35	Mostly fixed (might be reduced through conservation)
Electricity	150	Mostly fixed (might be reduced through conservation)
Telephone	50	Mostly fixed (could be reduced)
TRANSPORTATION:		
Payment on automobile #1	300	Fixed
Payment on automobile #2	150	Fixed
Insurance, registration, and taxes	50	Fixed
Gasoline	175	Mostly fixed (might be reduced)
CLOTHING:		
New clothing purchases	45	Variable
HEALTH:		
Medical expenses	75	Mostly fixed
Health insurance	165	Fixed
Life insurance	25	Fixed
ENTERTAINMENT/RECREATION		
Cable television	55	Variable (could be eliminated)
OTHER DEBT:		
Credit card payment	40	Fixed (could be increased to pay off faster)

Economics

The Balance Sheet: What You Own Versus What You Owe

Businesses are required both by stockholders and creditors to disclose what the firm holds and to whom money is owed. Just as it is a good practice for businesses regularly to publish their financial statements, it is an excellent idea for families periodically to take stock of their financial positions. Such an accounting is useful to potential lenders and insurance companies. All items which are "owned" by a family are called assets. Included in this category are automobiles, houses, furniture, savings accounts, moneys owed to the family by others, and clothing—in short, everything of value. Liabilities, on the other hand, are those amounts of money which are owed others. Included in the category of liabilities are taxes owed the government, mortgage loans, credit card balances, that $100 you owe your uncle Joe and aunt Mary, and all other forms of debt. For most families the dollar value of the family's assets is greater than its liabilities. In cases such as this, a family is said to enjoy some amount of "net worth," the difference between its assets and its liabilities. Since the typical financial statement places assets on the left side of the sheet and liabilities and net worth on the right, and since assets are

equal to liabilities plus net worth, this financial statement is commonly referred to as a "balance sheet."

Assets are generally broken down into three categories: monetary assets, tangible assets, and investment assets. Monetary assets include cash held and cash which will be forthcoming (what others owe you). The tangible assets section of the balance sheet includes actual physical things that the family owns, such as vehicles and property. Investment assets are those assets which are used as mediums of investment either to provide income or, hopefully, to go up in value; these include stocks, bonds, baseball card collections, and the like. Liabilities, amounts owed others, may be divided into two categories: short-term liabilities and long-term liabilities. Short-term liabilities are debts which one intends to pay within the next twelve months. Conversely, long-term liabilities are those debts which will not be paid in full within the next twelve months. Finally, as you saw earlier, net worth is determined by subtracting total liabilities from total assets. Given the following list of items and their values, develop a balance sheet for the Pete and Terri Jackson family.

Individual Retirement Account (IRA)	$12,000
Savings account	600
Credit cards (to be paid this year)	1,500
House & lot	115,000
Car loan	8,300
Mutual fund	4,400
Wal-Mart stock	6,300
Checking account	200
Income tax refund due	1,100
Personal property (clothes, jewelry, etc.)	16,000
Utility bills due	300
Cash on hand	100
Home loan	60,000
Car	12,000
Rent receivable owed from tenants	500
U.S. Savings Bonds	9,500
College savings account for Pete, Jr.	4,000

Balance Sheet for Pete and Terri Jackson
January 1, 1994

ASSETS			
Monetary Assets:			
Cash on hand	$100		
Checking account	200		
Savings account	600		
Rent receivable	500		
College savings account	4,000		
Income tax refund due	1,100		
Total Monetary Assets		$6,500	
Tangible Assets:			
House & lot	$115,000		
Car	12,000		
Personal property	16,000		
Total Tangible Assets		143,000	
Investment Assets:			
IRA	$12,000		
Mutual fund	4,400		
Wal-Mart stock	6,300		
U.S. Savings Bonds	9,500		
Total Investment Assets		32,200	
TOTAL ASSETS			$181,700
LIABILITIES			
Short-Term Liabilities:			
Credit cards	$1,500		
Utility bills due	300		
Total Short-Term Liabilities		$1,800	
Long-Term Liabilities:			
Car loan	$8,300		
Home loan	60,000		
Total Long-Term Liabilities		68,300	
Total Liabilities		70,100	
Net Worth (Total Assets – Total Liabilities)		111,600	
TOTAL LIABILITIES AND NET WORTH			$181,700

Economics

Balance Sheet Analysis: Calculation of Ratios

Once you have completed a family balance sheet (one every year at least), you can acquire valuable information by calculating a few personal financial ratios. A ratio compares two seemingly unrelated items in order to garner new and useful information. A common example would be information about your car. One piece of information tells you that you drove 200 miles since your last fuel purchase. A second piece of information is that when you filled up your car's gas tank, it took twenty gallons of gasoline. These two seemingly unrelated pieces of information, when combined, tell you that your car is getting only ten miles per gallon of gasoline. Likewise, personal financial ratios can give you a better understanding of your financial situation.

Ratio #1: Acid-Test Ratio

The acid-test ratio tells you how many times you can cover monthly expenses with your monetary assets. The acid-test ratio is calculated by dividing the family's monetary assets by its average monthly expenses. This ratio reveals how many months a family would be able to remain financially viable in case of a financial crisis that caused income to cease, such as a job loss or short-term disability. In the space provided below, calculate the Jacksons' acid-test ratio and comment on your findings. (Assume that their monthly expenses are $1,857.)

Acid-Test Ratio = Monetary Assets / Monthly Expenses
ANSWER: *$6,500/$1,857 = 3.5 months*

Comments: *Given the Jacksons' monthly expenses of $1,857 and their monetary assets of $6,500, they would be*

able to endure a financial crisis for approximately three and one-half months. This figure appears to be adequate,

especially if the Jacksons already have some sort of short-term disability insurance.

Ratio #2: Liquidity Ratio

The liquidity ratio is very similar to the acid-test ratio, but it tells how many times you can cover your monthly expenses with not only your monetary assets but your investments as well (in case of more drastic financial conditions, such as long-term disability, death of an income earner, and so on). The liquidity ratio is calculated by adding a family's monetary assets and investment assets and dividing by its average monthly expenses. In the space provided below, calculate the Jacksons' liquidity ratio and comment on your findings. (Again, assume that their monthly expenses are $1,857.)

Liquidity Ratio = (Monetary Assets + Investment Assets) / Monthly Expenses
ANSWER: *($6,500 + 32,200)/$1,857 = 20.8 months*

Comments: *Given the Jacksons' monthly expenses of $1,857 and their total monetary and investment assets of $38,700,*

they would be able to endure a financial crisis of nearly 21 months. This figure appears to be adequate; however,

it may not be wise to use family investments to meet current living expenses except in the most dire emergencies.

Ratio #3: Solvency Ratio

The solvency ratio tells you the percentage your debts are to your total assets. That is, it tells the percentage claim creditors have on your assets. This ratio is calculated by dividing the family's total liabilities by its total assets and multiplying by 100. As the percentage rises, a family is less solvent. If the percentage is greater than 100%, the family is technically insolvent. People in this situation may be able to pay their current bills, but they do not have enough to pay all their bills. Those who are insolvent usually have to hold some of their bills beyond the past due date in order to cover them with their next paycheck. Calculate the Jacksons' solvency ratio and comment on your findings.

Solvency Ratio % = (Total Liabilities / Total Assets) × 100
ANSWER: *($70,100/$181,700) x 100 = 38.58%*

Comment: *Given the Jacksons' total liabilities of $70,100 and their total assets of $181,700, their solvency ratio is*

38.58%. That is, for every dollar of assets they own, creditors have a claim on 38.58 cents.

Economics

Saving Money on Everyday Expenses

There is a saying that goes "If your income is less than your outgo, your upkeep will be your downfall!" Oftentimes, a family finds itself squeezed between its income and outgo, but while we have little control over our income, we do have some control over our expenses. In the spaces provided below, list ways in which a family could reduce each particular expense.

1. Food: *Purchase a freezer and buy frozen food in quantity when on sale. Use coupons for items which would have been purchased anyway. Prepare meals at home. Shop for groceries after eating. Shop with a list and purchase only needed items.*

2. Housing: *Double-check tax assessor's figures for accuracy. Shop around for a lower-priced homeowner's insurance policy. If you rent, search for a comparably appointed apartment or home in the same type of neighborhood for a lower price.*

3. Utilities: *Replace heating/cooling duct filters regularly. Add insulation to the home's ceiling, floor, and walls. Insulate the water heater and hot water pipes. When the heating/cooling system needs to be replaced, consider using a heat pump if the climate permits. Install storm doors and storm windows. Take advantage of your power company's special programs (i.e., load control on air conditioners). Install water conserving shower heads. Put a brick in the toilet tank to displace water. Turn off unnecessary lights. Limit time on long-distance telephone calls.*

4. Transportation: *Car-pool with coworkers to and from place of employment. Keep tires inflated to the proper pressure. Have automobile tuned up on a regular basis. Combine errands so that the automobile will be driven less often. Purchase gasoline at discount service stations and pay with cash. Shop for the best price for automobile insurance. Walk.*

5. Clothing: *Consider the purchase of good secondhand clothing. Make your own clothing. Avoid faddish designer clothing. Have shoes resoled.*

6. Health: *Purchase generic pharmaceuticals if approved by your physician. Use outpatient surgery centers rather than staying in a hospital. Shop for bargains in sundry health aisles (toothpaste, etc.).*

Economics

How to Constructively Show Dissatisfaction with Faulty Products and Services

One of man's greatest enemies (and poor business's greatest allies) is consumer timidity: a malady that strikes many of us when we receive shoddy merchandise or poor service. Rather than "cause trouble" by requesting repair, replacement merchandise, or a refund, we simply ignore the problem. However, good businesses want to know when and why customers are dissatisfied. Good businesses know that customer satisfaction is the key to future sales. Unhappy customers not only discontinue buying from that merchant but also complain to others, causing the loss of even more sales. This activity shows you how to respond to firms that will not give satisfaction for poor service or merchandise. To make this exercise realistic, the following hypothetical facts have been created.

PRODUCT:	Portable compact disc (CD) player
SERIAL NUMBER:	84179684
MODEL NUMBER:	TT6811 MK01
MANUFACTURER:	Transistor Town Corporation of America (TTCA)
	1 TTCA Building
	New York, New York 10019
PRICE YOU PAID:	$179.95
DATE OF PURCHASE:	January 2, 199X
STORE:	Transistor Town (You create an address in your town.)
PROBLEM:	When the "Play" button is pushed, the player goes into "Fast Forward." The problem began February 14.

The first principle to remember when trying to resolve a problem is to handle it on the lowest possible level. That is, first visit the store and speak to the salesperson or the store manager. In most cases a visit to the store will resolve the problem, but if it does not you must be willing to take your problem to the next level of management. The second principle is not to let anger get the best of you when dealing with others. Notice that this exercise does not mention the word *complaint*. Rather than an angry complainer, be a dissatisfied customer who expects to receive satisfaction. Occasionally, you will speak to a surly salesperson or manager. Always remember that the point of the visit is to receive an exchange or a refund, not to vent your anger. Try to gain the store representative's good will. In the heat of "battle," many dissatisfied customers fail to realize that the person with whom they have lost their temper is the only one who can help them at that time. Third, before you contact someone in the chain of communication, know what the next step will be. Specifically, know the name of the next person you will contact. Fourth, if you are not satisfied with the response of the person you have contacted, do not "threaten" him with going over his head to his supervisor. A threat of force in a business context will have the same consequences as other types of threats, namely, that the other party will immediately become defensive and refuse to help you. While you should never threaten, you should inform the person that you intend to speak to his supervisor (whom you identify by name). The usual chain of communication is as follows: the salesperson; the store manager; the customer service manager at the company's headquarters; the president of the company; and finally, the Better Business Bureau.

When speaking in person with another party, dress professionally; speak pleasantly; state the facts concisely; and, finally, ask for his help and wait for him to speak.

Step One: The Store Visit

On February 15, you go to Transistor Town to speak to the person who sold you the CD player. Upon arrival, you find that Brent, the man who sold you the player, is no longer employed there. He was fired for striking a complaining customer and is awaiting trial for assault and battery. You are referred to the store manager, Ms. Darlene Matthews. What will you say to her?

Answers will vary. The following is only a model. "Hello, Ms. Matthews. I purchased this CD player at Transistor

Town last month. I have a problem that I hope you can help me solve. Every time I press 'play,' it goes into fast

forward. As you can see by the sales receipt, it is still within the warranty period. Can you help me?"

She appears impatient, shifting her weight from one foot to the other and looking at her oversized watch. When you are almost finished relating the facts, she interrupts you with an exasperated "Gimme the player." Sighing, she looks it over and pushes a few buttons. She experiences the same problem. Looking up, she hands back the CD player and says, "Look, I'm really busy. I don't think we can help you. We don't service equipment here. Anyway, this is *your* problem. Take it home and try it for a few more weeks. Maybe the problem will go away." What will you do next?

Answers will vary. First, stay calm. Second, tell Ms. Matthews that you will not "try it for a few more weeks"

because the warranty will expire. Explain that you will be writing to the customer service department of Transistor

Town's corporate headquarters and that you will be explaining the problem and the poor service she gave you.

Step Two: The Letter of Dissatisfaction to Company Headquarters

A letter of dissatisfaction is, by nature, a formal document. Dissatisfaction letters should usually be directed to the corporation's director of customer service. At the top of the letter, state the technical data very simply. In the body of the letter be sure to do three things. First, explain the problem. Second, explain why you are contacting the company directly. Third, calmly explain how you feel. To prove your points, enclose photocopies of receipts and other documentation. Never include the originals; you may need them for future reference. Keep copies of all correspondence for your files. To avoid undue delay, you should mention a date after which you will contact them again to check on the progress of the case. To emphasize the seriousness of the matter, you may want to use "CC." The initials CC stand for "carbon copy" and are used at the bottom of the letter to indicate that a copy of the letter is being sent elsewhere. Letters may be copied to the corporation's president, the Better Business Bureau, the attorney general of your state, a consumer action hotline, or any other person or group who is able to initiate even greater action. In the space below, write a letter of dissatisfaction (dated March 1) to Transistor Town's customer service manager, Mr. Desmond Gruntle. The company's president is Mr. C. D. Rom.

Director of Customer Service   *March 1, 199X*
Transistor Town Corporation of America
1 TTCA Building
New York, New York 10019

Subject: Request for service on a Transistor Town CD player

Model #:	*TT6811 MK01*
Serial #:	*84179684*
Date Purchased:	*January 2, 199X*
Price Paid:	*$179.95*

Dear Sir:

On January 2, 199X, I purchased a compact disc player from your store in (name of city). The problem is that every time I press the "play" button, the player fast forwards. It is not a problem with the CD being played. It performs the same way with every disc. As you can see by the enclosed photocopy of my dated sales receipt, the CD player is within its established 90-day warranty.

I am contacting your office because I took the player to Ms. Darlene Matthews, the manager of the store from which I made my purchase and she was quite rude in her dealings with me, flatly refusing to repair or replace the player or issue a refund. Could you please tell me what I need to do to take care of this problem?

I have had many dealings with Transistor Town in the past, and I have never had an experience that has upset me so much. It is my hope that your office can provide the service that I demand from the firms with which I do business. To ensure that this matter receives its due attention, I am taking the liberty of sending a copy of this letter to the president of Transistor Town, Mr. C. D. Rom. If I do not hear from you by March 31, I will call his office to check on the progress of this matter.

Yours sincerely,

(Your signature)
(Your typed name)

Enclosure

CC: Mr. C. D. Rom, President, Transistor Town Corporation of America

---

March 31 goes by without a word from the company. On April 1, you call the president's office at (212) 555-1212, and his secretary says that yes, he received a copy of your letter but he does not deal with customer complaints. She suggests that you call the customer service manager, Mr. Desmond Gruntle. Without offering to transfer your call, she hangs up. You call Des Gruntle, and he explains that he too received a copy of the letter but he says, ''Look, buddy, I did not appreciate the rude tone of your letter. Turkeys like you waste our time and cause us nothing but trouble! I can't help it if you are stupid and can't figure out how to use your CD player!'' When you explain that you know how to use the player, that it is defective, and that you want it repaired or replaced, he laughs and slams down the telephone. By now, you are very angry, but you calmly take the next step, contacting the Better Business Bureau. You look up the telephone number of the local chapter and request a complaint form. Complete the form below, leaving blank any block for which you have no information.

BETTER BUSINESS BUREAU	CUSTOMER COMPLAINT		#12XXX
IMPORTANT! COMPLETE ALL 4 SECTIONS • WRITE FIRMLY			

1

DATE PROBLEM OCCURRED	DATE(S) YOU COMPLAINED TO CO.	TO WHOM **Mr. Gruntle**	PROD. OR SERVICE INVOLVED
February 14, 199X	**February 15, March 1, April 1**	**Ms. Matthews, Mr. Rom**	**CD Player**
BRAND NAME OR MFG.	MODEL, NAME, OR NO.	DATE PURCHASED	
Transistor Town	**CD Player TT6811MK01**	**January 2, 199X**	
AMOUNT INVOLVED $	NAME OF SALESPERSON	IF ADVERTISING INVOLVED, WHERE AND WHEN	
$179.95	**Brent**	**None**	

2

COMPANY PHONE NO.	CUSTOMER HOME PHONE NO.	CUSTOMER WORK PHONE NO.
(212) 555-1212	**student's home phone number**	**student's work phone number**

COMPANY NAME, ADDRESS, CITY, STATE, ZIP   CUSTOMER NAME, ADDRESS, CITY, STATE, ZIP

Transistor Town Corporation of America   **student's name**

1 TTCA Building   **student's address**

New York, New York 10019

3 WHAT IS YOUR COMPLAINT? *(Also be sure to enclose photocopies of contracts, receipts, cancelled checks or other relevant documents.)*

My CD player, which is still under its original 90-day warranty, goes into fast forward when ''Play'' is selected. Ms.

Matthews of the local Transistor Town store refuses to offer service, replacement, or refund. Likewise, Mr. Gruntle and

Mr. Rom, the customer service manager and president respectively, refuse to provide satisfaction.

4 WHAT SETTLEMENT WOULD YOU CONSIDER FAIR?

service, replacement, or refund

Upon receiving your form and copies of all documentation, the BBB called the firm and notified them of your complaint. The company offered to replace the CD player free of charge and sent you a certificate for ten free compact discs of your choice! Had the firm believed they were right and you were wrong, the BBB would have offered arbitration, a situation in which an unbiased BBB representative hears the facts and settles the dispute. Sometimes, firms are unwilling to provide satisfaction or submit to arbitration. At the very least, the BBB notes the incident in their files so that future prospective customers can be warned about the firm. If necessary, the BBB contacts the appropriate law enforcement agencies. If the problem involves a significant amount of money, you may want to consult an attorney.

Multiple Choice

Choose the response which best answers the question or completes the sentence.

__C__ 1. Which of the following would be considered an "impulse purchase"?
   A. the purchase of a part to fix a leaking faucet
   B. the purchase of laundry detergent that was accidentally left off a shopping list
   C. the purchase of a piece of jewelry from a television shopping network for which funds were not budgeted
   D. the purchase of needed clothing on sale at a department store

__D__ 2. What should be the first category in every Christian's household budget?
   A. savings
   B. food
   C. shelter
   D. none of the above

__A, D__ 3. Which of the following would *not* be included in a homeowner's escrow account? (Choose all that apply.)
   A. collision insurance
   B. property taxes
   C. property insurance
   D. maintenance expenses

__B__ 4. Which of the following is the type of insurance usually required by lenders to be carried on an automobile for which there is a loan outstanding?
   A. uninsured motorist
   B. collision
   C. comprehensive
   D. liability

__A__ 5. Whom might you contact for information about a local business of questionable honesty?
   A. Better Business Bureau
   B. Consumers Union
   C. Federal Trade Commission
   D. local police

__D__ 6. Which of the following is an example of the "bait and switch" method of sales?
   A. the high-pressure promotion of a product which was not advertised
   B. the promise of a valuable prize *only* if the customer purchases a certain product
   C. advertising nonexistent products in magazines and newspapers
   D. advertising a very low-priced, unobtainable product to lure consumers and then offering a higher-priced product

Modified True/False

If the statement is true, write the word *true* in the blank. If it is false, change the underlined words to make the statement true. Write the correct word(s) in the blank.

____do____ 1. Because the "love of money is the root of all evil," it is probably best if Christians do <u>not</u> engage in financial planning.

____True____ 2. One benefit of budgeting is that by doing so one can avoid <u>potential conflicts</u> with other family members.

__significantly more__ 3. Going out to dinner in restaurants is usually <u>less</u> expensive than preparing one's own meals.

____True____ 4. Most states require owners of automobiles to carry <u>liability</u> insurance.

____buyer____ 5. The Latin phrase "caveat emptor" literally means "let the <u>seller</u> beware!"

Economics

Chapter 16

Activity 1

Extent of Use of Consumer Credit

Examine the table below and answer the questions that follow.

		Consumer Credit Outstanding (Billions of Dollars)					
At End of Year	Non-Installment Credit	Installment & Revolving Credit				Total Consumer Credit Outstanding	Percentage Growth from Previous Period ((Pn-Po)/Po) x 100
		Total Installment Credit	Automobile	Revolving	Other		
1950	$8.129	$15.166	$6.035	$ —	$9.131	$23.295	
1955	12.076	29.809	13.485	—	16.324	41.885	79.80%
1960	15.700	44.335	18.108	—	26.227	60.035	*43.33*
1965	23.134	72.814	29.378	—	43.436	95.948	*59.82*
1970	27.695	103.905	36.348	4.900	62.657	131.600	*37.16*
1975	37.920	167.043	56.989	14.507	95.547	204.963	*55.75*
1980	52.115	298.154	111.991	55.111	131.053	350.269	*70.89*
1985	73.631	517.660	210.238	121.758	185.664	591.291	*68.81*
1990	59.509	738.765	284.739	222.552	231.474	798.274	*35.01*
1991	50.551	733.510	260.8981	243.564	229.048	784.061	*-1.78*
1992	52.082	741.093	259.627	254.299	227.167	793.175	*1.16*
1993*	50.322	783.115	277.576	279.273	226.266	833.437	*5.08*

*November
Source: Economic Report of the President, 1994 (Washington, D.C., 1994), Table B-76.

1. In what year did total consumer credit outstanding reach a peak? *1993* _____

2. Fill in the column labeled "Percentage Growth from Previous Period." Hint: To calculate growth, use the following formula: **(($ from latest period - $ from prior period) / $ from prior period) × 100**. For example, growth of total consumer credit outstanding between 1950 and 1955 = (($41.885 billion - $23.295 billion) / $23.295 billion) × 100 = 79.80%.

3. Which of the five-year periods between 1950 and 1990 saw the fastest growth? The slowest growth? *The fastest growth took place in the 1950-55 period; the slowest growth took place in the 1985-90* _____ *period.*

4. Among automobile, revolving, and other, which category experienced the greatest growth between 1970 and 1993? (Hint: Use the formula from question #2.) *Revolving credit experienced the* _____ *most growth—5,599.45%.*

Economics

Managing Revolving Credit

The Bible provides many cautions about credit. Revolving (or open-account) credit, if used injudiciously, will lead to financial ruin faster than any other type of credit. Revolving credit is most closely associated with credit cards, and a bit of advice to Christians is in order. First, if you believe that you need revolving credit, then keep only one bank credit card (such as MasterCard or Visa) and two or three oil company credit cards (which require the holder to pay all of the monthly charges each month). Second, use cards with low annual percentage interest rates (APR) and no additional fees. One bank credit card once advertised a "low" 13% APR, but the fine print said that if the balance of the account fell below $5,000 an "insurance fee" of 8% would be levied against the unpaid balance. Thus, any balances carried below $5,000 would carry an APR of 21%. Third, pay your entire balance at the end of the month. This usually ensures that no interest will need to be paid and will keep credit balances from getting out of control. Some people use a credit card to purchase items even when they have the money in their checking account to make the purchase. They deduct the amount of the charge from their check register to ensure that they will have the money to pay the bill when it arrives. The benefit of this system is that it leaves cash in an interest-bearing checking account for one more month, earning interest for the account holder. Fourth, insist that the credit card company not give you high credit limits. High credit limits can be a temptation to overspend. Fifth, do not use credit cards for everyday purchases at grocery stores and service stations. Use cash. Sixth, avoid temptation and possible theft by not carrying around credit cards, except a bank card for emergencies. Seventh, keep your eyes on your card when it is in the hands of another person. Knowledgeable thieves do not need the actual plastic card to charge items to your account as long as they know your credit card number and its expiration date. Thus, when you make a charge purchase, insist on keeping the carbon paper found between the customer and merchant receipts. Thieves are only too happy to purchase those discarded carbons. If a merchant "goofs" in the transaction and must run your card through the imprinter again, ask for all parts of the flawed receipt. Finally, keep your tissue receipts after each transaction and compare them to the bill when it arrives in order to audit each charge.

Reading the Credit Statement

On the next page is an example of a credit card monthly billing statement. Knowing how to read the statement will help you avoid credit problems. The first item to note is the billing date. The billing date, or the statement date, is the last day of the transaction reporting period. In our example the date is May 26, 1994. Any transaction made after that date will go on the next statement. The due date is the latest date that the credit card company must receive your payment in order to be credited on the next statement. Mr. Doe's payment must reach The First Bank by June 20, 1994. If the bill is to be paid in full each month, be sure your check for the entire balance reaches the credit card company by this date; otherwise, a finance charge will be added to next month's bill. If no payment is received by this date, the card holder is past due, and the company has legal right to begin collection procedures. Many companies impose a late fee if payment is not received by the due date.

The **balance** is the sum of any balance left over from the previous month plus any new purchases, cash advances, and finance charges and less any payments. Mr. Doe's balance is $263.56. The **minimum payment** is the minimum amount that the card holder can elect to pay by the due date if he chooses not to pay in full. In our example, the minimum payment is 5% of the total balance outstanding ($263.56 $\times$ .05 = $13.18). The **transaction dates** are the dates that purchases or payments were made; **posting dates** are the dates on which the credit card company recorded the transactions. The **average daily balance** is the sum of each day's balance during the billing cycle divided by the number of days in the billing cycle. The **credit limit** is the maximum balance that the account may have outstanding at any time. If the account holder charges more than his credit limit, the company may levy an overlimit fee or may require him to pay the overage immediately. The **available credit** is the difference between the credit limit and the current balance. Mr. Doe has a credit limit of $1,000, a current balance of $263.56, and an available credit amount of $736.44. Finally, interest rates are given as both annual percentage rates and as periodic (daily) rates. In our example, the APR on purchases is 18%, and the periodic rate is .0493% (18%/365 days). The APR for cash advances (withdrawals of cash from the credit account at the bank) is 15%, and the periodic rate is .0411% (15%/365).

MasterCard
589 West Main Street
Anytown, SC 29600

Account Number
5555 4444 3333 2222

The First Bank
589 West Main Street
Anytown, SC 29600

John L. Doe
211 Terrace Place
Anytown, SC 29601

Statement Date:	Payment Due Date:	PAY	Total New Balance:	OR AT LEAST	Total Minimum Payment:	Amount Paid:
05/26/94	06/20/94		$263.56		13.18	$_____

Reference	Transaction Date		Posting Date		Description of Transaction	Amount
7530586723	4	26	4	29	Flowers by Rita	27.95
7830581740	4	28	5	01	Montgomery Bicycle	84.63
3650573928	4	29	5	01	Anytown Automotive	102.54
2956730047	5	12	5	15	The Bookrack	14.76
3434839058	5	13	5	18	Tiretown	33.68
8832143120	5	13	5	18	Payment	145.97

SEND WRITTEN INQUIRIES TO:

DIRECT TELEPHONE INQUIRIES TO:

The First Bank
589 West Main Street
Anytown, SC 29600
(803) 555-0000

Account Number: **MasterCard**
5555 4444 3333 2222

Statement Date: 5/26/94	Minimum Payment: 13.18	Average Daily Balance
Days in Billing: 31	Credit Limit: 1,000.00	Purchases: 301.31
Next Statement Date: 6/26/94	Available Credit: 736.44	Cash Advances: .00

	Purchases	Cash Advances	Total
Previous Balance	145.97	.00	145.97
(-) Less Payments	145.97	.00	145.97
(-) Less Credits	.00	.00	.00
(+) Plus New Purchases	263.56	.00	263.56
(+) Plus Debits	.00	.00	.00
(+) Plus Cash Advances	.00	.00	.00
+ FINANCE CHARGES	.00	.00	.00
= New Balance	263.56	.00	263.56

	Purchases	Cash Advances
Periodic Rates:	.0493%	.0411%
Annual Percentage Rates:	18.00%	15.00%

Now that you are familiar with a billing statement, use the following information to complete the blank billing statement on the next page.

The card holder is Miss Matilda Grub of 301 Charger Avenue, San Diego, California 92117.

The statement date is December 13, 1995, and the payment is due 25 days after the statement date.

The revolving account is a VISA account #2621 9620 7559 9060 3818 0024 2510 held by The First Bank. The bank's address is 1 The First Building, San Diego, California 92115. The bank's telephone number is (619) 555-1212.

There are 31 days in each billing cycle. Thus, the next statement date will be 31 days after the most recent statement date.

Matilda had the following activity during this statement cycle:

She purchased a new Bible from the Hills Bible Bookstore on December 1 for $47.63. The transaction (Ref # 6936254011) was posted to the account on December 4.

She had her car serviced at City Ford on December 10 at a cost of $82.55. The transaction (Ref # 5527364090) was posted to the account on December 11.

The balance on her November statement was $27.25, which she paid in full on December 11. The transaction (Ref. #9485038421) was posted to the account on December 13.

Matilda's credit limit is $500.00.

The APR on the credit card is 21.00% for purchases and 17.00% for advances.

The First Bank has a policy that the minimum payment on a VISA account shall be 5% of the outstanding balance or $10.00, whichever is greater.

VISA
1 The First Building
San Diego, CA 92115

Account Number
2621 9620 7559 9060 3818 0024 2510

The First Bank   **Matilda Grub**
1 The First Building   **301 Charger Avenue**
San Diego, CA 92115   **San Diego, CA 92117**

Statement Date:	Payment Due Date:		PAY	Total New Balance:	OR AT LEAST	Total Minimum Payment:	Amount Paid:
12/13/95	**01/07/96**			**130.18**		**10.00**	$

Reference	Transaction Date		Posting Date		Description of Transaction	Amount
6936254011	12	01	12	04	**Hills Bible Bookstore**	47.63
5527364090	12	10	12	11	**City Ford**	82.55
9485038421	12	11	12	13	**Payment**	27.25

SEND WRITTEN INQUIRIES TO: **The First Bank**
1 The First Building
San Diego, CA 92115

DIRECT TELEPHONE INQUIRIES TO: **(619) 555-1212**

Account Number: **VISA**
2621 9620 7559 9060 3818 0024 2510

Statement Date:	Minimum Payment:	Average Daily Balance
12/31/95	**10.00**	Purchases: 43.77
Days in Billing:	Credit Limit:	
31	**500.00**	
		Cash Advances: .00
Next Statement Date:	Available Credit:	
1/31/96	**369.82**	

	Purchases	Cash Advances	Total
Previous Balance	**27.25**	**.00**	**27.25**
(-) Less Payments	**27.25**	**.00**	**27.25**
(-) Less Credits	**.00**	**.00**	**.00**
(+) Plus New Purchases	**130.18**	**.00**	**130.18**
(+) Plus Debits	**.00**	**.00**	**.00**
(+) Plus Cash Advances	**.00**	**.00**	**.00**
+ FINANCE CHARGES	**.00**	**.00**	**.00**
= New Balance	**130.18**	**.00**	**130.18**

	Purchases	Cash Advances	
Periodic Rates:	**.0575%**	**.0466%**	
Annual Percentage Rates:	**21.00%**	**17.00%**	

Computing the Average Daily Balance

Those who offer credit cards and other forms of revolving credit do so with full intention of making money from interest on outstanding balances. Card holders who pay off their balances each month are not the kind of customers revolving creditors prefer. Zealous to make as much money as possible, revolving creditors use many methods to compute finance charges on outstanding balances. One of the most popular methods is the **Average Daily Balance** method. The Average Daily Balance method of computing finance charges is one in which the periodic rate is multiplied by the average daily balance each day in the billing cycle. Some revolving creditors add new purchases to the average daily balance as soon as the purchases are made, while others do not add the new purchases until the next billing cycle.

The following example demonstrates the way to calculate the average daily balance. The original credit card billing statement which we used for John L. Doe (see p. 136) had an average daily balance of $301.31 for purchases. This amount was achieved by computing the balance on the account for each day of the billing cycle, adding the balances, and then dividing the sum by the number of days in the cycle.

4/26	145.97	(Balance due on the last statement)
4/27	145.97	
4/28	145.97	
4/29	173.92	($145.97 + $27.95 posted charge)
4/30	173.92	
5/01	361.09	($173.92 + $84.63 + $102.54 posted charges)
5/02	361.09	
5/03	361.09	
5/04	361.09	
5/05	361.09	
5/06	361.09	
5/07	361.09	
5/08	361.09	
5/09	361.09	
5/10	361.09	
5/11	361.09	
5/12	361.09	
5/13	361.09	
5/14	361.09	
5/15	375.85	($361.09 + $14.76 posted charge)
5/16	375.85	
5/17	375.85	
5/18	263.56	($375.85 + $33.68 posted charge − $145.97 posted payment
5/19	263.56	
5/20	263.56	
5/21	263.56	
5/22	263.56	
5/23	263.56	
5/24	263.56	
5/25	263.56	
5/26	263.56	
SUM	$9,340.60	

$$\$9,340.60 \,/\, 31 = \$301.31 \text{ AVERAGE DAILY BALANCE}$$

If a person had an average daily balance of $400.00 in purchases and an APR of 21.00%, the finance charge would be $400 × (21.00%/365 days) = $23.01. In John Doe's case, the company was not using the Average Daily Balance method. Fortunately for Mr. Doe, interest was not being charged on balances until they had accumulated past the payment due date.

The following is a copy of John Doe's next credit card statement. Calculate the average daily balance and write in the amount on the statement.

MasterCard
589 West Main Street
Anytown, SC 29600

Account Number

5555 4444 3333 2222

The First Bank	**John L. Doe**
589 West Main Street	**211 Terrace Place**
Anytown, SC 29600	**Anytown, SC 29601**

Statement Date:	Payment Due Date:	**PAY**	Total New Balance:	**OR AT LEAST**	Total Minimum Payment:	Amount Paid:
06/26/94	07/20/94		$236.56		13.18	$

Reference	Transaction Date		Posting Date		Description of Transaction	Amount
4284759211	5	27	5	29	**Sunshine Farms**	10.24
4957749301	5	27	5	29	**Safeway Drugstore**	24.51
5069384274	5	31	6	02	**5th Street Cleaners**	6.10
2315364792	6	04	6	07	**Roebuck Dept. Store**	121.32
4961833983	6	15	6	20	**Annual Fee**	50.00
4456090087	6	17	6	20	**Payment**	263.56

SEND WRITTEN INQUIRIES TO:

DIRECT TELEPHONE INQUIRIES TO:

The First Bank
589 West Main Street
Anytown, SC 29600
(803) 555-0000

Account Number: **MasterCard**
5555 4444 3333 2222

Statement Date: **6/26/94**	Minimum Payment: **10.61**	Average Daily Balance
Days in Billing: **31**	Credit Limit: **1,000.00**	Purchases: ___**331.04**___
Next Statement Date: **7/27/94**	Available Credit: **787.83**	Cash Advances: .00

	Purchases	Cash Advances	Total
Previous Balance	263.56	.00	263.56
(-) Less Payments	263.56	.00	263.56
(-) Less Credits	.00	.00	.00
(+) Plus New Purchases	212.17	.00	212.17
(+) Plus Debits	.00	.00	.00
(+) Plus Cash Advances	.00	.00	.00
+ FINANCE CHARGES	.00	.00	.00
= New Balance	212.17	.00	212.17

	Purchases	Cash Advances
Periodic Rates:	.0493%	.0411%
Annual Percentage Rates:	18.00%	15.00%

Average Daily Balance Calculation Sheet:

Date	Balance	
5/27	263.56	*(Balance due on the last statement)*
5/28	263.56	
5/29	298.31	*($263.56 + $10.24 + $24.51 posted charges)*
5/30	298.31	
5/31	298.31	
6/01	298.31	
6/02	304.41	*($298.31 + $6.10 posted charge)*
6/03	304.41	
6/04	304.41	
6/05	304.41	
6/06	304.41	
6/07	425.73	*($304.41 + $121.32 posted charge)*
6/08	425.73	
6/09	425.73	
6/10	425.73	
6/11	425.73	
6/12	425.73	
6/13	425.73	
6/14	425.73	
6/15	425.73	
6/16	425.73	
6/17	425.73	
6/18	425.73	
6/19	425.73	
6/20	212.17	*($425.73 + $50.00 posted charge − $263.56 posted payment)*
6/21	212.17	
6/22	212.17	
6/23	212.17	
6/24	212.17	
6/25	212.17	
6/26	212.17	
SUM	$10,262.09	

$10,262.09 / 31 = $331.04 AVERAGE DAILY BALANCE

Economics

Credit Application, Scoring, and Qualification

Completing a Credit Application

To borrow money from a bank or a savings and loan association, you must first truthfully fill out a credit application. Fill out this credit application using the information on the next page.

[X] INDIVIDUAL CREDIT—Not relying on the assets of another person as the basis of repayment of the credit requested. Complete Section A. If the requested credit is to be secured, also complete Sections C and D.

[ ] JOINT CREDIT WITH ANOTHER PERSON—Complete Sections A and B. If the requested credit is to be secured, also complete Sections C and D.

Consumer Application
(Not for Fair Housing Act Loans)

If this loan will be secured by real estate, you can choose your own attorney and insurance agent.

Attorney: _____

Insurance Agent (Hazard) _____

(Flood) _____

AMOUNT REQUESTED **$8,000**	PURPOSE OF LOAN **purchase of used car**

SECTION A—INFORMATION REGARDING APPLICANT

NAME: **student's name** FIRST, MIDDLE, LAST	AGE **29**	BIRTHDATE **9/4/XX** +15
PRESENT ADDRESS **student's address**	YRS. THERE **8**	SOC. SEC. NO. **Answers will vary.** +18

CITY **Answers will vary.**	STATE **Answers will vary.**	ZIP **Answers will vary.**	TELEPHONE NUMBER **Answers will vary.** +11

PREVIOUS ADDRESS **None**		YEARS THERE _____

NAME AND ADDRESS OF PRESENT EMPLOYER **Smith Construction**	TELEPHONE NUMBER **Answers will vary.**

POSITION OR TITLE **Foreman**	LENGTH OF EMPLOYMENT **4** Years **0** Months +06

PRESENT SALARY OR COMMISSION [X] NET [ ] GROSS $ **3,500** PER **Mo.**	NUMBER OF DEPENDENTS **4**	AGES OF DEPENDENTS **27, 4, 3, 1** +16

OTHER INCOME $ _____ PER _____	SOURCES OF OTHER INCOME **None**	IS ANY INCOME LISTED IN THIS SECTION LIKELY TO BE REDUCED BEFORE THE CREDIT REQUESTED IS PAID OFF?	[ ] YES [ ] NO

NAME AND ADDRESS OF PREVIOUS EMPLOYER **None**	YEARS THERE

NAME OF NEAREST RELATIVE NOT LIVING WITH YOU	RELATIONSHIP

ADDRESS	TELEPHONE NUMBER

OUTSTANDING DEBTS (INCLUDE CHARGE ACCOUNTS, INSTALLMENT CONTRACTS, CREDIT CARDS, RENT, MORTGAGES, ETC.)

CREDITOR	TYPE OF DEBT OR ACCT. NO.	NAME IN WHICH ACCT. CARRIED	ORIGINAL DEBT	PRESENT BALANCE	PAST DUE?	MONTHLY PAYMENTS	
(LANDLORD OR MORTGAGE HOLDER) **Robert Reynolds**	[X] RENT PAYMENT [ ] MORTGAGE	**student's name**				$485	–40
1. **Sears**	123456789	**student's name**		$500		$25	+06
2.							
3.							
BANK REFERENCE **The First Bank**	[X] CHECKING [X] SAVINGS	[ ] CREDIT CARD [ ] REAL ESTATE	[ ] INSTALLMENT LOAN [ ] COMMERCIAL LOAN	TOTAL PAYMENTS			+30 62

OTHER OBLIGATIONS—(E.G., LIABILITY TO PAY ALIMONY, CHILD SUPPORT, SEPARATE MAINTENANCE. USE SEPARATE SHEET IF NECESSARY.)

[ ] If checked here, the collateral involved is being acquired with the proceeds of the loan hereby applied for and Association may disburse proceeds directly to Seller of said collateral.

The collateral is being used primarily for: [ ] Business   [ ] Personal, family, household use   [ ] Farming

WARRANTY OF APPLICANT(S)

The undersigned Applicant(s) warrants and represents that all statements, representations and warranties appearing hereon are correct, being made by them (and expressly relied upon by the Association) to induce this Association to approve their within Loan Application. I specifically additionally here warrant, unless otherwise noted herein: That title to any collateral securing this loan is free and clear of all encumbrances and will remain so until this is fully repaid.

____**student's signature**____ (SEAL)   _____ (SEAL)
APPLICANT   CO-APPLICANT/GUARANTOR

You want to borrow $8,000 from The First Bank, 1 The First Building, Westchester, MO, for the purchase of a used car.

Your age is 29, and your date of birth is September 4 (adjust the year to fit).

You rent the home in which you live from Robert Reynolds for $485 per month.

You have lived at your current residence for eight years. You have no previous residence.

Enter your own address and telephone number.

You have a spouse (age 27) and three children (ages 4, 3, and 1) for a total of four dependents.

You have been a foreman at Smith Construction for four years. You have no previous employment.

Your spouse is not employed, and your net monthly income is $3,500.

You have a checking account at The First Bank and a savings account.

You are applying for this loan without a co-applicant.

You have no bank cards (i.e., MasterCard or VISA), travel cards (i.e., American Express), or entertainment cards (i.e., Diner's Club).

You have a Sears credit card (#123456789) with a balance outstanding of $500 and a monthly payment of $25. Your payment history has been excellent.

You state that besides your Sears credit card, you have no other credit experience.

Credit Scoring

While some of the questions asked on a standard credit application are quite personal, they are geared to guide the potential lender to a fair credit decision that will be profitable for the institution and will guarantee that the borrower does not become overburdened with debt. To guard against unfair discrimination in lending, many large institutional lenders use the "discriminant analysis" or "credit scoring" method to judge the credit worthiness of applicants. After conducting extensive audits of credit applications of both good and bad borrowers, lenders isolate the characteristics that are statistically significant in showing the applicant's character and ability to repay. Each characteristic is further broken down into favorable and unfavorable gradations, with progressively higher scores being assigned to progressively more attractive characteristics.

Given the credit scoring system below, score your credit application on the preceding page (in the column to the right of the application).

CREDIT SCORING ITEMS AND SCORES

Age:		Years at current address:	
< 25 years old	(+10)	< 1 year	(−13)
25 - 29 years old	(+15)	1 - 2 years	(−04)
30 - 34 years old	(+13)	3 years	(000)
35 - 39 years old	(+08)	4 - 5 years	(+06)
40 - 44 years old	(+18)	6 - 9 years	(+18)
45 - 49 years old	(+23)	> 9 years	(+33)
> 49 years old	(+31)		
		Years at current job:	
Residence status:		< 1 year	(−18)
Own your home	(+38)	1 - 3 years	(000)
Rent your home	(−40)	4 - 6 years	(+06)
Other (live with parents, etc.)	(000)	7 - 8 years	(+11)
		> 8 years	(+20)

Types of bank accounts currently held:

Checking & savings	(+30)
Savings only	(+14)
Checking only	(+08)
Neither	(000)

Do you have a telephone?

Yes	(+11)
No	(000)

How many major department store credit cards do you have?

None	(000)
1 - 2	(+06)
3 or more	(+10)

How many loans from small finance companies do you have (besides automobile financing companies)?

None	(000)
1 only	(–05)
> 1	(–15)

Do you have a bank loan currently outstanding?

Yes	(+04)
No	(000)

How many bank, travel, and entertainment cards do you have?

None	(000)
1 only	(–05)
> 1	(–15)

How many marginal (poor) credit references do you have?

None	(000)
1 or more	(–08)

Annual income:

< $14,000	(–09)
14,001 - 21,000	(000)
21,001 - 26,000	(+06)
26,001 - 35,000	(+10)
> 35,000	(+16)

The policy of the bank to which you have applied is that if the applicant's credit score is—

131 to 193	Verify employment and income. Approve loan.
068 to 129	Verify employment and income. Verify credit references via credit bureau. Approve loan
004 to 067	Verify employment and income. Verify credit references via credit bureau. Require qualified cosigner (under section 1B of the Statement of Action Taken form). The applicant has two weeks to respond. Approve loan.
- 92 to 003	Reject (under section 2 of Statement of Action Taken form).

Given the above policies, assume that the bank has requested and received all required verifications. On the next page is a ''Statement of Action Taken.'' Complete the form in the way that the bank would deem necessary based upon your credit score. The loan officer's name is Chad Mallory.

Statement of Action Taken

Address

_____1 The First Building_____

_____Westchester , MO_____ Zip _____

Phone _____ Date _____

To: _student's name and address_ _____

_____

_____

1. Thank you for your request for $_____8,000_____ to _____purchase a used automobile ._____

     _____A. We regret to inform you that we have taken the following action:

         _____(a) Denied your request

         _____(b) Not accepted you as an endorser

         _____(c) Other _____

     __X__ B. We are unable to offer you credit on the terms you requested for the reason(s) listed.

          We can, however, offer you credit on the following terms: _____**To approve this loan request, we will**_____

          _**require a qualifying cosigner .**_____

          If this offer is acceptable to you, please notify us at the above address by _____

                                                                Date

     _____C. We require the following information to evaluate your application:

          _____

          If we do not receive this information by _____, we will be unable to give further

          consideration to your credit request.   (Date)

2. We have taken this action or made this counteroffer for the following principal reason(s):

_____(a) Insufficient number of credit references provided	_____(m)	Unable to verify residence
_____(b) Unable to verify credit references	_____(n)	No credit file
_____(c) Temporary or irregular employment	_____(o)	Insufficient credit file
_____(d) Unable to verify employment	_____(p)	Delinquent past or present credit
_____(e) Length of employment		obligations with others
_____(f) Insufficient income for amount of credit requested	_____(q)	Garnishment, attachment, foreclosure,
_____(g) Excessive obligations in relation to income		repossession, or suit
_____(h) Unable to verify income	_____(r)	Bankruptcy
_____(i) Limited credit experience	_____(s)	Previous delinquent credit obligations
_____(j) Amount requested exceeds loan value of collateral		with us
_____(k) Too short a period of residence	_____(t)	Other, specify _____
_____(l) Temporary residence		_____

3. If this section is completed, our decision was based in part on information we received from an outside source or the failure of that source to provide sufficient information to us.

    Our credit decision was based in whole or in part on information obtained in a report from the consumer reporting agency listed below. The agency is unable to supply specific reasons why we have denied your request. You do, however, have the right under the Fair Credit Reporting Act to know the information contained in your credit file. Any questions regarding such information should be directed to:

    Name of agency _____

    Street address and phone _____

    _____

    _____ Information was obtained from an outside source other than a consumer reporting agency. You have the right to make a written request of us within 60 days for disclosure of the nature of this information.

The Federal Equal Credit Opportunity Act prohibits creditors from discriminating against credit applicants on the basis of race, color, religion, national origin, sex, marital status, age (provided that the applicant has the capacity to enter into a binding contract) because all or part of the applicant's income derives from any public assistance program; or because the applicant has in good faith exercised any right under the Consumer Credit Protection Act. The federal agency that administers compliance with the law concerning this creditor is the Federal Deposit Insurance Corporation, 245 Peachtree Center Ave. N.E., Suite 1200, Atlanta, GA 30303.

If you have any questions, contact us at the address or phone number above.   _Chad Mallory_

                                                                     _____

                                                                     Loan officer

Note & Security Agreement

After receiving the Statement of Action Taken, you visited Mr. Mallory and convinced him that you are not a bad credit risk. He decided to grant the loan without requiring a cosigner. Use the following information to complete the Note & Security Agreement.

Proceeds (amount of the loan) are $8,000.

The loan will have a fixed interest rate of 13.00%.

For "Office" place your city's name.

The note will be note number 78-6082.

The term of the loan will be for 36 months, beginning on the first day of next month (you enter the appropriate date).

To find the monthly payment, use the table found in your text on page 265.

The total of payments is found by multiplying the payment by the term of the loan.

Find the Total Finance Charge by subtracting the amount financed from the total of payments.

There are no registration or filing fees.

You are giving the bank a security interest in the "goods or property being purchased."

You do not wish to purchase credit life or disability insurance.

Mr. Mallory's loan officer number is 2620.

You are authorizing the bank to draft your checking account (#54321) for the monthly payment.

The car you are purchasing is a used 199X Pontiac 6000 LS, four-door sedan, serial number H6000M3037525LS.

Note and Security Agreement

Borrower _____ *student's name* _____ Date _____ *today's date* _____, 19 **XX** Proceeds $ _____ **8,000** _____ **13** %

Address _____ *student's address* _____ Office _____ *name of city* _____

Phone *student's phone no.* Note # _____ **78-6082** _____

We are happy to be able to make this loan to you. We want you to understand how your loan works, so read this agreement carefully and ask us if we have not made part of it clear to you. If you agree to be bound by the promises in this agreement, sign your name below. If more than one person signs, each will be responsible for repaying the loan in full. The words "you" and "your" refer to the borrower and anyone else who signs this agreement. "BANK" refers to the lending institution.

☐ If checked here, your loan has a variable interest rate of _____ (index) plus _____ percent ☐ but never less than _____ percent.

Amount Financed	FINANCE CHARGE	Total of Payments	ANNUAL PERCENTAGE RATE	You have the right to receive at this time an itemization of the Amount Financed. Please initial here if you want an itemization.
The amount of credit provided to you or on your behalf	*The dollar amount the credit will cost*	*The amount you will have paid after you have made all payments as scheduled*	*The cost of your credit as a yearly rate*	
$ **8,000**	$ **1,702.72**	$ **9,702.72**	**13.00** %	_____

☐ **Variable Rate Loans:**

1) The interest rate may increase during the term of this loan if ☐ the BANK's Prime Rate increases ☐ The Wall Street Journal Prime Interest Rate increases ☐ Other _____

2) Any increase will take the form of: ☐ more payments of the same amount ☐ larger payments ☐ a larger amount due at maturity

3) The rate on this loan will not rise above _____ %.

4) The rate may not increase more often than _____.

5) If this loan is secured by your principal dwelling and is over one year: Your loan contains a variable rate feature. Disclosures about the variable rate feature have been provided to you earlier.
Your payment schedule will be:

Number of Payments	Amount of Payments	When Payments Are Due
36	**$269.52**	**Answers will vary.**

Registration and Filing Fees $ _____.

Security: You are giving the BANK a security interest in:
☒ the goods or property being purchased ☐ motor vehicles ☐ other _____
Collateral securing other loans (but not including your primary residence or household goods) may also secure this loan.

Late Charges: If your installment payment is 10 days late, you will be charged $10.00 or 5% of the payment, whichever is less.

Prepayment: If you pay off early, you will not have to pay an interest penalty and you may be entitled to a refund of part of the credit insurance premium. *Please read the rest of this Agreement for additional information about nonpayment, default, any required repayment in full before the scheduled date, and prepayment refunds and penalties.*

Credit Insurance: Credit life insurance and credit disability insurance are not required to obtain this loan and will not be provided unless you sign here, agreeing to pay the premium given below.

Credit Life: Insured _____ Premium $ _____ Date _____ Birthdate _____
Insured _____ Date _____ Birthdate _____
Credit Disability: Insured _____ Premium $ _____ Date _____ Birthdate _____

Promise to Pay: You promise to pay the BANK the amount financed plus finance charges calculated before and after maturity at the rate(s), according to the payment schedule(s), and at the office set forth herein. You agree to waive presentment for payment, protest and notice of dishonor and non-payment of this Note. You waive defense on the ground of any extension of time or release of other borrowers, guarantors, owners, or collateral. Each borrower acknowledges receipt of a copy of this Note fully completed prior to signing.
The terms and conditions printed on both sides of this instrument are part of this Note.

Borrower _____ *student's name* _____ (seal) For BANK use only _____ Officer # _____ **2620**

Borrower _____ (seal) Purpose _____

Borrower _____ (seal) Social Security # _____

I authorize the BANK to draft my account (# _____ **54321** _____) for any amount that may be due.
Signature of borrower _____ *student's signature* _____

Security Agreement: *If this section is not completed, there is no specific collateral for this loan. "You" in this section refers to anyone who signs as owner. Each person in whose name the collateral is titled must sign this section, unless a separate mortgage or other security agreement has been signed. Unless the security you pledge is in the possession of the BANK, you promise to maintain adequate insurance on the collateral, with the BANK named as lienholder on the policy. You may obtain insurance from anyone you want that is acceptable to the BANK. If you fail to purchase this insurance, the BANK may purchase the insurance and add its cost to your loan.*

The collateral for this loan is described on this Mortgage dated _____ **Answers will vary.** _____, 19 **XX** for $ _____ **8,000**
As collateral for this loan, you give the BANK a security interest in the following property:

New or Used	Year	Make	Type of Body	Serial Number
used	**199X**	**Pontiac 6000 LS**	**4-door sedan**	**H6000M3037525LS**

☐ The collateral is described on the attached Schedule A. ☐ If checked, sign Consumer Code Agreement on reverse.

Owner _____ *student's signature* _____ Owner _____

Economics

Multiple Choice

Choose the response which best answers the question or completes the sentence.

___B___ 1. According to your text, excluding a home mortgage, at what point does a person's credit become "overextended"?
  A. 5% of a person's take-home pay
  B. 20% of a person's take-home pay
  C. 20% of a person's gross pay
  D. 5% of a person's gross pay

___D___ 2. According to your text, which of the following represent the two purposes for consumer borrowing?
  A. fixed expenses and revolving expenses
  B. installment and revolving expenses
  C. impulse borrowing and investment borrowing
  D. consumption borrowing and investment borrowing

___B___ 3. What is the "term" of a loan?
  A. the total interest one will pay on the loan
  B. the number of months of the loan
  C. the sum of all of the payments of the loan
  D. the interest rate of the loan

___C___ 4. A table which illustrates the amount of principal, interest, and remaining balance after each loan payment is known as a(n)
  A. loan table.
  B. loan schedule.
  C. amortization schedule.
  D. loan amortization schedule table.

___B___ 5. A _____ clause stipulates that the balance of the loan's principal is due on the last payment date.
  A. bubble
  B. balloon
  C. principal
  D. acceleration

___A___ 6. What is used for collateral on a first mortgage?
  A. a house
  B. the equity one has in one's house
  C. a savings assignment
  D. some item of value such as jewelry

Modified True/False

If the statement is true, write the word *true* in the blank. If it is false, change the underlined word(s) to make the statement true. Write the correct word(s) in the blank.

___A secured loan___ 1. An <u>unsecured loan</u> is backed by some form of collateral.

___Revolving credit___ 2. <u>Installment credit</u> is what is used when one wants an open-ended loan.

___True___ 3. "<u>Equity</u>" is the difference between a house's value and its outstanding loan balance.

___True___ 4. "<u>Character</u>" is the most important "C" of credit.

___seven years___ 5. Bad credit remains in one's credit report for <u>the lifetime of the person.</u>

Economics

©1995 BJU Press. Reproduction prohibited.

Maintaining a Checking Account

Writing Checks

Opening a checking account is a relatively simple proposition. Maintaining such an account is an altogether different prospect. On the following pages are several blank checks and deposit slips, a blank check register, and checks which were written to you during the month of April.

1. Follow the directions for each day.
2. Use each item in order. Do not tear out checks or deposit tickets. If you make a mistake writing a check or deposit ticket, cross it out and use the next one provided. Extra checks and deposit tickets have been provided for use in case of mistakes.
3. All expenditures will be by check.
4. Properly write each check indicated in the order given, beginning with check #101.
5. Enter all transactions into the check register and compute a balance after each transaction.
6. Examine all checks to be deposited for correctness and properly endorse all checks to be deposited.
7. Completely fill out deposit tickets as needed.
8. Upon receipt of your monthly statement, reconcile your account. Remember to subtract service charges!

April 1	Today is the day you open your checking account. Account name: Bob or Mary Kirkpatrick. The account is opened with an initial deposit of $1,127.35 consisting of Bob's regular biweekly $953.84 paycheck from the Siegel Corporation, a check for $100.00 from John Smith, and $73.51 in cash.
	Write a check to the Calvary Baptist Church for $180 for your tithe and offering. (Note: On this check and all others, you should make a notation on the "for" line to indicate the purpose of the check.)
	Write a check to the Second American Mortgage Company for $523.19, representing your April house payment.
	Your daughter needs a check for $40.00 made out to Calvary Christian School for the purchase of lunch tickets for the month of April.
	Write a check to Bell Northwest for your telephone charges for the month of March: $34.87.
	To celebrate payday you took your family to dinner. Write a check to Harris Steak House for $23.43.
April 3	You received a rebate check for $8.50 for your purchase of Bunny Batteries back around Christmas. Endorse the check and deposit it to your account.
	You went grocery shopping at the Diamond Food Store. Total bill: $185.43.
April 6	Two bills need to be paid today—Front Range Natural Gas Company (for March gas service): $64.33; Better Lawns and Soil magazine subscription: $17.99.
	You received a check from your brother-in-law Fred for the $250 he has owed you for ten years.
April 7	Three more bills are due today. Boy, are you getting tired of bills! Twenty-third Century Mutual Fund (deposit to investment account): $150.00; Gasco Oil Company (March gasoline): $54.23; Edison Electric Company (March electricity): $110.00.
April 15	It is payday again! Deposit your $953.84 paycheck.
	Write a check to Calvary Baptist Church for $110.00 for your tithe and offering.

It is not only payday but also April 15, and you know what that means! Write two checks in the following order: Internal Revenue Service, $57.00; State Department of Revenue, $102.00.

Payment is due to Calvary Christian School for your daughter's monthly school bill: $285.00.

April 17   You ordered some rosebushes through Rosebushes-by-Mail. Total check amount was $43.87.

April 20   A payment is due on your automobile loan. Make a check payable to The First Bank for $201.41.

April 21   You received a check from the Twenty-third Century Mutual Fund for $559.28. You deposit $500.00 of the check and receive the balance as cash back on the deposit.

April 22   You went to the Diamond Food Store again for groceries. Total bill: $193.55.

Your City Water Company bill of $143.22 is due today (for January through March water and sewer service).

Your quarterly life insurance premium is due today to the Federated Life Insurance Company: $110.00.

Your monthly automobile insurance bill is due today to the Farm State Insurance Company: $72.44.

April 23   You deposit an $800.00 personal check for the sale of a computer you had advertised in your local newspaper.

You received a bill from the Herald Star newspaper for $14.50, representing the cost of the classified advertising used to sell your computer.

April 30   Your bank notifies you that the $800.00 check you deposited was returned. The fellow who bought your computer wrote you a check from an account which did not have sufficient funds.

May 1   Payday again! $953.84.

Write a check to Calvary Baptist Church for $110.00 for your tithe and offering.

Write a check to the Second American Mortgage Company for $523.19, representing your May house payment.

Your daughter needs a check for $40.00 made out to Calvary Christian School for the purchase of lunch tickets for the month of May.

Write a check to Bell Northwest for your telephone charges for the month of April: $32.28.

May 7   You receive a checking account statement from The First Bank for your April checking account activity. Reconcile your check register with the bank's statement.

Siegel Corporation
Westchester, Missouri

001001

$\dfrac{00\text{-}001}{123}$

Date
04/01/XX

Void After 90 Days

PAY NINE HUNDRED FIFTY-THREE DOLLARS AND EIGHTY-FOUR CENTS $953.84

NET AMOUNT

TO THE
ORDER OF

Robert Kirkpatrick
11 Kendall Green Drive
Westchester, MO 64498

The First Bank
Westchester, Missouri

Jared P. Cooper

Treasurer

1450

2X-1000/1234

John Smith
P.O. Box 1500
Westchester, MO 64498

April 1, 19 *9X*

PAY TO THE
ORDER OF *Bob Kirkpatrick* $ *100.00*

One hundred and 00/100 ——————————— DOLLARS

Central Savings and Loan
Springfield, Missouri

John Smith

FOR _____

Bob or Mary Kirkpatrick
11 Kendall Green Drive
Westchester, MO 64498

DATE ____ **April 1,** ____ 19 **9X**
DEPOSITS MAY NOT BE AVAILABLE FOR IMMEDIATE WITHDRAWAL

_____
SIGN HERE IF CASH RECEIVED FROM DEPOSIT

CURRENCY	73	00
COIN		51
CHECKS	953	84
	100	00
TOTAL FROM OTHER SIDE		
TOTAL	1,127	35
LESS CASH	—	—
NET DEPOSIT	1,127	35

01-0000/0001

DEPOSIT TICKET

USE OTHER SIDE FOR
ADDITIONAL LISTINGS

TOTAL ITEMS
2

BE SURE EACH ITEM IS
PROPERLY ENDORSED

The First Bank
Westchester, Missouri

Deposit Slip / Endorsement Form

Endorsement Section 1

ENDORSE HERE

x *Bob Kirkpatrick*

DO NOT WRITE, STAMP, OR SIGN BELOW THIS LINE
◆ RESERVED FOR FINANCIAL INSTITUTION USE ◆

Endorsement Section 2

ENDORSE HERE

x *Robert Kirkpatrick*

DO NOT WRITE, STAMP, OR SIGN BELOW THIS LINE
◆ RESERVED FOR FINANCIAL INSTITUTION USE ◆

Deposit Slip

Please List Each Check Separately by Financial Institution Number

CHECKS	DOLLARS	CENTS
1		
2		
3		
4		
5		
6		
7		
8		
9		
10		
11		
12		
13		
14		
15		
16		

TOTAL THIS SIDE
ENTER THIS TOTAL
ON REVERSE SIDE

CASH COUNT—FOR FINANCIAL INSTITUTION'S USE ONLY

x	100	
x	50	
x	20	
x	10	
x	5	
x	2	
x	1	
TOTAL	$	

160

101

01-0000/0001

Bob or Mary Kirkpatrick
11 Kendall Green Drive
Westchester, MO   64498

April 1,   19 **9X**

PAY TO THE
ORDER OF   *Calvary Baptist Church* $ **180.00**

One hundred eighty and 00/100 ————————————— DOLLARS

The First Bank
Westchester, Missouri

FOR   *tithe/offering*   *Bob (or Mary) Kirkpatrick*

102

01-0000/0001

Bob or Mary Kirkpatrick
11 Kendall Green Drive
Westchester, MO   64498

April 1,   19 **9X**

PAY TO THE
ORDER OF   *Second American Mortgage Company* $ **523.19**

Five hundred twenty-three and 19/100 ————————— DOLLARS

The First Bank
Westchester, Missouri

FOR   *April house payment*   *Bob (or Mary) Kirkpatrick*

103

01-0000/0001

Bob or Mary Kirkpatrick
11 Kendall Green Drive
Westchester, MO   64498

April 1,   19 **9X**

PAY TO THE
ORDER OF   *Calvary Christian School* $ **40.00**

Forty and 00/100 ————————————————— DOLLARS

The First Bank
Westchester, Missouri

FOR   *lunch tickets*   *Bob (or Mary) Kirkpatrick*

ENDORSE HERE

X

DO NOT WRITE, STAMP, OR SIGN BELOW THIS LINE

RESERVED FOR FINANCIAL INSTITUTION USE

ENDORSE HERE

X

DO NOT WRITE, STAMP, OR SIGN BELOW THIS LINE

RESERVED FOR FINANCIAL INSTITUTION USE

ENDORSE HERE

X

DO NOT WRITE, STAMP, OR SIGN BELOW THIS LINE

RESERVED FOR FINANCIAL INSTITUTION USE

162

Bob or Mary Kirkpatrick
11 Kendall Green Drive
Westchester, MO   64498

104

01-0000/0001

April 1,   19 **9X**

PAY TO THE
ORDER OF   **Bell Northwest** $ | **34.87**

Thirty-four and 87/100 ————————————————————— DOLLARS

The First Bank
Westchester, Missouri

FOR   **phone bill**   *Bob (or Mary) Kirkpatrick*

Bob or Mary Kirkpatrick
11 Kendall Green Drive
Westchester, MO   64498

105

01-0000/0001

April 1,   19 **9X**

PAY TO THE
ORDER OF   **Harris Steak House** $ | **23.43**

Twenty-three and 43/100 ————————————————————— DOLLARS

The First Bank
Westchester, Missouri

FOR   **out to eat with family**   *Bob (or Mary) Kirkpatrick*

Bunny Batteries
P.O. Box 60
Chicago, IL   60617

188

3X-1000/1234

March 30, 19 *9X*

PAY TO THE
ORDER OF   *Bob Kirkpatrick* $ | *8.50*

Eight and 50/100 ————————————————————— DOLLARS

First Federal Savings Bank
Chicago, Illinois

FOR _____   *Marilyn Jenson*
                                      Treasurer

ENDORSE HERE

x

DO NOT WRITE, STAMP, OR SIGN BELOW THIS LINE ➤
➤ RESERVED FOR FINANCIAL INSTITUTION USE

ENDORSE HERE

x

DO NOT WRITE, STAMP, OR SIGN BELOW THIS LINE ➤
➤ RESERVED FOR FINANCIAL INSTITUTION USE

ENDORSE HERE

x *Bob Kirkpatrick*

DO NOT WRITE, STAMP, OR SIGN BELOW THIS LINE ➤
➤ RESERVED FOR FINANCIAL INSTITUTION USE

Deposit Ticket

Bob or Mary Kirkpatrick
11 Kendall Green Drive
Westchester, MO   64498

DATE _____ **April 3,** ___ 19 **9X**
DEPOSITS MAY NOT BE AVAILABLE FOR IMMEDIATE WITHDRAWAL

_____
SIGN HERE IF CASH RECEIVED FROM DEPOSIT

CURRENCY		
COIN		
CHECKS	8	50
TOTAL FROM OTHER SIDE		
TOTAL	8	50
LESS CASH	—	—
NET DEPOSIT	8	50

01-0000/0001

DEPOSIT TICKET

USE OTHER SIDE FOR
ADDITIONAL LISTINGS

TOTAL ITEMS
1

BE SURE EACH ITEM IS
PROPERLY ENDORSED

The First Bank
Westchester, Missouri

106
01-0000/0001

Bob or Mary Kirkpatrick
11 Kendall Green Drive
Westchester, MO   64498

April 3, ___ 19 **9X**

PAY TO THE
ORDER OF   **Diamond Food Store** $ **185.43**

One hundred eighty-five and 43/100 ——————— DOLLARS

The First Bank
Westchester, Missouri

FOR _____ **groceries** _____   *Bob (or Mary) Kirkpatrick*

107
01-0000/0001

Bob or Mary Kirkpatrick
11 Kendall Green Drive
Westchester, MO   64498

April 6, ___ 19 **9X**

PAY TO THE
ORDER OF   **Front Range Natural Gas Company** $ **64.33**

Sixty-four and 33/100 ——————— DOLLARS

The First Bank
Westchester, Missouri

FOR _____ **March gas bill** _____   *Bob (or Mary) Kirkpatrick*

Please List Each Check Separately by Financial Institution Number

	CHECKS	DOLLARS	CENTS
1			
2			
3			
4			
5			
6			
7			
8			
9			
10			
11			
12			
13			
14			
15			
16			

TOTAL THIS SIDE
ENTER THIS TOTAL
ON REVERSE SIDE

CASH COUNT—FOR FINANCIAL INSTITUTION'S USE ONLY

x	100	
x	50	
x	20	
x	10	
x	5	
x	2	
x	1	
TOTAL	$	

ENDORSE HERE

X

DO NOT WRITE, STAMP, OR SIGN BELOW THIS LINE
→ RESERVED FOR FINANCIAL INSTITUTION USE →

ENDORSE HERE

X

DO NOT WRITE, STAMP, OR SIGN BELOW THIS LINE
→ RESERVED FOR FINANCIAL INSTITUTION USE →

Check 108

Bob or Mary Kirkpatrick
11 Kendall Green Drive
Westchester, MO   64498

108
01-0000/0001

April 6, 19 _9X_

PAY TO THE
ORDER OF   **Better Lawns and Soil** $ **17.99**

Seventeen and 99/100 ———————————————————— DOLLARS

The First Bank
Westchester, Missouri

FOR ___ **magazine subscription** ___   _Bob (or Mary) Kirkpatrick_

Check 361

Fred McAllister
810 Birch Street
San Diego, CA   92115

361
4X-1000/1234

April 2, 19 _9X_

PAY TO THE
ORDER OF ___ _Bob Kirkpatrick_ ___ $ _250.00_

Two hundred fifty and 00/100 ———————————— DOLLARS

Pacific National Bank
San Diego, California

FOR _____   _Fred McAllister_

Deposit Ticket

Bob or Mary Kirkpatrick
11 Kendall Green Drive
Westchester, MO   64498

DATE ___ **April 6,** 19 **9X** ___
DEPOSITS MAY NOT BE AVAILABLE FOR IMMEDIATE WITHDRAWAL

_____
SIGN HERE IF CASH RECEIVED FROM DEPOSIT

CURRENCY		
COIN		
CHECKS	250	00
TOTAL FROM OTHER SIDE		
TOTAL	250	00
LESS CASH	—	—
NET DEPOSIT	250	00

01-0000/0001

DEPOSIT TICKET

USE OTHER SIDE FOR
ADDITIONAL LISTINGS

TOTAL ITEMS
1

BE SURE EACH ITEM IS
PROPERLY ENDORSED

The First Bank
Westchester, Missouri

Left section (deposit slip):

Please List Each Check Separately by Financial Institution Number

CHECKS	DOLLARS	CENTS
1		
2		
3		
4		
5		
6		
7		
8		
9		
10		
11		
12		
13		
14		
15		
16		

TOTAL THIS SIDE
ENTER THIS TOTAL ON REVERSE SIDE

CASH COUNT—FOR FINANCIAL INSTITUTION'S USE ONLY

x	100	
x	50	
x	20	
x	10	
x	5	
x	2	
x	1	
TOTAL	$	

Middle section (endorsement):

ENDORSE HERE

x *Bob Kirkpatrick*

DO NOT WRITE, STAMP, OR SIGN BELOW THIS LINE
→ RESERVED FOR FINANCIAL INSTITUTION USE →

Right section (endorsement):

ENDORSE HERE

x

DO NOT WRITE, STAMP, OR SIGN BELOW THIS LINE
→ RESERVED FOR FINANCIAL INSTITUTION USE →

Check 109

Bob or Mary Kirkpatrick
11 Kendall Green Drive
Westchester, MO   64498

109
01-0000/0001

April 7,   19 **9X**

PAY TO THE
ORDER OF   **Twenty-third Century Mutual Fund** $ **150.00**

One hundred fifty and 00/100 ———————————————— DOLLARS

The First Bank
Westchester, Missouri

FOR   **investment account**   *Bob (or Mary) Kirkpatrick*

Check 110

Bob or Mary Kirkpatrick
11 Kendall Green Drive
Westchester, MO   64498

110
01-0000/0001

April 7,   19 **9X**

PAY TO THE
ORDER OF   **Gasco Oil Company** $ **54.23**

Fifty-four and 23/100 ———————————————— DOLLARS

The First Bank
Westchester, Missouri

FOR   **March gasoline bill**   *Bob (or Mary) Kirkpatrick*

Check 111

Bob or Mary Kirkpatrick
11 Kendall Green Drive
Westchester, MO   64498

111
01-0000/0001

April 7,   19 **9X**

PAY TO THE
ORDER OF   **Edison Electric Company** $ **110.00**

One hundred ten and 00/100 ———————————————— DOLLARS

The First Bank
Westchester, Missouri

FOR   **March electricity bill**   *Bob (or Mary) Kirkpatrick*

ENDORSE HERE

X

DO NOT WRITE, STAMP, OR SIGN BELOW THIS LINE
RESERVED FOR FINANCIAL INSTITUTION USE

ENDORSE HERE

X

DO NOT WRITE, STAMP, OR SIGN BELOW THIS LINE
RESERVED FOR FINANCIAL INSTITUTION USE

ENDORSE HERE

X

DO NOT WRITE, STAMP, OR SIGN BELOW THIS LINE
RESERVED FOR FINANCIAL INSTITUTION USE

Siegel Corporation
Westchester, Missouri

001002

00-001
123

Date
04/15/XX

Void After 90 Days

PAY NINE HUNDRED FIFTY-THREE DOLLARS AND EIGHTY-FOUR CENTS $953.84

NET AMOUNT

TO THE
ORDER OF

Robert Kirkpatrick
11 Kendall Green Drive
Westchester, MO   64498

The First Bank
Westchester, Missouri

Jared P. Cooper

Treasurer

Bob or Mary Kirkpatrick
11 Kendall Green Drive
Westchester, MO   64498

DATE ____ **April 15,** ___ 19 **9X**
DEPOSITS MAY NOT BE AVAILABLE FOR IMMEDIATE WITHDRAWAL

_____
SIGN HERE IF CASH RECEIVED FROM DEPOSIT

CURRENCY		
COIN		
CHECKS	953	84
TOTAL FROM OTHER SIDE		
TOTAL	953	84
LESS CASH	—	—
NET DEPOSIT	953	84

The First Bank
Westchester, Missouri

01-0000/0001

DEPOSIT TICKET

USE OTHER SIDE FOR
ADDITIONAL LISTINGS

TOTAL ITEMS
1

BE SURE EACH ITEM IS
PROPERLY ENDORSED

112

01-0000/0001

Bob or Mary Kirkpatrick
11 Kendall Green Drive
Westchester, MO   64498

April 15, ___ 19 **9X**

PAY TO THE
ORDER OF   *Calvary Baptist Church* _____ $ **110.00**

One hundred ten and 00/100 _____ DOLLARS

The First Bank
Westchester, Missouri

Bob (or Mary) Kirkpatrick

FOR _____ *tithe / offering* _____

ENDORSE HERE

x *Robert Kirkpatrick*

DO NOT WRITE, STAMP, OR SIGN BELOW THIS LINE
◆ RESERVED FOR FINANCIAL INSTITUTION USE ◆

Please List Each Check Separately by Financial Institution Number

CHECKS	DOLLARS	CENTS
1		
2		
3		
4		
5		
6		
7		
8		
9		
10		
11		
12		
13		
14		
15		
16		

TOTAL THIS SIDE
ENTER THIS TOTAL
ON REVERSE SIDE

CASH COUNT—FOR FINANCIAL INSTITUTION'S USE ONLY

x	100	
x	50	
x	20	
x	10	
x	5	
x	2	
x	1	
	$	
TOTAL		

ENDORSE HERE

x

DO NOT WRITE, STAMP, OR SIGN BELOW THIS LINE
◆ RESERVED FOR FINANCIAL INSTITUTION USE ◆

Check 113

Bob or Mary Kirkpatrick
11 Kendall Green Drive
Westchester, MO   64498

April 15,   19 _9X_

113
01-0000/0001

PAY TO THE ORDER OF _Internal Revenue Service_ $ _57.00_

Fifty-seven and 00/100 ———————————————— DOLLARS

The First Bank
Westchester, Missouri

FOR _federal income tax_

Bob (or Mary) Kirkpatrick

Check 114

Bob or Mary Kirkpatrick
11 Kendall Green Drive
Westchester, MO   64498

April 15,   19 _9X_

114
01-0000/0001

PAY TO THE ORDER OF _State Department of Revenue_ $ _102.00_

One hundred two and 00/100 ———————————————— DOLLARS

The First Bank
Westchester, Missouri

FOR _state income tax_

Bob (or Mary) Kirkpatrick

Check 115

Bob or Mary Kirkpatrick
11 Kendall Green Drive
Westchester, MO   64498

April 15,   19 _9X_

115
01-0000/0001

PAY TO THE ORDER OF _Calvary Christian School_ $ _102.00_

Two hundred eighty-five and 00/100 ———————————————— DOLLARS

The First Bank
Westchester, Missouri

FOR _April school bill_

Bob (or Mary) Kirkpatrick

ENDORSE HERE

X

DO NOT WRITE, STAMP, OR SIGN BELOW THIS LINE
RESERVED FOR FINANCIAL INSTITUTION USE

ENDORSE HERE

X

DO NOT WRITE, STAMP, OR SIGN BELOW THIS LINE
RESERVED FOR FINANCIAL INSTITUTION USE

ENDORSE HERE

X

DO NOT WRITE, STAMP, OR SIGN BELOW THIS LINE
RESERVED FOR FINANCIAL INSTITUTION USE

174

Check 116

Bob or Mary Kirkpatrick
11 Kendall Green Drive
Westchester, MO   64498

116
01-0000/0001

April 17,   19 **9X**

PAY TO THE ORDER OF **Rosebushes-by-Mail** $ **43.87**

Forty-three and 87/100 ———————————————— DOLLARS

The First Bank
Westchester, Missouri

FOR **rosebushes**   *Bob (or Mary) Kirkpatrick*

Check 117

Bob or Mary Kirkpatrick
11 Kendall Green Drive
Westchester, MO   64498

117
01-0000/0001

April 20,   19 **9X**

PAY TO THE ORDER OF **The First Bank** $ **201.41**

Two hundred one and 41/100 ———————————————— DOLLARS

The First Bank
Westchester, Missouri

FOR **April car payment**   *Bob (or Mary) Kirkpatrick*

Check 1901

Twenty-third Century Mutual Fund
Atlanta, Georgia   30321

1901
5X-1000/1234

April 15, 19 *9X*

PAY TO THE ORDER OF *Bob Kirkpatrick* $ *559.28*

Five hundred fifty-nine and 28/100 ———————————————— DOLLARS

Central Bank
Atlanta, Georgia

FOR _____   *Raymond G. Wells*
                                        Treasurer

ENDORSE HERE

x

DO NOT WRITE, STAMP, OR SIGN BELOW THIS LINE ➧
➧ RESERVED FOR FINANCIAL INSTITUTION USE ➧

ENDORSE HERE

x

DO NOT WRITE, STAMP, OR SIGN BELOW THIS LINE ➧
➧ RESERVED FOR FINANCIAL INSTITUTION USE ➧

ENDORSE HERE

x *Bob Kirkpatrick*

DO NOT WRITE, STAMP, OR SIGN BELOW THIS LINE ➧
➧ RESERVED FOR FINANCIAL INSTITUTION USE ➧

Deposit Ticket

Bob or Mary Kirkpatrick
11 Kendall Green Drive
Westchester, MO 64498

DATE _____ **April 21,** ___ 19 **9X**
DEPOSITS MAY NOT BE AVAILABLE FOR IMMEDIATE WITHDRAWAL

Bob (or Mary) Kirkpatrick
SIGN HERE IF CASH RECEIVED FROM DEPOSIT

CURRENCY		
COIN		
CHECKS	559	28
TOTAL FROM OTHER SIDE		
TOTAL	559	28
LESS CASH	59	28
NET DEPOSIT	500	00

01-0000/0001

DEPOSIT TICKET

USE OTHER SIDE FOR
ADDITIONAL LISTINGS

TOTAL ITEMS
1

BE SURE EACH ITEM IS
PROPERLY ENDORSED

The First Bank
Westchester, Missouri

118
01-0000/0001

Bob or Mary Kirkpatrick
11 Kendall Green Drive
Westchester, MO 64498

_____ **April 22,** ___ 19 **9X**

PAY TO THE ORDER OF ___ **Diamond Food Store** ___ $ | **193.55**

One hundred ninety-three and 55/100 _____ DOLLARS

The First Bank
Westchester, Missouri

FOR _____ **groceries** _____   _Bob (or Mary) Kirkpatrick_

119
01-0000/0001

Bob or Mary Kirkpatrick
11 Kendall Green Drive
Westchester, MO 64498

_____ **April 22,** ___ 19 **9X**

PAY TO THE ORDER OF ___ **City Water Company** ___ $ | **143.22**

One hundred forty-three and 22/100 _____ DOLLARS

The First Bank
Westchester, Missouri

FOR _____ **water/sewer service bill** _____   _Bob (or Mary) Kirkpatrick_

178

ENDORSE HERE

X _____

DO NOT WRITE, STAMP, OR SIGN BELOW THIS LINE
☛ RESERVED FOR FINANCIAL INSTITUTION USE ☛

_____

ENDORSE HERE

X _____

DO NOT WRITE, STAMP, OR SIGN BELOW THIS LINE
☛ RESERVED FOR FINANCIAL INSTITUTION USE ☛

_____

Please List Each Check Separately by Financial Institution Number

CHECKS	DOLLARS	CENTS
1		
2		
3		
4		
5		
6		
7		
8		
9		
10		
11		
12		
13		
14		
15		
16		

TOTAL THIS SIDE

ENTER THIS TOTAL
ON REVERSE SIDE

CASH COUNT—FOR FINANCIAL INSTITUTION'S USE ONLY

	x	100		
	x	50		
	x	20		
	x	10		
	x	5		
	x	2		
	x	1		
TOTAL		$		

120

01-0000/0001

Bob or Mary Kirkpatrick
11 Kendall Green Drive
Westchester, MO   64498

April 22,   19 **9X**

PAY TO THE
ORDER OF   **Federated Life Insurance Company** $ **110.00**

One hundred ten and 00/100 ———————————————— DOLLARS

The First Bank
Westchester, Missouri

FOR   **life insurance premium**   *Bob (or Mary) Kirkpatrick*

121

01-0000/0001

Bob or Mary Kirkpatrick
11 Kendall Green Drive
Westchester, MO   64498

April 22,   19 **9X**

PAY TO THE
ORDER OF   **Farm State Insurance Company** $ **72.44**

Seventy-two and 44/100 ———————————————— DOLLARS

The First Bank
Westchester, Missouri

FOR   **April auto insurance**   *Bob (or Mary) Kirkpatrick*

612

6X-1000/1234

Joey Wilson
Rt. 5, Box 91
Westchester, MO   64498

April 22, 19 *9X*

PAY TO THE
ORDER OF   *Bob Kirkpatrick* $ *800.00*

Eight hundred and 00/100 ———————————————— DOLLARS

Midwest Independent Bank
Westchester, Missouri

FOR   *computer*   *Joey Wilson*

ENDORSE HERE

x *Bob Kirkpatrick*

DO NOT WRITE, STAMP, OR SIGN BELOW THIS LINE
◆ RESERVED FOR FINANCIAL INSTITUTION USE ◆

ENDORSE HERE

x

DO NOT WRITE, STAMP, OR SIGN BELOW THIS LINE
◆ RESERVED FOR FINANCIAL INSTITUTION USE ◆

ENDORSE HERE

x

DO NOT WRITE, STAMP, OR SIGN BELOW THIS LINE
◆ RESERVED FOR FINANCIAL INSTITUTION USE ◆

Deposit Ticket

CURRENCY		
COIN		
CHECKS	800	00
TOTAL FROM OTHER SIDE		
TOTAL	**800**	**00**
LESS CASH	—	—
NET DEPOSIT	**800**	**00**

Bob or Mary Kirkpatrick
11 Kendall Green Drive
Westchester, MO   64498

DATE _____ **April 22,** __ 19 **9X** __
DEPOSITS MAY NOT BE AVAILABLE FOR IMMEDIATE WITHDRAWAL

_____
SIGN HERE IF CASH RECEIVED FROM DEPOSIT

01-0000/0001

DEPOSIT TICKET

USE OTHER SIDE FOR
ADDITIONAL LISTINGS

TOTAL ITEMS
1

BE SURE EACH ITEM IS
PROPERLY ENDORSED

The First Bank
Westchester, Missouri

Bob or Mary Kirkpatrick
11 Kendall Green Drive
Westchester, MO   64498

122
01-0000/0001

_____ **April 23,** _____ 19 **9X**

PAY TO THE
ORDER OF   **Herald Star Newspaper** _____ $ **14.50**

Fourteen and 50/100 _____ DOLLARS

The First Bank
Westchester, Missouri

FOR _____ **classified ad** _____   *Bob (or Mary) Kirkpatrick*

Siegel Corporation
Westchester, Missouri

001003

00-001
123

Date
05/01/XX

Void After 90 Days

Pay NINE HUNDRED FIFTY-THREE DOLLARS AND EIGHTY-FOUR CENTS $953.84

TO THE
ORDER OF

Robert Kirkpatrick
11 Kendall Green Drive
Westchester, MO   64498

The First Bank
Westchester, Missouri

NET AMOUNT

Jared P. Cooper
Treasurer

ENDORSE HERE

x *Robert Kirkpatrick*

DO NOT WRITE, STAMP, OR SIGN BELOW THIS LINE
◆ RESERVED FOR FINANCIAL INSTITUTION USE ◆

ENDORSE HERE

x

DO NOT WRITE, STAMP, OR SIGN BELOW THIS LINE
◆ RESERVED FOR FINANCIAL INSTITUTION USE ◆

Please List Each Check Separately by Financial Institution Number

	CHECKS	DOLLARS	CENTS
1			
2			
3			
4			
5			
6			
7			
8			
9			
10			
11			
12			
13			
14			
15			
16			

TOTAL THIS SIDE
ENTER THIS TOTAL
ON REVERSE SIDE

CASH COUNT—FOR FINANCIAL INSTITUTION'S USE ONLY

	x	100	
	x	50	
	x	20	
	x	10	
	x	5	
	x	2	
	x	1	
TOTAL		$	

Deposit Ticket

CURRENCY			
COIN			
CHECKS		953	84
TOTAL FROM OTHER SIDE			
TOTAL		953	84
LESS CASH		—	—
NET DEPOSIT		953	84

Bob or Mary Kirkpatrick
11 Kendall Green Drive
Westchester, MO 64498

DATE ___**May 1,**___ 19 **9X**

DEPOSITS MAY NOT BE AVAILABLE FOR IMMEDIATE WITHDRAWAL

_____
SIGN HERE IF CASH RECEIVED FROM DEPOSIT

01-0000/0001

DEPOSIT TICKET

USE OTHER SIDE FOR ADDITIONAL LISTINGS

TOTAL ITEMS
1

BE SURE EACH ITEM IS PROPERLY ENDORSED

The First Bank
Westchester, Missouri

123
01-0000/0001

Bob or Mary Kirkpatrick
11 Kendall Green Drive
Westchester, MO 64498

___**May 1,**___ 19 **9X**

PAY TO THE ORDER OF ___**Calvary Baptist Church**___ $ **110.00**

One hundred ten and 00/100 _____ DOLLARS

The First Bank
Westchester, Missouri

FOR ___**tithe/offering**___ *Bob (or Mary) Kirkpatrick*

124
01-0000/0001

Bob or Mary Kirkpatrick
11 Kendall Green Drive
Westchester, MO 64498

___**May 1,**___ 19 **9X**

PAY TO THE ORDER OF ___**Second American Mortgage Company**___ $ **523.19**

Five hundred twenty-three and 19/100 _____ DOLLARS

The First Bank
Westchester, Missouri

FOR ___**May house payment**___ *Bob (or Mary) Kirkpatrick*

Deposit Slip / Check Listing

Please List Each Check Separately by Financial Institution Number

	CHECKS	DOLLARS	CENTS
1			
2			
3			
4			
5			
6			
7			
8			
9			
10			
11			
12			
13			
14			
15			
16			

TOTAL THIS SIDE
ENTER THIS TOTAL ON REVERSE SIDE

CASH COUNT—FOR FINANCIAL INSTITUTION'S USE ONLY

x	100	
x	50	
x	20	
x	10	
x	5	
x	2	
x	1	
TOTAL	$	

ENDORSE HERE

X _____

DO NOT WRITE, STAMP, OR SIGN BELOW THIS LINE
➤ RESERVED FOR FINANCIAL INSTITUTION USE ➤

ENDORSE HERE

X _____

DO NOT WRITE, STAMP, OR SIGN BELOW THIS LINE
➤ RESERVED FOR FINANCIAL INSTITUTION USE ➤

Bob or Mary Kirkpatrick
11 Kendall Green Drive
Westchester, MO   64498

May 1,   19_**9X**_

PAY TO THE
ORDER OF   **Calvary Christian School** $ | **40.00** |

Forty and 00/100 ———————————————— DOLLARS

The First Bank
Westchester, Missouri

FOR   **lunch tickets**   _Bob (or Mary) Kirkpatrick_

Bob or Mary Kirkpatrick
11 Kendall Green Drive
Westchester, MO   64498

May 1,   19_**9X**_

PAY TO THE
ORDER OF   **Bell Northwest** $ | **32.28** |

Thirty-two and 28/100 ———————————————— DOLLARS

The First Bank
Westchester, Missouri

FOR   **phone bill**   _Bob (or Mary) Kirkpatrick_

01-0000/0001

Bob or Mary Kirkpatrick
11 Kendall Green Drive
Westchester, MO   64498

———————— 19————

PAY TO THE
ORDER OF $ | |

———————————————— DOLLARS

The First Bank
Westchester, Missouri

FOR

ENDORSE HERE

X

DO NOT WRITE, STAMP, OR SIGN BELOW THIS LINE
RESERVED FOR FINANCIAL INSTITUTION USE

ENDORSE HERE

X

DO NOT WRITE, STAMP, OR SIGN BELOW THIS LINE
RESERVED FOR FINANCIAL INSTITUTION USE

ENDORSE HERE

X

DO NOT WRITE, STAMP, OR SIGN BELOW THIS LINE
RESERVED FOR FINANCIAL INSTITUTION USE

186

Bob or Mary Kirkpatrick
11 Kendall Green Drive
Westchester, MO   64498

_____ 19 _____

01-0000/0001

PAY TO THE
ORDER OF _____ $ [   ]

_____ DOLLARS

The First Bank
Westchester, Missouri

FOR _____   _____

Bob or Mary Kirkpatrick
11 Kendall Green Drive
Westchester, MO   64498

_____ 19 _____

01-0000/0001

PAY TO THE
ORDER OF _____ $ [   ]

_____ DOLLARS

The First Bank
Westchester, Missouri

FOR _____   _____

Bob or Mary Kirkpatrick
11 Kendall Green Drive
Westchester, MO   64498

_____ 19 _____

01-0000/0001

PAY TO THE
ORDER OF _____ $ [   ]

_____ DOLLARS

The First Bank
Westchester, Missouri

FOR _____   _____

ENDORSE HERE

X

DO NOT WRITE, STAMP, OR SIGN BELOW THIS LINE
RESERVED FOR FINANCIAL INSTITUTION USE

ENDORSE HERE

X

DO NOT WRITE, STAMP, OR SIGN BELOW THIS LINE
RESERVED FOR FINANCIAL INSTITUTION USE

ENDORSE HERE

X

DO NOT WRITE, STAMP, OR SIGN BELOW THIS LINE
RESERVED FOR FINANCIAL INSTITUTION USE

188

Bob or Mary Kirkpatrick
11 Kendall Green Drive
Westchester, MO   64498

_____ 19_____

01-0000/0001

PAY TO THE
ORDER OF _____ $ [   ]

_____ DOLLARS

The First Bank
Westchester, Missouri

FOR _____   _____

Bob or Mary Kirkpatrick
11 Kendall Green Drive
Westchester, MO   64498

DATE _____ 19_____
DEPOSITS MAY NOT BE AVAILABLE FOR IMMEDIATE WITHDRAWAL

_____
SIGN HERE IF CASH RECEIVED FROM DEPOSIT

CURRENCY		
COIN		
CHECKS		
TOTAL FROM OTHER SIDE		
TOTAL		
LESS CASH		
NET DEPOSIT		

01-0000/0001

DEPOSIT TICKET

USE OTHER SIDE FOR
ADDITIONAL LISTINGS

TOTAL ITEMS

BE SURE EACH ITEM IS
PROPERLY ENDORSED

The First Bank
Westchester, Missouri

Bob or Mary Kirkpatrick
11 Kendall Green Drive
Westchester, MO   64498

DATE _____ 19_____
DEPOSITS MAY NOT BE AVAILABLE FOR IMMEDIATE WITHDRAWAL

_____
SIGN HERE IF CASH RECEIVED FROM DEPOSIT

CURRENCY		
COIN		
CHECKS		
TOTAL FROM OTHER SIDE		
TOTAL		
LESS CASH		
NET DEPOSIT		

01-0000/0001

DEPOSIT TICKET

USE OTHER SIDE FOR
ADDITIONAL LISTINGS

TOTAL ITEMS

BE SURE EACH ITEM IS
PROPERLY ENDORSED

The First Bank
Westchester, Missouri

ENDORSE HERE

X

DO NOT WRITE, STAMP, OR SIGN BELOW THIS LINE
→ RESERVED FOR FINANCIAL INSTITUTION USE →

Please List Each Check Separately by Financial Institution Number

CHECKS	DOLLARS	CENTS
1		
2		
3		
4		
5		
6		
7		
8		
9		
10		
11		
12		
13		
14		
15		
16		

TOTAL THIS SIDE
ENTER THIS TOTAL
ON REVERSE SIDE

CASH COUNT—FOR FINANCIAL INSTITUTION'S USE ONLY

x	100	
x	50	
x	20	
x	10	
x	5	
x	2	
x	1	
TOTAL	$	

Please List Each Check Separately by Financial Institution Number

CHECKS	DOLLARS	CENTS
1		
2		
3		
4		
5		
6		
7		
8		
9		
10		
11		
12		
13		
14		
15		
16		

TOTAL THIS SIDE
ENTER THIS TOTAL
ON REVERSE SIDE

CASH COUNT—FOR FINANCIAL INSTITUTION'S USE ONLY

x	100	
x	50	
x	20	
x	10	
x	5	
x	2	
x	1	
TOTAL	$	

190

Date		Check Number	Checks Issued to or Deposit Received from	Amount of Deposit		T	Amount of Check		Balance	
4	1		*Initial Deposit*	1,127	35	X			1,127	35
4	1	101	*Calvary Baptist Church*			X	180	00	947	35
4	1	102	*Second American Mortgage Company*			X	523	19	424	16
4	1	103	*Calvary Christian School*			X	40	00	384	16
4	1	104	*Bell Northwest*			X	34	87	349	29
4	1	105	*Harris Steak House*				23	43	325	86
4	3		*Deposit (rebate check)*	8	50	X			334	36
4	3	106	*Diamond Food Store*				185	43	148	93
4	6	107	*Front Range Natural Gas Company*			X	64	33	84	60
4	6	108	*Better Lawns and Soil*				17	99	66	61
4	6		*Deposit*	250	00	X			316	61
4	7	109	*Twenty-third Century Mutual Fund*			X	150	00	166	61
4	7	110	*Gasco Oil Company*			X	54	23	112	38
4	7	111	*Edison Electric Company*			X	110	00	2	38
4	15		*Deposit*	953	84	X			956	22
4	15	112	*Calvary Baptist Church*			X	110	00	846	22
4	15	113	*Internal Revenue Service*				57	00	789	22
4	15	114	*State Department of Revenue*				102	00	687	22
4	15	115	*Calvary Christian School*				285	00	402	22
4	17	116	*Rosebushes-by-Mail*				43	87	358	35
4	20	117	*The First Bank (car payment)*			X	201	41	156	94
4	21		*Deposit*	500	00	X			656	94
4	22	118	*Diamond Food Store*			X	193	55	463	39
4	22	119	*City Water Company*			X	143	22	320	17
4	22	120	*Federated Life Insurance Company*				110	00	210	17
4	22	121	*Farm State Insurance Company*				72	44	137	73
4	23		*Deposit (sale of computer)*	800	00	X			937	73
4	23	122	*Herald Star Newspaper*				14	50	923	23
4	30		*Check returned*				800	00	123	23
5	1		*Deposit*	953	84				1,077	07
5	1	123	*Calvary Baptist Church*				110	00	967	07
5	1	124	*Second American Mortgage Company*				523	19	443	88
5	1	125	*Calvary Christian School*				40	00	403	88
5	1	126	*Bell Northwest*				32	28	371	60
4	27		*Service Charge*			X	6	40	365	20

The First Bank
1 The First Building
Westchester, Missouri

Mr. or Mrs. Robert Kirkpatrick
11 Kendall Green Drive
Westchester, MO   64498

STATEMENT PERIOD			STATEMENT OF ACCOUNTS	
FROM	TO		ACCOUNT NUMBER	PAGE NUMBER
03/28/9X	04/27/9X		101101	1 of 1

Balance Forwarded	Number of Credits	Total Credits	Number of Debits	Total Debits	Less: Fees	Closing Balance
0.00	6	3,639.69	12	1,804.80	6.40	1,828.49

Date	Credit Amount	Date	Credit Amount
4/01	1,127.35		
4/03	8.50		
4/06	250.00		
4/15	953.84		
4/21	500.00		
4/23	800.00		

Check Number	Date Posted	Amount	Daily Balance	Check Number	Date Posted	Amount	Daily Balance
102	4/08	523.19	862.66				
104	4/08	34.87	827.79				
101	4/08	180.00	647.79				
103	4/08	40.00	607.79				
107	4/10	64.33	543.46				
111	4/10	110.00	433.46				
112	4/18	110.00	1,277.30				
117	4/21	201.41	1,575.89				
110	4/22	54.23	1,521.66				
118	4/24	193.55	2,128.11				
109	4/24	150.00	1,978.11				
119	4/26	143.22	1,834.89				
SVC CHG	4/27	6.40	1,828.49				

TO RECONCILE YOUR CHECKING ACCOUNT BALANCE, FOLLOW THESE SIX SIMPLE STEPS

1. Subtract from your check register all service charges, check printing charges, and any other miscellaneous charges which we have deducted from your account as shown on the front of this statement.

2. Add to your check register all credits, service charge refunds, NOW account interest, and any other miscellaneous additions which we have made to your account as shown on the front of this statement.

3. Compare the checks shown on this statement to your check register and indicate checks which have cleared by placing an X beside them in your check register.

4. List all checks which have not yet cleared the bank:

CHECKS OUTSTANDING	
CHECK NUMBER	AMOUNT
105	$23.43
106	185.43
108	17.99
113	57.00
114	102.00
115	285.00
116	43.87
120	110.00
121	72.44
122	14.50
CHECK RETURNED	800.00*
123	110.00
124	523.19
125	40.00
126	32.28
TOTAL	$2,417.13

5. Enter the ending balance as shown on the front of this statement:

   Add deposits made after the statement closing date:

   Total:

   Subtract your outstanding checks:

6. This figure should agree with the balance in your check register:

$1,828.49
953.84
$2,782.33
2,417.13
$365.20

*Note to teacher: The $800.00 returned check was posted on 4/30, three days after this statement's closing date. The returned check would appear in the next monthly statement.

Understanding Investments: Time Value of Money

Future Value

Nearly everyone has heard the old saying ''time is money,'' but few fully understand the truth of the statement. The principle of the time value of money simply holds that money today is more valuable than the same amount of money at a later time. Consider the following hypothetical situation. You have been offered $100 and have been given two options as to the form in which it may be received. Option #1: You may receive $100 in cash today. Option #2: You may receive $100 at the end of one year. Question: If you could invest at an interest rate of 8%, which option would you choose? According to economists, the rational investor will select option #1 because, by taking the $100 today, he could invest it so that it would grow to $108 by the end of the year. The value of the investment at the future time (in this case one year) is called its ''future value,'' or, more simply, its FV. It is relatively simple to calculate future values if you know the formula:

$$\text{FV} = \text{TODAY'S VALUE} \times (1 + i)^n$$

i= interest rate and n=number of periods

Thus, $100 earning 8% would, at the end of one year be worth

$$\$100 \times (1 + .08)^1 =$$

$$\$100 \times 1.08 =$$

$$\$108.00$$

What would be the FV of the same $100 at 7% after two years?

$$\$100 \times (1 + .07)^2 =$$

$$\$100 \times 1.1449 =$$

$$\$114.49$$

The previous examples calculate future values based upon annual compounding. If the interest is compounded at a greater rate, you must make two simple adjustments to the formula. First, divide the annual interest rate (i) by the number of compounding periods in a year. For example, if the annual interest rate is 7% and compounding is performed semiannually, then the interest rate you insert into your formula is .035 (.07/2). If compounding is quarterly, then you would use .0175 (.07/4). The second adjustment is even easier. The power used (n) is found by multiplying the number of years the deposit is being held by the number of compounding periods per year. For example, if your deposit is being compounded quarterly and the deposit is being held for two years, you would use a factor of 8 (2 × 4). Thus, $100 held for 2 years at 7% compounded quarterly would be worth

$$\$100 \times [1 + (.07/4)]^{(2 \times 4)} =$$

$$\$100 \times (1 + .0175)^8 =$$

$$\$100 \times 1.1489 =$$

$$\$114.89$$

Compare the results of your two investments. If your $100 was earning 7% and was compounded annually, you would have $114.49 at the end of the two years. If, however, your deposit was being compounded quarterly, you would have a return of $114.89. The principle is clear: As compounding becomes more frequent, your wealth increases at a greater rate.

You may find the following exercises easier to perform if you have a calculator which has a ''y^x'' key, which calculates powers. If, however, your calculator does not have this capability, you may perform the calculation by manually calculating the power (i.e., $1.07^2 = 1.07 \times 1.07$).

What will be the future values of the following deposits? (Round decimal numbers to four decimal places. Show all of your work.)

1. $73,000 for three years compounded annually at 10%

$$\$73{,}000 \times (1 + .10)^3 =$$
$$\$73{,}000 \times 1.331 =$$
$$\$97{,}163.00$$

2. $50,000 for two years compounded semiannually at 6%

$$\$50{,}000 \times [1 + (.06/2)]^{(2 \times 2)} =$$
$$\$50{,}000 \times (1 + .03)^4 =$$
$$\$50{,}000 \times 1.1255 =$$
$$\$56{,}275.00$$

3. $100,000 for seven years compounded quarterly at 10%

$$\$100{,}000 \times [1 + (.10/4)]^{(7 \times 4)} =$$
$$\$100{,}000 \times (1 + .025)^{28} =$$
$$\$100{,}000 \times 1.9965$$
$$\$199{,}650.00$$

4. $100 for two years compounded monthly at 18%

$$\$100 \times [1 + (.18/12)]^{(2 \times 12)} =$$
$$\$100 \times (1 + .015)^{24}$$
$$\$100 \times 1.4295$$
$$\$142.95$$

Present Value

You just saw that the future value of an investment is found by multiplying the initial deposit by its compounded interest factor. Economists refer to the initial deposit as the investment's "present value," or, simply, PV. As you will see, the ability to calculate an investment's PV is very important to investors, bankers, and economists. Calculating an investment's PV is nothing more than working backwards, using an investment's future value to determine its initial amount. PV is found by multiplying the FV (future value) by the inverse of the compounded interest factor. The formula for finding the PV of an investment is

$$\mathbf{PV = FV \times [\,1\,/\,(1 + i)^n\,]}$$

For example, the PV of an 8% investment compounded annually for one year which has an FV of $108 would be

$$\$108 \times [1/(1 + .08)^1] =$$
$$\$108 \times (1/1.08) =$$
$$\$108 \times .9259 =$$
$$\$100$$

Again, if interest is being compounded more frequently than once per year, the interest factor (i) is found by dividing the annual interest rate by the number of periods per year the investment is compounded (i.e., semiannually = 2, quarterly = 4, etc.). The procedure for finding the power factor (n) was discussed previously. Simply multiply the number of years the investment is held by the number of compounding periods per year (i.e., three years compounded quarterly = 3 × 4 = 12).

196

For example, what is the PV of a 7% investment compounded quarterly for two years which has an FV of $12,500?

$$\$12,500 \times \{1/[1 + (.07/4)]^{(2 \times 4)}\} =$$
$$\$12,500 \times [1/(1.0175)^8] =$$
$$\$12,500 \times (1/1.1489) =$$
$$\$12,500 \times .8704 =$$
$$\$10,880.00$$

Calculate the following PVs. (Remember to round all decimal figures to the fourth decimal place.)

5. A 5% investment compounded semiannually for three years which has an FV of $308,115

$$\$308,115 \times \{1/[1 + (.05/2)]^{(3 \times 2)}\} =$$
$$\$308,115 \times [1/(1.025)^6] =$$
$$\$308,115 \times (1/1.1597) =$$
$$\$308,115 \times .8623$$
$$\$265,687.56$$

6. An 8.3% investment compounded quarterly for two years whose FV is $45,000

$$\$45,000 \times \{1/[1 + (.083/4)]^{(2 \times 4)}\} =$$
$$\$45,000 \times [1/(1.0208)^8] =$$
$$\$45,000 \times (1/1.1790) =$$
$$\$45,000 \times .8482 =$$
$$\$38,169.00$$

7. A 10% investment compounded monthly for one year whose FV is $50,000

$$\$50,000 \times \{1/[1 + (.10/12)]^{(1 \times 12)}\} =$$
$$\$50,000 \times [1/(1.0083)^{12}] =$$
$$\$50,000 \times (1/1.1043) =$$
$$\$50,000 \times .9056 =$$
$$\$45,280.00$$

8. Now for a practical application: You are in the process of selling a rather expensive piece of equipment, and you are faced with a dilemma. You may receive either $10 million in cash today or $20 million ten years from now. (Assume that you can earn 8% quarterly compounded interest on deposits.) Since it is impractical to compare the two amounts, you decide to compare present values. In the space below show your computations and give your recommendation.

Obviously, the present value of the first option ($10 million today) is $10 million; therefore, you need to compute the PV of option #2. If the PV of option #2 is greater than $10 million, it should be accepted. If the PV of option #2 is less than $10 million, it should be rejected.

$$\$20,000,000 \times \{1/[1 + (.08/4)]^{(10 \times 4)} =$$
$$\$20,000,000 \times \{1/(1.02^{40})] =$$
$$\$20,000,000 \times (1/2.2080) =$$
$$\$20,000,000 \times .4529 =$$
$$\$9,058,000.00$$

The PV of option #2 is less than $10 million; therefore, it should be rejected.

Time Value Tables

If there is one thing that students appreciate, it is a short cut. Economists have created Time Value Tables, which consist of tables of factors which enable us to find present values and future balues without having to use the formulas.

Below is a future value table. In order to determine the future value of a deposit, simply determine the number of periods the investment will be held and its periodic interest rate, locate the factor which corresponds to those two factors, and multiply the deposit by the factor. For example, we determined that the future value of a $100 deposit for two periods at 7% was

$$\$100 \times (1 + .07)^2 =$$
$$\$100 \times 1.145 =$$
$$\$114.50$$

Now, use the short-cut method. Look up the factor corresponding to 7% for two periods. What do you find? You should have found the factor of 1.145. Now, instead of having to use the formula, all you have to do is multiply your deposit of $100 by the factor 1.145 to determine its future value.

Future Value Table

| | | | | | | Percent | | | | | | | | |
Period	1	2	3	4	5	6	7	8	9	10	12	14	16	18
1	1.010	1.020	1.030	1.040	1.050	1.060	1.070	1.080	1.090	1.100	1.120	1.140	1.160	1.180
2	1.020	1.040	1.061	1.082	1.103	1.124	1.145	1.166	1.188	1.210	1.254	1.300	1.346	1.392
3	1.030	1.061	1.093	1.125	1.158	1.191	1.225	1.260	1.295	1.331	1.405	1.482	1.561	1.643
4	1.041	1.082	1.126	1.170	1.216	1.262	1.311	1.360	1.412	1.464	1.574	1.689	1.811	1.939
5	1.051	1.104	1.159	1.217	1.276	1.338	1.403	1.469	1.539	1.611	1.762	1.925	2.100	2.288
6	1.062	1.126	1.194	1.265	1.340	1.419	1.501	1.587	1.677	1.772	1.974	2.195	2.436	2.700
7	1.072	1.149	1.230	1.316	1.407	1.504	1.606	1.714	1.828	1.949	2.211	2.502	2.826	3.185
8	1.083	1.172	1.267	1.369	1.477	1.594	1.718	1.851	1.993	2.144	2.476	2.853	3.278	3.759
9	1.094	1.195	1.305	1.423	1.551	1.689	1.838	1.999	2.172	2.358	2.773	3.252	3.803	4.435
10	1.105	1.219	1.344	1.480	1.629	1.791	1.967	2.159	2.367	2.594	3.106	3.707	4.411	5.234
11	1.116	1.243	1.384	1.539	1.710	1.898	2.105	2.322	2.580	2.853	3.479	4.226	5.117	6.176
12	1.127	1.268	1.426	1.601	1.796	2.012	2.252	2.518	2.813	3.138	3.896	4.818	5.936	7.288
13	1.138	1.294	1.469	1.665	1.886	2.133	2.410	2.720	3.066	3.452	4.363	5.492	6.886	8.599
14	1.149	1.319	1.513	1.732	1.980	2.261	2.579	2.937	3.342	3.797	4.887	6.261	7.988	10.147
15	1.161	1.346	1.558	1.801	2.079	2.397	2.759	3.172	3.642	4.177	5.474	7.138	9.266	11.974
16	1.173	1.373	1.605	1.873	2.183	2.540	2.952	3.426	3.970	4.595	6.130	8.137	10.748	14.129
17	1.184	1.400	1.653	1.948	2.292	2.693	3.159	3.700	4.328	5.054	6.866	9.276	12.468	16.672
18	1.196	1.428	1.702	2.206	2.407	2.854	3.380	3.996	4.717	5.560	7.690	10.575	14.463	19.673
19	1.208	1.457	1.754	2.107	2.527	3.026	3.617	4.316	5.142	6.116	8.613	12.056	16.777	23.214
20	1.220	1.486	1.806	2.191	2.653	3.207	3.870	4.661	5.604	6.727	9.646	13.743	19.461	27.393
21	1.232	1.516	1.860	2.279	2.786	3.400	4.141	5.034	6.109	7.400	10.804	15.668	22.574	32.324
22	1.245	1.546	1.916	2.370	2.925	3.604	4.430	5.437	6.659	8.140	12.100	17.861	26.186	38.142
23	1.257	1.577	1.974	2.465	3.072	3.820	4.741	5.871	7.258	8.954	13.552	20.362	30.376	45.008
24	1.270	1.608	2.033	2.563	3.225	4.049	5.072	6.341	7.911	9.850	15.179	23.212	35.236	53.109
25	1.282	1.641	2.094	2.666	3.368	4.292	5.427	6.848	8.623	10.835	17.000	26.462	40.874	62.669

Use the future value table to determine the future values of the following deposits.

9. $100 at 8% for one year $100 x 1.080 = $108.00

10. $73,000 at 10% for three years $73,000 x 1.331 = $97,163.00

11. $83,235 at 18% for sixteen years $83,235 x 14.129 = $1,176,027.32

Note that the table uses periods instead of years. This is because of periodic compounding. If an investment is earning 12% for 6 years compounded semiannually, you should use the factor corresponding to 6% (12%/2 periods per yr.) for 12 periods (6 yrs. × 2 periods per yr.). If interest is compounded quarterly, then you should use the factor corresponding to 3% for 24 periods.

Determine the following future values using your future value tables.

12. $76,435 at 12% for two years compounded semiannually $76,435 x 1.262 (6% for 4 periods) = $96,460.97

13. $76,435 at 12% for two years compounded quarterly $76,435 x 1.267 (3% for 8 periods) = $96,843.15

14. $76,435 at 12% for two years compounded monthly $76,435 x 1.270 (1% for 24 periods) = $97,072.45

Just as economists have developed future value tables to determine the future value of an investment when the interest rate, duration of the deposit, and the present value are known, they have also created present value tables. An example of a present value table is found below. Using present value tables, one can determine the present value of some future value as long as the interest rate and duration of the deposit are known. For example, rather than using the formula to determine the PV of an 8% investment that was held for one year which has an FV of $108.00 as we did earlier, we can multiply $108.00 by .926 with the result being $100.00.

As in the case of finding future values, if the deposit is compounded, we multiply the number of years by the number of compounding periods, and we divide the interest rate by the number of compounding periods in a year. Thus, the PV factor for a deposit which was held for 10 years at 10% compounded semiannually would be .377, the factor corresponding to 5% for twenty periods.

Use the present value table to determine the present values for the problems below.

15. A 22% investment compounded annually for ten years with a future value of $108,995.00

$108,995 x .137 (22% for 10 periods) = $14,932.32

16. A 12% investment compounded semiannually for ten years with a future value of $10,000.00

$10,000 x .312 (6% for 20 periods) = $3,120.00

17. A 48% investment compounded monthly for two years with a future value of $1,000,000

$1,000,000 x .390 (4% for 24 periods) = $390,000.00

Present Value Table

Period	Percent											
	2	4	6	8	10	12	14	16	18	20	22	24
1	.980	.962	.943	.926	.909	.893	.877	.862	.847	.833	.820	.807
2	.961	.925	.890	.857	.826	.797	.769	.743	.718	.694	.672	.650
3	.942	.889	.840	.794	.751	.712	.675	.641	.609	.579	.551	.525
4	.924	.855	.792	.735	.683	.636	.592	.552	.516	.482	.451	.423
5	.906	.822	.747	.681	.621	.567	.519	.476	.437	.402	.370	.341
6	.888	.790	.705	.630	.564	.507	.456	.410	.370	.335	.303	.275
7	.871	.760	.665	.584	.513	.452	.400	.354	.314	.279	.249	.222
8	.853	.731	.627	.540	.467	.404	.351	.305	.266	.233	.204	.179
9	.837	.703	.592	.500	.424	.361	.308	.263	.226	.194	.167	.144
10	.820	.676	.558	.463	.386	.322	.270	.227	.191	.162	.137	.116
12	.788	.625	.497	.397	.319	.257	.208	.168	.137	.112	.092	.076
14	.758	.577	.442	.340	.263	.205	.160	.125	.099	.078	.062	.049
16	.728	.534	.394	.292	.218	.163	.123	.093	.071	.054	.042	.032
18	.700	.494	.350	.250	.180	.130	.095	.069	.051	.038	.028	.021
20	.673	.456	.312	.215	.149	.104	.073	.051	.037	.026	.019	.014
22	.647	.422	.278	.184	.123	.083	.056	.038	.026	.018	.013	.009
24	.622	.390	.247	.158	.102	.066	.043	.028	.019	.013	.008	.006

Valuing Bonds

The philosopher La Rochefoucauld once said, "The greatest of all gifts is the power to estimate things at their true worth." Most of us know the chagrin of purchasing something only to find later that we paid too much. When investing money, however, the sums of money are far greater, and the consequences of paying too much for an asset could be financially ruinous. The key in purchasing investments such as bonds, therefore, is to determine whether the price is right at the time of purchase.

A bond is evidence of a loan that an individual has made to a corporation or a government entity. When a consumer purchases a house, he signs a note which legally obligates him to pay principal and interest over the life of the note. If the holder of the note (the bank) needs some money in a hurry, it may sell the note to another bank. Thus, a home mortgage may have many owners over the life of the loan. Likewise, bonds issued by corporations are bought and sold as investments. How can an investor know whether he is paying the right price for a bond?

When a person purchases a bond upon its issuance by the corporation (usually for $1,000), he is receiving two promises. First, he is promised periodic interest. That is, if a bond is carrying a 6% interest rate, the bondholder will receive $60 at the end of each year. Second, he is promised repayment of the principal. If the bond has a maturity of twenty years, the bondholder is legally entitled to receive his $1,000 principal at the end of the twenty-year period. Since a bond is an investment instrument like a savings account and has a set future value, it is easy to determine the price for which it should be sold today. The price of a bond today is the present value of all future interest and principal payments with one twist: the interest rate used is the interest rate being offered on brand-new bonds.

The following example will illustrate how bond valuation works. What should you be willing to pay for a $1,000, 6% bond with five years left to maturity, assuming that new bonds are carrying a 10% interest rate?

PRESENT VALUE (PV) OF THE INTEREST PAYMENTS REMAINING DURING THE LIFE OF THE BOND:

Year #1 interest payment: $60 (6% of $1,000)	x .909 (PV figure for 10% period #1)	=	$54.54
Year #2 interest payment: $60	x .826	=	49.56
Year #3 interest payment: $60	x .751	=	45.06
Year #4 interest payment: $60	x .683	=	40.98
Year #5 interest payment: $60	x .621	=	37.26

PRESENT VALUE OF THE FINAL PRINCIPAL PAYMENT DUE UPON MATURITY:

$1,000	x .621 (PV figure for 10% period #5)	=	621.00

TOTAL PRESENT VALUE OF INTEREST PLUS PRINCIPAL: = $848.40

You are in the market to purchase a bond. Your neighbor has offered to sell you his $1,000, 10% bond for $1,000. Assuming that new bonds are carrying a 6% rate and that your neighbor's bond has five years left to maturity, calculate the price you should be willing to pay. Is your neighbor trying to rip you off or give you a bargain? Use your present value tables and show all work below.

PRESENT VALUE (PV) OF THE INTEREST PAYMENTS REMAINING DURING THE LIFE OF THE BOND:

Year #1 interest payment: $100 (10% of $1,000)	*x .943 (PV figure for 6% period #1)*	*=*	*$94.30*
Year #2 interest payment: $100	*x .890*	*=*	*89.00*
Year #3 interest payment: $100	*x .840*	*=*	*84.00*
Year #4 interest payment: $100	*x .792*	*=*	*79.20*
Year #5 interest payment: $100	*x .747*	*=*	*74.70*

PRESENT VALUE OF THE FINAL PRINCIPAL PAYMENT DUE UPON MATURITY:

$1,000	*x .747 (PV figure for 6% period #5)*	*=*	*747.00*

TOTAL PRESENT VALUE OF INTEREST PLUS PRINCIPAL: *=* *$1,168.20*

Buy the bond. You are getting a bond worth $1,168.20 for a bargain price of $1,000.

Multiple Choice

Choose the response which best answers the question or completes the sentence.

__C__ 1. According to your text, which of the following is not one of the basic purposes for holding cash?
   A. to pay for routine transactions
   B. to pay for unexpected emergencies
   C. to pay for valuable coins
   D. to provide a store of value

__D__ 2. Which of the following is not a transaction account?
   A. a super-NOW account at a savings and loan association
   B. a checking account at a commercial bank
   C. a share-draft account at a credit union
   D. All of the above are types of transactions accounts.

__B__ 3. If a savings account becomes the property of a widow, then the account was one of
   A. tenants in common.
   B. rights of survivorship.
   C. corporate tenants de facto.
   D. nonrecisionary contract de facto.

__B__ 4. A postdated check is one
   A. which has a date which is too old.
   B. which is dated for some date in the future.
   C. on which the date has been posted by the payee.
   D. which is missing a date.

__A__ 5. Which of the following types of guaranteed checks has the bank place a hold on the check buyer's funds?
   A. certified check
   B. traveler's check
   C. cashier's check
   D. money order

__B__ 6. The formula $100 \times \{[1 + (i/n)]^n - 1\}$ calculates the
   A. nominal rate of interest.
   B. effective rate of interest.
   C. yield to maturity.
   D. present value of an investment.

Modified True/False

If the statement is true, write the word *true* in the blank. If it is false, change the underlined word(s) to make the statement true. Write the correct word(s) in the blank.

__six months__ 1. A bank is not legally required to cash a check that is dated more than three months old.

__True__ 2. FSLIC stands for Federal Savings and Loan Insurance Corporation.

__words__ 3. If the two amounts on a check disagree, the one written in numerals is accepted as the legally correct amount.

__True__ 4. It is possible for interest to be compounded daily but posted only quarterly.

__Escheat__ 5. Fraud is a term that is associated with a bank's turning dormant accounts over to the government.

Writing a Will

The most important step, by far, in developing a comprehensive financial plan is executing a valid will. If you die intestate, that is, without a will, the government of the state in which you live will determine who will receive your possessions and take care of your children. Generally, when an unmarried person dies intestate one-half of the estate will go to each living parent; if only one parent is living, he or she will receive the entire estate. If neither parent is living, the estate will be divided among surviving brothers and sisters. If a married person dies, on the other hand, the state usually dictates that one-half of the estate is given to the surviving spouse while the other half is given equally to any surviving children. Finally, if a person dies intestate without any surviving parents, spouse, children, or any other next of kin, the entire estate is usually given to the state.

"So what?" you may be saying. "When I'm dead, I don't care what happens to my possessions. I'll never see them again!" Nevertheless, it is important what happens to your possessions after you die. Scripture places a very high responsibility upon all of us to make wise choices with what has been placed into our care. After all, we really do not own anything. We are merely stewards of those things with which we have been entrusted, be they houses, automobiles, bank accounts, jewelry, or children. To allow the state to make choices according to its laws that we should be making according to God's commandments is ignorant at best and poor stewardship at worst. Also, you may not see your possessions again, but you may see your children again. It is very important to specify their guardians in your will. Otherwise, the state will select someone to care for them without regard for their spiritual well-being. Do you remember the story of Job? In the end he received twice as many goods as he had before. The only exception to his doubled prosperity was his children. Prior to the disasters which befell him he had ten children. When his tribulations were over he had another ten children. You might be wondering why he didn't have twenty children. The answer is simple: He never lost his first children; they merely went to another place. In the end he had twenty children. Since your children are your most important gift from God, you must provide for their spiritual well-being even after your death.

The execution of a valid will is the way to legally make your wishes known. There is a definite format that a legal will should follow. For the Christian, the will should begin with a declaration of the decedent's testimony. Then the will should specify an executor and a guardian for all minor children, list all specific gifts, list other gifts, provide instructions for the payment of any estate taxes, and provide full authority to the executor. In addition to a legal will, many provide a document commonly known as a letter of last instructions. A *letter of last instructions* (officially known as a *letter precatory*) is usually a signed, handwritten letter which, in many cases, is very personal and sentimental and gives the executor details which may not be provided in a will. Items usually contained in a letter of last instruction include information pertaining to the location of bank accounts and account numbers, locations of various items which the executor might otherwise have a difficult time locating, and burial instructions.

Given the information below, construct a last will and testament and a letter of last instructions.

Your name is Patty Jones. You are 32 years old, and you reside at 1223 Spruance Road in Dayton, Ohio. Your husband, Carey Jones, died two years ago as a result of a prolonged illness. You have two children: Mark, age 7, and Kimberly, age 4. You have checking and savings accounts which are located in the Suburban Bank of Dayton, Ohio. Your checking account number is 376-376-5, and your savings account number is 476-17290-357. Your safe-deposit box is located at the Second Citizens National Bank in Dayton. In your safe-deposit box is your life insurance policy (worth $300,000), $14,000 worth of U.S. Savings Bonds, the diamond engagement ring which once belonged to your mother (value $3,500), and a coin collection which belonged to your father (value $2,750). Also enclosed in the safe-deposit box are your important personal papers: the deed to your home, the title to your car, all birth certificates and Social Security cards, and all the documents pertaining to stocks, bonds, and mutual funds (worth $700,000). Upon your death you would like for your daughter to receive the diamond ring and for your son to receive the coin collection. Your brother, Buddy Bierman, a pastor in Manhattan, Kansas, has agreed to serve as executor of your estate. Should Buddy be unable to serve as executor, Mr. Donald Worthington, a businessman in your church, has agreed to serve as substitute executor. Your brother, Buddy, and his wife, Sarah, have agreed to serve as legal guardians for your children should the need arise. Your late husband's parents, Cory and Matilda Jones, are another godly couple who, now in their mid-50s, have also agreed to serve as guardians for Mark and Kimberly. Because of age factors, you would prefer

to have your children go to your brother and sister-in-law, but if they, at the time of your death, cannot serve as legal guardians, you want your children to live with your in-laws in their home in Dayton, Ohio. You want to give $5,000 of your estate to your home church, Faith Baptist Church, for its building fund. You desire for all funeral arrangements to be made through the Madison Funeral Home (owned by a member of your church), and you wish to be buried in the Green Lawn Cemetery beside your late spouse (at the time of your spouse's death you purchased two plots). You would like to have Psalm 119:112, the verse you chose as your life's verse after you were saved on June 1, 1977, inscribed on your headstone.

LAST WILL AND TESTAMENT OF PATTY JONES

Believing that faithful stewardship to my Lord and Savior Jesus Christ is as important in death as well as in life, I, Patty Jones of 1223 Spruance Road, Dayton, Ohio, state that this is my last will and testament, revoking all previous wills. On June 1, 1977, after reading Romans 3:23, "For all have sinned and come short of the glory of God," I realized that I was a sinner. Further realizing that "the wages of sin is death; but the gift of God is eternal life through Jesus Christ our Lord" (Romans 6:23), I accepted Jesus Christ as my personal Savior in accordance to Romans 10:13: "For whosoever shall call upon the name of the Lord shall be saved." I urge all readers and hearers of this will to claim Jesus Christ as their personal Savior that they may know the forgiveness of their sins and the gift of eternal life in heaven.

1. EXECUTORS: *I appoint my brother, Mr. Buddy Bierman, of Manhattan, Kansas, executor of this will. If Buddy is unable or unwilling to do so or ceases to do so, I appoint Mr. Donald Worthington of Dayton, Ohio, to serve as substitute executor.*

2. GUARDIANS: *I appoint my brother and his wife, Buddy and Sarah Bierman, of Manhattan, Kansas, to serve as guardians over the persons and property of my children until they are eighteen (18) years of age. I also appoint my late husband's parents, Cory and Matilda Jones of Dayton, Ohio, to serve as substitute guardians in the event that Buddy and Sarah are unwilling or unable to serve as guardians or cease to do so.*

3. SPECIFIC GIFTS: *I leave the diamond ring which once belonged to my mother to my daughter, Kimberly. I leave the coin collection which belonged to my father to my son, Mark. Should either of my children die before I do, or at the same time, the specific gifts they were to receive shall be given to my brother, Buddy Bierman.*

4. GENERAL GIFTS: *I leave to my church, Faith Baptist Church in Dayton, Ohio, five thousand dollars ($5,000) for its building fund. Should this gift not be accepted or should the church not be in existence at the time of my death, this gift shall become part of my residuary estate.*

5. RESIDUARY ESTATE: *I give all of the rest of my property to my children, Mark and Kimberly Jones. If they die before me or at the same time, I give all this property to my brother, Buddy Bierman.*

6. TAXES AND ADMINISTRATIVE EXPENSES: *All taxes and expenses related to my estate are to be paid out of the residuary estate.*

7. EXECUTOR'S OPTIONS: *In order to expedite the distribution of my estate, I give my executor full power to sell, lease, mortgage, reinvest, or otherwise dispose of the assets in my estate.*

Signed _____*Patty Jones*_____ Dated Signed ____*today's date*____

    WITNESSES: At Patty Jones's request, we met on the date inserted above to witness the signing of this will. With all of us present at the same time, Patty Jones signed it and affirmed it to be the last will and testament.

Signed _____ **Address** _____

Signed _____ **Address** _____

Signed _____ **Address** _____

Dear Buddy,

If you are reading this letter, it can only mean that I have gone to be with the Lord. I thank God that He privileged you and me to be reared by the godly parents we had and that we were both saved at an early age. I thank you for the love you and Sarah expressed to Kimberly, Mark, and me over the years, especially during Carey's illness and the difficult time afterward. Now Carey and I are both in heaven in a far better place, but I cannot help but be concerned about the welfare of the children God gave Carey and me. As you have no doubt already realized, I have named you executor of my estate, as well as naming you and Sarah guardians for Kimberly and Mark. I know you have loved them as if they were your own children over the past several years. Now they are your own. Please love them as I have sought to love them and be sure to bring them up in the "nurture and admonition of the Lord." They are wonderful children, but they are individuals with totally different personalities. Kimberly is rather headstrong and determined, while Mark tends to be a follower. Both of these qualities can be assets or liabilities as they grow up. Do all that you can to make sure that they grow up to love the Lord and seek to serve Him. I want Kimberly and Mark to receive a Christian education; therefore, it is up to you to select a good Christian school for them to attend. I know that your legal authority over them ends when they turn eighteen, but please do all that you can to urge them to attend a good Christian college. Since they will probably find their life's partners in college, as did Carey and I, I want to make sure that they are pointed in the right direction.

The following are a few details which I am sure will prove helpful as you try to "tie up all of the loose ends" as executor of the estate. First, I have a checking account (#376-376-5) and a savings account (#476-17290-357) in the Suburban Bank of Dayton, Ohio. I also have a safe-deposit box at the Second Citizens National Bank in Dayton, Ohio. In my safe-deposit box you will find a $300,000 life insurance policy naming Kimberly and Mark as beneficiaries. Also in the safe-deposit box are $14,000 worth of U.S. Savings Bonds, the diamond engagement ring I have left for Kimberly (It was Mom's, you might remember), Dad's old coin collection I have left to Mark, and an assortment of miscellaneous papers, including all of our Social Security cards, the deed to the house, the title to my car, all of our birth certificates, and the papers on all of my stocks, bonds, and mutual funds worth $700,000.

Regarding my funeral, I would like to be buried next to Carey at the Green Lawn Cemetery. When Carey was buried I purchased the second plot. I would like for all of the funeral arrangements to be made through the Madison Funeral Home since Mr. Madison is a member of my church and has been a good friend for years. He took care of all of Carey's arrangements and was very helpful. Please don't spend a lot of money on my funeral. I would like for Pastor Connell to preach my funeral. I know that he will preach the gospel and I have several friends who really need to be saved. Finally, I would like to have my life verse inscribed on my headstone:

I have inclined my heart to perform thy statutes alway,
even unto the end.

Psalm 119:112

Thank you, Buddy,

Patty

Duties of an Executor

Probate is the name for the court procedure for settling and disposing of an estate with or without a valid will. Probate is often a very slow process, tying up the assets of the estate for months or even years. One of the most important aspects of composing your last will and testament is the careful selection of an executor for your estate and his or her substitute. The task of serving as an executor is not an easy one; it involves hours of labor with attorneys, bankers, clerks, creditors, debtors, and family members. In the space below, list what you believe are some of the most important duties of an executor. *Student answers will vary, but the answers below are some of the most important duties of an executor.*

1. *Assist in making funeral arrangements: Carefully read the last will and testament and the letter of last instructions and contact immediate family members to determine the wishes of the deceased and family. There may be special considerations. If the deceased was ever a member of the armed forces, he may be eligible for a military funeral.*

2. *Collect all amounts due to the decedent's estate: Search through the decedent's business papers in filing cabinets, desks, and safe-deposit boxes to determine whether any money is owed his estate from others, including wages, life insurance proceeds, pensions, Social Security benefits, and personal loans he had made.*

3. *Determine the value of the deceased's estate by having real estate and other property appraised; having the contents of safe-deposit boxes inventoried; determining amounts of funds in checking, saving, and other bank accounts; and liquidating securities such as stocks, bonds, and other investments.*

4. *Determine all debts owed by the deceased and pay them as expeditiously as possible. In some cases a debt must remain unpaid for a short period of time until the estate is liquidated. In such cases, the executor should notify the creditor so that unpleasant collection procedures are not initiated against a grieving widow or widower.*

5. *Enlist the assistance of lawyers and accountants in completing estate, income, and inheritance tax forms.*

6. *Ensure that the dependents of the deceased have been properly cared for during the estate settlement process. Do the dependents have enough money to purchase food, clothing, shelter, and other necessities? In this way, the executor becomes almost a substitute provider for a short period of time.*

7. *If the deceased was a business owner or partner, the executor may have to step in and oversee his business until the estate is settled.*

8. *Ensure that distribution of the liquidated estate is in accordance with the will of the deceased and with all applicable laws.*

9. *Other possible answers include the following: Submit all necessary reports with the court regarding your activities as executor. / If the will is contested, testify in court as required. / Console grieving family members.*

Economics

Calculating Estate Value and Estate Taxes Owed
Calculating Gross Estate and Net Taxable Estate

Mark Twain once remarked that there are a lot of uncertainties in life, but two certainties are ''death and taxes.'' A big problem for beneficiaries of an estate is that often those two certainties go hand in hand. Upon the death of a person, the value of his estate is totaled and taxes are levied. Three questions are often asked by those unfamiliar with the process of settling an estate. First, how does one calculate the size of a decedent's estate? Second, how are estate taxes calculated? Third, is there any way to avoid paying estate taxes?

The first question is relatively simple to answer. A person's gross estate includes virtually everything that he owns plus amounts due him from others at the time of his death. A person's estate taxes are not figured on the gross estate but rather on his net taxable estate, which is calculated by subtracting from the gross estate all of the decedent's debts, expenses arising from the settling of the estate, charitable bequests in the will, properties that were passed to others by law or contract, and any taxable gifts received after 1976. Proceeds from life insurance are not considered part of a decedent's gross estate and thus are not taxed.

In the space below, calculate Patty Jones's gross estate and net taxable estate given the following information.

Value of a home in Dayton, Ohio	$120,000
Proceeds of life insurance policy	300,000
Total value of checking account	800
Value of automobile	2,500
Total value of savings account	3,200
U.S. Savings Bonds	14,000
Value of personal possessions and home furnishings	18,000
Value of investments in stocks, bonds, and mutual funds	700,000
Amount owed on home mortgage	15,000
Balance owed on MasterCard	300
Balance owed to dentist	700
Total of amounts owed on utility bills	400
Funeral costs	3,000
Costs of settling the estate (court costs)	32,000
Bequest to church building fund	5,000

Gross Estate:

Value of home in Dayton, Ohio	**$120,000**
Total value of checking account	**800**
Value of automobile	**2,500**
Total value of savings account	**3,200**
U.S. Savings Bonds	**14,000**
Value of personal possessions and home furnishings	**18,000**
Value of investments in stocks, bonds, and mutual funds	**700,000**
TOTAL GROSS ESTATE	**$858,500**

Net Taxable Estate:

Gross Estate	**$858,500**

Less:

Amount owed on home mortgage	**$15,000**
Balance owed on MasterCard	**300**
Balance owed to dentist	**700**
Total of amounts owed on utility bills	**400**
Funeral costs	**3,000**
Costs of settling the estate (court costs)	**32,000**
Charitable bequest to church building fund	**5,000**
TOTAL NET TAXABLE INCOME	**$802,100**

Calculating Estate Taxes

While death is a certainty for all of us as long as the Lord tarries, estate taxes are not. The way that current estate tax law is written, less than 10% of all Americans will be subject to estate taxes. Congress has written estate tax laws in such a way that there is no tax liability on net taxable estates of $600,000 or less. This is because there is an estate tax credit which reduces all estate tax liabilities by $192,800. Using the table below, note how estate taxes are computed. For example, assume that a person dies with a net taxable estate of $400,000. Since $400,000 falls between the ''more than'' of

$250,000 and the ''but not greater than'' of $500,000, the tax would be $70,800 plus 34% of $150,000 ($400,000 NTE minus $250,000) for a total of $121,800. Since the tax is $121,800 but the unified estate tax credit is $192,800, the estate is not liable to pay any taxes.

Let us try one more example. What would be the tax liability for Patty Jones's estate from the previous exercise? We determined that the Net Taxable Estate was $802,100. This NTE is more than $750,000 and less than $1,000,000, causing the tax to be $248,300 plus 39% of the excess of the NTE over $750,000.

Tax	$248,300
Excess Tax [.39 × (802,100 − 750,000)]	+ 20,319
Total Tax	$268,619
Less: Unified Estate Tax Credit	− 192,800
Total Adjusted Estate Tax	$75,819

GIFT AND ESTATE TAXES				
NET TAXABLE ESTATE (NTE)		TAX	RATE OF TAX ON EXCESS ABOVE AMOUNT IN COLUMN 1	UNIFIED GIFT AND ESTATE TAX CREDIT
MORE THAN	BUT NOT GREATER THAN			
$ 0	$10,000	18% OF NTE	0%	$192,800
10,000	20,000	$1,800	20	192,800
20,000	40,000	3,800	22	192,800
40,000	60,000	8,200	24	192,800
60,000	80,000	13,000	26	192,800
80,000	100,000	18,200	28	192,800
100,000	150,000	23,800	30	192,800
150,000	250,000	38,800	32	192,800
250,000	500,000	70,800	34	192,800
500,000	750,000	155,800	37	192,800
750,000	1,000,000	248,300	39	192,800
1,000,000	1,250,000	345,800	41	192,800
1,250,000	1,500,000	448,300	43	192,800
1,500,000	2,000,000	555,800	45	192,800
2,000,000	2,500,000	780,800	49	192,800
2,500,000	3,000,000	1,025,800	53	192,800
3,000,000	—	1,290,800	55	192,800

Source: Internal Revenue Service.

Using the table on the previous page, calculate the total estate tax owed on the following Net Taxable Estates. (Round all answers to the nearest whole dollar.)

A. $600,000

Tax	*$155,800*
Excess Tax [.37 x (600,000–500,000)]	*+ 37,000*
Total Tax	*192,800*
Less Unified Estate Tax Credit	*– 192,800*
Total Adjusted Estate Tax	*$0*

B. $845,310

Tax	*$248,300*
Excess Tax [.39 x (845,310–750,000)]	*+ 37,171*
Total Tax	*285,471*
Less Unified Estate Tax Credit	*– 192,800*
Total Adjusted Estate Tax	*$92,671*

C. $1,234,567

Tax	*$345,800*
Excess Tax [.41 x (1,234,567–1,000,000)]	*+ 96,172*
Total Tax	*441,972*
Less Unified Estate Tax Credit	*– 192,800*
Total Adjusted Estate Tax	*$249,172*

D. $4,982,559

Tax	*$1,290,800*
Excess Tax [.55 x (4,982,559–3,000,000)]	*+1,090,407*
Total Tax	*2,381,207*
Less Unified Estate Tax Credit	*– 192,800*
Total Adjusted Estate Tax	*$2,188,407*

Economics

Determining Amount of Life Insurance to Purchase

Virtually all insurance is designed to replace what was lost. Automobile collision insurance replaces your vehicle should you damage or totally destroy your car; homeowner's insurance will replace your home if it is lost in a fire. Life insurance cannot replace a loved one, but it can replace the income which was lost as a result of his or her death. The first step in the process of obtaining life insurance is to determine the amount of life insurance which will meet death related expenses, pay outstanding medical expenses, pay off outstanding credit obligations, and provide a predetermined amount of income to survivors (above any income provided by Social Security).

The formula to determine the amount of life insurance one needs to purchase, therefore, is:

Necessary Life Insurance = Death Related Expenses +

+ Medical Expenses of Deceased
+ Outstanding Credit Obligations
+ (Desired Annual Income – Interest Income on Current Investments – Annual Social Security Income)/Interest Rate You Can Earn on Low Risk Investments

Sam Ramey attended a personal financial management seminar in which he realized the importance of personal financial planning. He just completed his last will and testament and letter of last instructions and is now ready to purchase a life insurance policy, but he does not know how much he needs. Sam is 37 years old, and his wife is also 37 years old. Sam brings home $1,400 per month ($16,800 per year) after taxes. He estimates that it will cost approximately $8,000 for death related expenses and $10,000 for possible outstanding medical bills. He has a $50,000 mortgage outstanding on his house, $10,000 in outstanding loans on their two cars,

$1,500 outstanding balance on a recent school loan, and miscellaneous small credit balances totaling $800. Sam's insurance agent advised Sam to purchase a $500,000 life insurance policy at a cost of $300 per year per $100,000 for a total of $1,500 per year. Should Sam do it? Justify your answer. Assume that investments of life insurance proceeds can be invested to return a stable 6% rate of return after taxes and that he has investments which provide $100 per month in interest. Also assume that Sam's family will be eligible to receive $800 per month in Social Security benefits.

ESTIMATION OF NEEDED LIFE INSURANCE		
CATEGORY OF NEED		AMOUNT
DEATH RELATED EXPENSES		*$8,000*
ANTICIPATED MEDICAL EXPENSES		*10,000*
OUTSTANDING CREDIT OBLIGATIONS:		
Home mortgage	*$50,000*	
Automobile loans	*10,000*	
School loan	*1,500*	
Miscellaneous loans	*800*	
TOTAL OUTSTANDING CREDIT OBLIGATIONS		*$62,300*
(ANNUAL INCOME – INTEREST INCOME ON CURRENT INVESTMENTS – ANNUAL SOCIAL SECURITY BENEFITS) / INTEREST RATE ON LOW RISK INVESTMENTS: ($16,800 – 1,200 – 9,600) / .06		*100,000*
TOTAL LIFE INSURANCE NEED		*$180,300*

Answer: *It appears that Sam is being asked to purchase more life insurance than he really needs. He could meet his needs with a $200,000 policy at a cost of $600 per year ($50 per month) as opposed to spending a total of $1,500 per year for a $500,000 policy.*

Term Life Insurance Versus Whole Life Insurance

Your text points out that the two basic forms of life insurance are term life insurance and whole life insurance. Term life insurance provides only death protection, while whole life insurance provides a savings element. Many financial experts point out that the sole motive for the purchase of life insurance should be to provide income protection for those who are dependent upon one's income and that one should not look to a life insurance policy as an investment medium. They point out that when one combines any kind of purchase with a savings plan, the purchaser usually ends up losing money. For example, several years ago gas stations gave out savings stamps which, after accumulated, could be used for the purchase of merchandise. Many gas stations offered five, ten, and sometimes up to fifteen times the normal quantity of savings stamps for a much higher price per gallon of gasoline. It took some time, but the public realized that they could have saved money by purchasing gasoline without savings stamps, accumulated the difference that they would have paid, and been able to purchase their desired merchandise much sooner. Likewise, many personal financial planners advise their clients to avoid purchasing the significantly more expensive whole life insurance and purchase basic term life insurance. The amount saved should be personally invested. Otherwise, the insurance company invests your money, keeps out a portion of your earnings for expenses, fees, and profits, and remits to you a fraction of what you could have earned.

The table provided on the next page illustrates how you will actually make money by purchasing term life insurance and investing the difference. The table has five columns. The first column shows the age of the insured. Column 2 gives the premium for a $100,000 policy for annual renewable term life insurance. (Note that these values have come from the rate chart for a male in good health from an earlier exercise.) Column 3 is the savings one would experience for that year by purchasing term over whole life insurance. (We are assuming that the whole life policy premium is $850 per year.) If the policy holder pays for his term insurance at the beginning of each year and invests the difference, he will earn interest during the year; therefore, the amounts in column 4 are found by adding any previous years' balance to the savings for that particular year and adding 6%. (We are assuming that even an inexperienced investor could earn at least 6%.) For example, in the first year of this program (age 30), the term life insurance purchaser would save $679 ($850 - $171 ART premium). If the $679 were invested at 6%, the invested savings would become $719.74 by the end of the year, bringing the estate's value to $100,719.74 (the sum of the insurance proceeds of $100,000 plus the invested savings). Likewise, in the second year (age 31), the savings is $679. This savings, added to the previous year's total savings of $719.74, is $1,398.74. When invested at 6% for all of year 2, the balance becomes $1,482.66. Simply stated, the formula for computing the new value for column 4 is as follows: (last year's ending balance + this year's savings) $\times$ 1.06. For age 30: ($0 + $679) $\times$ 1.06 = $719.74. For age 31: ($719.74 + $679 $\times$ 1.06) = $1,482.66.

Fill in the empty blanks in columns 4 and 5 from age 46 through age 60. What will be the total *increase* in the estate's value if the client purchases term insurance and invests the difference?

Age	Premium for Annual Renewable Term	Difference ($850 Whole Life Premium Less ART Premium)	Total of Savings and Earnings at 6%	Total Estate ($100,000 + Total Savings and Earnings)
		ESTATE BUILD-UP IF INSURED PURCHASES TERM LIFE INSURANCE INSTEAD OF WHOLE LIFE AND INVESTS THE DIFFERENCE		
30	$171	$679	$719.74	$100,719.74
31	171	679	1,482.66	101,482.66
32	172	678	2,290.30	102,290.30
33	177	673	3,141.10	103,141.10
34	180	670	4,039.77	104,039.77
35	183	667	4,989.18	104,989.18
36	190	660	5,988.13	105.988.13
37	198	652	7,138.54	107.138.54
38	206	644	8,143.49	108,143.49
39	218	632	9,302.02	109,302.02
40	231	619	10,516.28	110,516.28
41	243	607	11,790.68	111,790.68
42	260	590	13,123.52	113,123.52
43	282	568	14,513.01	114,513.01
44	308	542	15,958.31	115,958.31
45	340	510	17.456.41	117,456.41
46	372	478	*19,010.47*	*119,010.47*
47	403	447	*20,624.92*	*120,624.92*
48	429	421	*22,308.68*	*122,308.68*
49	465	385	*24,055.30*	*124,055.30*
50	498	352	*25,871.74*	*125,871.74*
51	542	308	*27,750.52*	*127,750.52*
52	587	263	*29,694.33*	*129,694.33*
53	643	207	*31,695.41*	*131,695.41*
54	701	149	*33,755.07*	*133,755.07*
55	772	78	*35,863.05*	*135,863.05*
56	839	11	*38,026.49*	*138,026.49*
57	910	-60	*40,244.48*	*140,244.48*
58	997	-147	*42,503.33*	*142,503.33*
59	1,078	-228	*44,811.85*	*144,811.85*
60	1,183	-333	*47,147.58*	*147,147.58*

Economics

Completing a Life Insurance Application and Computing Premiums

The Life Insurance Application

After a person knows how much life insurance he needs, he must complete a life insurance application. On the next three pages is a typical life insurance application. Use the following information to complete the application for Mr. Samuel Paul Ramey.

His Social Security number is 111-22-3333.

He works for United Semiconductors as a quality assurance inspector and has held this position since April 24, 1982.

He is naming his wife, Glenda, as the first-class beneficiary of the policy and his children, Lisa and Ben, as the second-class beneficiaries.

Mr. Ramey's address for the past fifteen years has been 374 Cone Circle, San Diego, California, 92115 in San Diego County.

His home telephone number is (619) 555-1212, and his work telephone number is (619) 555-1213.

Mr. Ramey was born 37 years ago today in the state of California.

He is 5' 11" and weighs 175 lbs.

He is in excellent health because of his regular bicycling, running, and swimming regimen in which he works out for at least one hour per day.

He has never smoked cigarettes.

His driver's license number is CA1654903424.

Mr. Ramey will be the owner of the policy.

He is requesting $250,000 in annual term insurance with no optional benefits.

He is eligible for the nonsmoker good health discount.

His doctor's name is Robert Preston of 4545 Doctor's Drive in San Diego, California, 92124, telephone number (619) 555-1214.

Two years ago today, Mr. Ramey was suffering from the flu, so he visited his doctor. The doctor prescribed antibiotics.

Mr. Ramey answered all of the health and behavior questions in the negative.

He will pay his premium annually.

HOMETOWN LIFE INSURANCE COMPANY
Hometown, USA 10000

Part 1 - Application for
Annual Term and Five-Year Term

1. PERSONS PROPOSED FOR INSURANCE			Sex	Birthdate Mo. Day Yr.	Actual Age	Birth Place	Marital Status	Social Security #	Height and Weight
First	Middle	Last							
a. Insured Samuel Paul Ramey			M	today's date 37 yrs. ago	37	(state) CA	M	111-22-3333	Ht. 5' 11" / Wt. 175
b. Children (if to be insured) **(The children are to be beneficiaries; they are not being insured. Nothing should be entered here.)**						Must be age 17 or less at last birthday, be children or stepchildren of the Insured, and be living with the Insured.			

2. ADDRESS

No./Street **374 Cone Circle**	Phone # Home **(619) 555-1212** Bus. **(619) 555-1213**
City/State **San Diego, California**	Driver's License # **CA1654903424** State **CA**
Zip Code/County **92115 / San Diego County**	Prior address (if at present address less than 1 year)
Date Moved to Address (Mo./Yr.) **Present month 15 yrs. ago**	

3. OWNER (if other than 1a)

	Address	Relationship	Soc. Sec. #	Home Ph. #

4. BENEFICIARY

First Class	Relationship	Second Class	Relationship
Glenda Ramey	**wife**	**Lisa and Ben Ramey**	**children**

5. EMPLOYMENT

Occupation **Quality assurance inspector**

Employer Name/Date of Employment (Mo./Yr.) **United Semiconductors / April 1982**

6. INSURANCE REQUESTED

Face Amount $ **$250,000**

Plan (check one) [X] Annual Term   [ ] Five-Year Term

7. FIVE-YEAR TERM OPTIONAL BENEFITS/RIDERS

[ ] Waiver of Premium
[ ] Accidental Death Benefit
[ ] Children's Level Term Rider _____ Units

8. DISCOUNTS

a. Has anyone proposed for this insurance smoked cigarettes in the last twelve months?   [ ] Yes   [X] No
b. [X] Good Health (Complete attached Healthy American Questionnaire - LR536)

9. PAYMENT PLAN

[X] Annual   [ ] Semi-Annual   [ ] Quarterly   [ ] Pre-Authorized Method (Complete attached form.)
[ ] Payroll Deduction (Attach LB1)   [ ] Military Allotment (Five-Year Term only)   [ ] Other _____
[ ] Account Bill (Check one payment plan above and list all policies for account bill in REMARKS.)

10. LAST PHYSICIAN CONSULTED - Please answer completely. If none, state "NONE."

When? (Mo./Yr.) **Present month 2 yrs. ago**	Physician's Name **Robert Preston**
Why? **flu**	No./Street **4545 Doctor's Drive**
Treatment/Medication **antibiotics**	City/State/Zip **San Diego, CA 92124**
	Phone # **(619) 555-1214**

Complete the following, if available (this will expedite processing):
Dr. Tax I.D. #   Patient #   Fee: $

11. Has anyone proposed for this insurance: Yes No

    a. **Ever** used narcotics, hallucinatory or mind-altering substances not prescribed by a physician or been arrested for the use, possession, sale, or delivery of such substances? . . . . ☐   ☒

    b. **Ever** sought or received treatment or advice for the use of alcohol? . . . . ☐   ☒

    c. Had a driver's license revoked or suspended due to a moving violation within the **last 5 years** or **ever** been charged with driving under the influence of alcohol or drugs? . . . . ☐   ☒

    d. Been charged with 3 or more moving violations, or had 2 or more accidents while driving a motor vehicle within the **last 3 years?** . . . . ☐   ☒

    e. Been convicted of, or pled guilty to, a felony charge within the **last 5 years?** . . . . ☐   ☒

    f. **Ever** been diagnosed or received treatment by a medical practitioner for Acquired Immune Deficiency Syndrome, AIDS Related Complex, or any AIDS related condition? . . . . ☐   ☒

    g. **Ever** sought or received treatment for, been diagnosed as having, or had symptoms of heart attack, stroke, cancer, or malignancy? . . . . ☐   ☒

12. Has anyone proposed for this insurance EVER been treated for, had any symptom of, or been told that he/she has: Yes No

    a. High blood pressure . . . . ☐   ☒

    b. Pain, pressure, or discomfort in the chest; palpitation, heart murmur, rheumatic fever, or other heart disorder? . . . . ☐   ☒

    c. Anemia, aneurysm, or other disorder of the blood or blood vessels? . . . . ☐   ☒

    d. Asthma, shortness of breath, emphysema, or other disorder of the respiratory system? . . . . ☐   ☒

    e. Epilepsy, convulsions, retardation, fainting spells, paralysis, mental illness, nervous breakdown, depression, or other disorder of the brain or nervous system? . . . . ☐   ☒

    f. Ulcer, colitis, hepatitis, or other disorder of the stomach, liver, intestines, pancreas, or rectum? . . . . ☐   ☒

    g. Diabetes, thyroid, pituitary, or glandular disorder? . . . . ☐   ☒

    h. Arthritis; back trouble; gout; or disorder of the skin, muscles, bones, or joints? . . . . ☐   ☒

    i. A polyp, tumor, or cancer? . . . . ☐   ☒

    j. Sugar, albumin, or blood in the urine? . . . . ☐   ☒

    k. Nephritis, urethritis, or other disorder of the kidney or urinary tract? . . . . ☐   ☒

    l. Mastitis, prostatitis, venereal disease, or other disease of the genital or reproductive organs? . . . . ☐   ☒

    m. Any disease or enlargement of the lymph nodes, night sweats, fatigue, or unexplained fever? . . . . ☐   ☒

    n. Any disorder of eyes? . . . . ☐   ☒

13. Does anyone proposed for this insurance now take prescription medication or receive treatment of any kind? ☐   ☒

14. Other than shown above, within the last 5 years has anyone proposed for this insurance:

    a. Had any mental disorder, physical disorder, or congenital abnormality? . . . . ☐   ☒

    b. Had surgery? . . . . ☐   ☒

    c. Had an x-ray, EKG (ECG) or other diagnostic test? . . . . ☐   ☒

    d. Been a patient in a hospital, clinic, or other facility? . . . . ☐   ☒

    e. Been advised to have any diagnostic test, hospitalization or surgery which was not complete? . . . . ☐   ☒

DETAILS OF EACH "YES" ANSWER TO QUESTIONS 11, 12, 13, AND 14—Attach additional sheet if necessary.

Ques. #	Name of Person	Name of Disease, Sympton, Injury, Etc.	Date/ Duration	Treatment/ Medication	Name & Address of Dr./Hospital/Clinic and, if available, Patient #/Dr. Tax I.D. # and Fee

---

15. In the last 3 years, or in the next 12 months, will anyone proposed for this insurance have: Yes No

    a. Flown other than as a scheduled airline passenger? . . . . ☐   ☒

    b. Engaged in vehicle racing, scuba diving, hang gliding, or parachuting? . . . . ☐   ☒

    c. Lived, traveled, or worked outside of the United States, or had a temporary or student visa? . . . . ☐   ☒

17. Does anyone proposed for this insurance now have any life insurance or annuity:

		Yes	No
a.	In force in any company?	☐	☒
b.	Application pending in any company?	☐	☒
c.	Which will be replaced or changed because of this application?	☐	☒

If "Yes," give details below.

Person	Company Name and Address	Policy #	Amount of Insurance		Date Applied or Issued
			Face Amt.	ADB Amt.	

18. Within the **last 3 years** has anyone proposed for this insurance been rated, postponed, or denied for

	Yes	No
☐ life or ☐ health insurance? If yes, give name or company and reason.	☐	☒

	Yes	No
19. Has the proposed insured been told that any medical exams or tests are required?	☐	☒

REMARKS:

Premium notices will be sent to address of Owner in either section 3 or section 1a unless another address is shown above.

FOR OFFICE USE ONLY:

I do declare that all answers written on this Application are full and correct, to the best of my knowledge and belief.

A. Waiver of Premium, Accidental Death Benefit, and Children's Level Term Rider are optional benefits/riders, available on Five-Year Term only. They will be in effect only if applied for and approved.

B. A medical exam may be required of any person proposed for this insurance, even if Question 19 is answered no.

C. This insurance will start only as provided in the Receipt and Temporary Insurance Agreement issued in connection with this Application. If no receipt is issued, or if insurance under it has stopped and not started again, no insurance will start by reason of this Application until the policy is delivered and the first payment is received. In this case, the insurance will start on the date shown in the policy. No insurance will start if on the start date of the policy the health of the person(s) proposed for this insurance is not as described in this Application.

D. Only an insurance officer may change this Application or waive a right or requirement. No agent may do this.

PLEASE REVIEW ALL INFORMATION BEFORE SIGNING

DATED AT	City San Diego	State CA	DATED ON	Mo. Day Yr. today's date	INSURED X _Samuel Paul Ramey_

FOR AGENT USE ONLY

Writing Agent:
Name:_____
Agt.#:_____ Region:_____ Loc.:_____

To the best of my knowledge, replacement of life insurance or annuity ☐ is ☐ is not involved in this sale.

Participating Agent:
Name:_____
Agt.#:_____ Region:_____ Loc.:_____

RECEIVED
PAYMENT OF $

☐ Check
☐ Cash
☐ Other

Sales Producer: (Writing agent's signature also required)
Name:_____
Agt.#:_____ Region:_____ Loc.:_____

☐ Discover ☐ MasterCard ☐ VISA
Card #_____ Exp. Date____ /___
Auth. # _____ Auth. Date _____

The Premium Chart

Life insurance companies do not provide life insurance free of charge. Rather they charge a "premium," which represents the annual payment required to purchase coverage. Below and on the next page are sample rate charts for annual renewable term life insurance (ART). The following charts show the premiums that are required for men and women of various ages under various circumstances. The chart below shows the rates for standard males, male nonsmokers, and males in good health (involved in personal exercise programs). The chart on the next page shows the rates for females in the same categories. Refer to the charts to complete the questions on the next page.

Ages	Male Standard—ART				Male Nonsmoker—ART				Male Good Health—ART			
	50K	100K	150K	250K	50K	100K	150K	250K	50K	100K	150K	250K
25	$160	$233	$302	$440	$135	$189	$241	$344	$124	$170	$214	$302
26	162	236	306	447	135	189	241	344	124	170	214	302
27	164	238	309	451	135	189	241	344	124	170	214	302
28	165	240	312	456	136	190	242	347	125	171	216	305
29	165	241	314	458	136	190	242	347	125	171	216	305
30	167	243	317	463	136	190	242	347	125	171	216	305
31	170	249	324	475	136	190	242	347	125	171	216	305
32	173	254	331	486	137	192	245	351	125	172	217	307
33	178	262	343	505	140	197	251	361	128	177	223	316
34	183	272	356	526	142	201	257	370	130	180	228	323
35	190	283	373	551	144	205	263	379	132	183	232	330
36	199	298	393	584	149	214	275	398	136	190	242	347
37	208	315	417	621	154	222	287	417	140	198	253	363
38	219	334	444	663	160	232	300	438	145	206	265	382
39	232	356	475	712	168	245	319	468	152	218	281	407
40	246	381	509	765	176	260	340	500	159	231	299	435
41	263	409	549	828	185	275	361	533	167	243	317	463
42	280	437	588	890	197	295	389	577	176	260	340	500
43	299	471	636	964	212	321	426	635	189	282	371	549
44	319	505	683	1039	229	351	467	700	204	308	407	605
45	341	543	736	1122	252	390	522	786	223	340	453	677
46	363	582	790	1207	273	427	574	867	242	372	497	747
47	388	625	850	1302	294	463	624	946	259	403	540	814
48	414	669	912	1399	312	493	667	1013	275	429	577	872
49	443	719	983	1510	337	536	727	1108	296	465	627	951
50	474	772	1057	1627	360	575	781	1194	315	498	674	1025
51	510	834	1144	1763	390	627	853	1307	340	542	734	1120
52	551	904	1242	1917	420	679	927	1422	367	587	798	1219
53	598	984	1354	2094	459	746	1021	1570	399	643	877	1344
54	650	1074	1480	2291	498	813	1114	1717	433	701	958	1471
55	706	1171	1615	2504	547	897	1232	1901	474	772	1057	1627
56	767	1276	1762	2734	592	975	1341	2073	513	839	1151	1775
57	831	1385	1915	2976	641	1058	1458	2257	555	910	1251	1931
58	899	1502	2079	3233	700	1160	1600	2481	605	997	1372	2121
59	972	1627	2254	3507	756	1256	1734	2691	652	1078	1485	2300
60	1052	1766	2448	3813	828	1379	1907	2962	714	1183	1632	2531

Ages	Female Standard—ART				Female Nonsmoker—ART				Female Good Health—ART			
	50K	100K	150K	250K	50K	100K	150K	250K	50K	100K	150K	250K
25	$132	$183	$232	$330	$120	$164	$205	$289	$111	$148	$183	$254
26	133	186	237	337	121	165	207	291	112	149	185	256
27	135	189	241	344	122	167	210	296	113	151	188	261
28	138	194	247	354	124	169	213	300	114	153	191	265
29	140	198	253	363	125	171	216	305	115	154	192	268
30	143	203	260	375	127	174	220	312	117	158	197	275
31	146	208	268	386	128	177	223	316	118	160	199	279
32	149	214	275	398	130	180	228	323	119	162	202	284
33	152	219	282	410	132	183	232	330	121	165	207	291
34	157	227	294	428	134	187	238	340	123	168	211	298
35	162	235	305	444	136	191	244	349	125	171	216	305
36	163	246	321	470	140	197	251	361	128	177	223	316
37	176	260	340	500	143	202	259	372	130	181	229	326
38	186	276	362	535	146	207	266	384	133	185	235	335
39	197	295	389	577	150	215	277	400	136	191	244	349
40	210	317	420	626	155	223	288	419	141	199	254	365
41	223	340	453	677	161	234	303	442	146	207	266	384
42	237	365	487	730	168	246	321	470	152	219	282	410
43	251	388	519	781	176	260	340	500	159	231	299	435
44	265	412	553	835	186	277	364	538	167	244	318	465
45	280	437	588	890	197	295	389	577	176	260	340	500
46	294	463	624	946	209	316	419	623	187	278	365	540
47	310	490	662	1006	221	337	448	670	197	296	390	579
48	327	520	703	1071	235	362	482	723	209	316	419	623
49	346	551	747	1140	250	386	516	777	221	337	448	670
50	366	586	796	1217	266	414	556	839	235	362	482	723
51	388	624	849	1300	284	446	600	909	251	388	519	781
52	412	664	906	1390	304	480	647	983	267	416	559	844
53	440	713	974	1496	327	520	703	1071	288	451	608	920
54	468	761	1041	1602	351	561	761	1161	308	486	656	997
55	498	812	1113	1715	376	604	821	1256	329	523	708	1078
56	527	863	1185	1827	403	649	884	1355	351	561	761	1161
57	556	912	1253	1935	429	694	947	1454	374	599	815	1247
58	583	958	1318	2036	448	727	994	1528	390	628	855	1309
59	612	1008	1388	2147	476	774	1060	1632	414	668	911	1397
60	645	1065	1467	2270	500	816	1119	1724	434	703	961	1475

In the spaces provided, answer the following questions.

1. What will be the premium for Mr. Ramey? *$363*

2. Find the premium for a 57-year-old female smoker who wants a $250,000 ART policy? *$1,935*

3. What will be the premium for a male nonsmoker who is age 32 and who wants a $100,000 ART policy? *$192* For a female under the same circumstances? *$180*

4. What would be the premium for a male in good health at age 25 for a $250,000 ART policy? *$302* For a male under the same circumstances at age 60? *$2,531*

5. Why is it that one's premiums rise as he ages? *As a person ages, the risk of his dying goes up, increasing the chance that the insurance company will have to pay life insurance proceeds. In order to stay in business and maintain an adequate profit, the company must charge higher premiums as the ages of their clients increase.*

6. Why is it that, everything else being equal, premiums for females are lower than those for males? *Statistically, it has been found that females outlive males; therefore, since the risk of paying out insurance proceeds is less, insurance companies can charge a lower premium for females and still maintain their profitability.*

Multiple Choice

Choose the response which best answers the question or completes the sentence.

__B__ 1. "But if any provide not for his own, and specially for those of his own _____, he hath denied the faith, and is worse than an infidel." (I Timothy 5:8)
A. church
B. house
C. brethren
D. faith

__D__ 2. What should be the first step in developing a comprehensive financial plan?
A. the purchase of life insurance
B. making regular contributions to retirement accounts
C. the purchase of disability insurance
D. the preparation of a will

__A__ 3. What is the main purpose for purchasing life insurance?
A. to replace lost income
B. to provide a lump sum of money for the retirement of outstanding debts
C. to pay funeral expenses
D. to pay the home mortgage

__A__ 4. Which of the following types of life insurance has no savings component?
A. term life insurance
B. whole life insurance
C. universal life insurance
D. "single pay" life insurance

__D__ 5. Which of the following is a "defined-contribution" retirement plan?
A. IRA
B. Social Security
C. Keough plan
D. 401(k) plan

__A__ 6. By what percentage does the government reduce one's Social Security benefits if a person retires at age 62 instead of 65?
A. 20%
B. 10%
C. 5%
D. 1%

Modified True/False

If the statement is true, write the word *true* in the blank. If it is false, change the underlined words to make the statement true. Write the correct word(s) in the blank.

____*True*____ 1. When making financial plans, the Christian should include plans to care for <u>his parents in their old age</u>.

____*Few*____ 2. <u>Most</u> adults in the United States have written wills.

____*$600,000*____ 3. The value of an estate must exceed <u>$1 million</u> before it is subject to federal estate taxes.

____*True*____ 4. Term insurance provides <u>more</u> death protection per dollar of premium than any other type of life insurance.

____*True*____ 5. Employer-sponsored health insurance is a <u>nontaxable</u> benefit.